George H. Lauff

CRA

EVOLUTION AND CLASSIFICATION OF THE MOUNTAIN CADDISFLIES

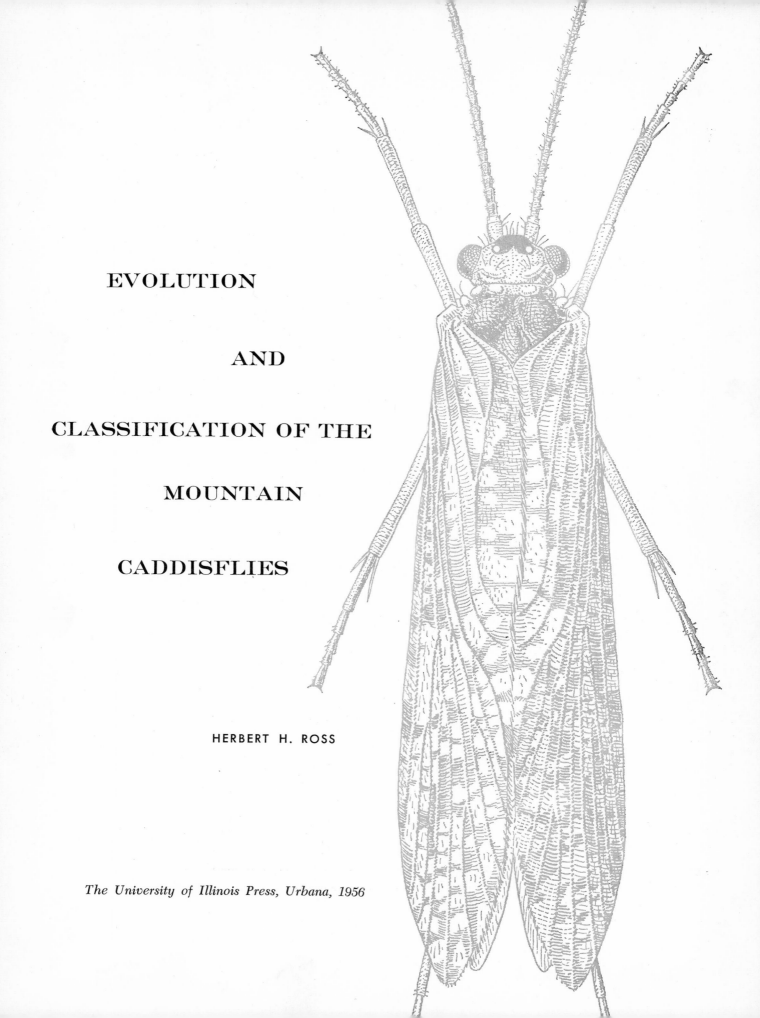

# EVOLUTION

# AND

# CLASSIFICATION OF THE

# MOUNTAIN

# CADDISFLIES

HERBERT H. ROSS

*The University of Illinois Press, Urbana, 1956*

# FOREWORD

Without aid from many sources it would have been impossible to bring together the information in this report. To the following institutions and their personnel I wish to express my gratitude for loans of material and the opportunity to work with their collections: American Museum of Natural History, British Museum (Natural History), Natural History Museum of Basel, Brussels Museum, Congo Museum, California Academy of Sciences, Canadian National Museum, Carnegie Museum, Chicago Natural History Museum, Cornell University, Genoa Natural History Museum, Lausanne University Museum, Leyden Museum, Museum of Comparative Zoology (Harvard), Paris Museum, University of Minnesota, University of Saskatchewan, and the United States National Museum.

A host of colleagues have made available enormous amounts of caddisfly material, much of it in the families treated here. I wish to thank especially Lewis Berner, University of Florida; Federico Bonet, Escuela Nacional de Ciencias (Mexico); B. D. Burks, U. S. National Museum; Harry Chandler, Red Bluff, California; Jared Davis, Radiological Sciences Department, General Electric Company; P. W. Fattig, Emory University; Arden Gaufin, University of Utah; C. C. Hoff, University of New Mexico; Harry Hoogstraal, U. S. Naval Medical Research Unit No. 3; Stanley G. Jewett, Portland, Oregon; G. H. Knowlton and his students, Utah State Agricultural College; Mrs. M. Kohno, Wakamatsu City, Japan; Hugh B. Leech, California Academy of Sciences; J. W. and Fannie A. Leonard, Michigan Department of Conservation; Don Merkeley, Montana State College; Boyd Palmer, Puerto Rico Polytechnic Institute; W. E. Ricker, Pacific Biological Station; E. S. Ross, California Academy of Science; M. W. Sanderson, Illinois Natural History Survey; Fernand Schmid, Lausanne, Switzerland; L. J. Stannard, Illinois Natural History Survey; G. J. Spencer, University of British Columbia; Matsunae Tsuda, Nara Women's University, Japan; Felix Woytkowski, Lima, Peru.

For help and encouragement I am deeply indebted to the following: Cornelius Betten, Asheville, North Carolina; D. G. Denning, Berkeley, California; D. E. Kimmins, British Museum (Natural History); E. W. King, Cornell College, Iowa; G. Marlier, Biological Laboratory of the LRSAC, Belgian Congo; the L. J. Milnes, University of New Hampshire; the late Martin E. Mosely, British Museum (Natural History), and Georg Ulmer, Hamburg, Germany. Dr. Ulmer was especially kind in arranging for Mrs. Ross and me to work on his extremely valuable collection at his home in Hamburg. Dr. Betten, Mr. Kimmins, and Dr. Ulmer have been generous with good advice and valuable suggestions.

In few insect groups is the student so aided by contributions already in the literature as in this order. Pertinent citations are given elsewhere, but I feel that especial attention should be called here to the pioneer and comprehensive works of Betten, Martynov, McLachlan, and Ulmer, and to the remarkable research collections assembled by Banks and Mosely.

I am indebted to the Research Board of the Graduate College, University of Illinois, for providing graduate assistance with many details of study, and to the John Simon Guggenheim Memorial Foundation for providing the opportunity for Mrs. Ross and me to study collections on this continent and in Europe. Mrs. Ross has been of inestimable assistance especially as my technician during study trips and in abstracting geological literature. To Mrs. Robert Hull, formerly of the Survey staff, I am greatly indebted for typing and editing the manuscript and many of the charts; and to Mr. James Curfman, formerly of the Survey staff, I wish to express my thanks for valued assistance with the illustrations.

Members of our local discussion group on insect evolution have provided much information from the literature, collected material, aided in discussion, or assisted in other ways. I wish to acknowledge especially, in addition to persons mentioned in preceding paragraphs, the assistance of E. C. Becker, Mrs. L. K. Gloyd, J. F. McAlpine, T. E. Moore, W. R. Richards, S. S. Roback, R. B. Selander, J. L. Slater, E. H. N. Smith, P. W. Smith, Kathryn M. Sommerman, and Glenn Ulrich.

To the Board of Natural Resources, State of Illinois, I am deeply indebted for support of this project, and especially to Dr. Alfred E. Emerson, University of Chicago, and Dr. H. B. Mills, Chief, Illinois Natural History Survey, for encouragement, discussion, and advice during the progress of this work.

Finally I want to express my deep gratitude to the members of the Editorial Board of the Illinois Biological Monographs for reading the manuscript and offering constructive criticism of great value.


HERBERT H. ROSS

*Systematic Entomologist, Illinois Natural History Survey; Professor of Entomology, University of Illinois*

# CONTENTS

chapter one | # INTRODUCTION

The Trichoptera or caddisflies comprise one of the few aquatic orders of insects. Of the 30 families belonging to the Trichoptera, the three most primitive—Philopotamidae, Rhyacophilidae, and Glossosomatidae—have proved to be of unusual interest biogeographically. An investigation of the phylogeny and dispersal of these families has resulted in deductions which contribute significantly to our knowledge of the age and history of the cool-adapted biota.

Information concerning warm-adapted groups, such as the gall wasps, the termites, and the camels, has allowed us to form fairly definite ideas concerning the past dispersal patterns of these forms. The successful reconstruction of these historical data has been possible because of either extensive fossil records, or the persistence of large numbers of genera or species in widely separated areas of the world. In contrast, the evolutionary history of that part of the biota adapted to cool or cold conditions has remained an enigma. In the case of the cool-adapted families of terrestrial animals, the fossil record is meager, and most or all of their existing genera and species groups are widely distributed throughout the Holarctic region. These conditions obscure the place and time of origin of such groups.

The peculiar distributional and survival features of the three caddisfly families under discussion appear to afford an excellent opportunity to obtain abundant and tangible data relating to this problem. Most of the species are dependent for existence not only on cool water but also on swift water, and hence are restricted primarily to hilly terrain or mountain systems. Furthermore, related groups occur in mountains throughout the entire world, each group often being confined to a mountainous area a great distance from its relatives, and on the opposite side of the equator. A great number of phyletic lines have survived in such restricted mountain areas, indicating that these insects have been able to exist for long periods of time in a small total range. As a result, the primitive caddisfly families present an opportunity to trace dispersal patterns further into the past than has been possible with other cool-adapted groups that have been investigated.

## PROBLEMS AND PROCEDURES

In theory, the method used here is a simple one; in practice, many difficulties may be encountered. First, the characteristics of a world-wide group including both fossil and living species are studied and organized, and from these data the phylogenetic tree is deduced. The distribution pattern of each branch is then indicated on the tree, and if correlations appear between phylogenetic development and distribution, part or all of the dispersal pattern responsible for the present distribution of the group may be deduced.

Assuming results of significance up to this step, the next is to correlate the dispersal pattern with the geologic time scale. Accurately dated fossils give indisputable evidence of minimum age of the line to which they belong. Known geologic data, such as time and position of land bridges, time and extent of past climates, and time of mountain building or peneplaning, furnish evidence of the possible periods when dispersals could have occurred. Finally, comparisons may be made with the dispersal patterns of other groups of organisms whose evolutionary histories have been studied.

From this assembled evidence the investigator must attempt to visualize a possible dispersal pattern into which all his data will fit harmoniously. A probable explanation can be devised when the phylogeny, distribution, fossil evidence, and deduced dispersal pattern for the group under consideration integrate reasonably with the known geologic time factors. The more definitive and abundant the data which can be brought to bear on each point, the more reliable are the conclusions. In brief, biogeographic interpretations are based on a simple type of hypothetical reasoning. The worker attempts to create a mental picture of past happenings which will explain the known facts. A brief but lucid discussion of this method is given by Lobeck (1939:20-21).

If, through investigations of the three caddisfly families, it could be demonstrated that biogeographic correlations exist among them, the over-all implications would be of considerably greater significance than would those resulting from study of a single family. A preliminary survey showed that the Philopotamidae, Rhyacophilidae, and Glossosomatidae share several important characters: each family has a core of primitive genera which are cool-adapted, confined generally to mountainous areas, and widely distributed throughout the Holarctic region. It was therefore considered highly desirable to study the three families in detail.

In each family a sufficient number of annectent forms have survived to allow us to ascertain basic phylogeny and many points of the dispersal patterns. In each family, also, there are available a few fossils which have proved of great aid in dating possible times of dispersal. Each of these families can be traced back to Cretaceous ancestors, making them antique as terrestrial animals. The primitive genera in their early evolutional stages were intimately associated with a marked restriction to cool mountain streams. It seems clear that their development has been inextricably bound to the continuous existence of mountain ranges extending back through a similar span of time. In this connection, excellent stratigraphic evidence for the longevity of mountain systems has been presented by such authors as Love (1939), Spieker (1946), Umbgrove (1947), and Gilluly (1949).

To test the hypothesis that these three families arose from a cool-adapted ancestral form it was desirable to investigate the phylogeny of the entire order Trichoptera. Since no documented family tree was available, it was necessary to start from the beginning and recheck every character that appeared to offer evidence of relationships. The analysis has given rise to many interesting ideas concerning the evolution of the families of Trichoptera.

Study of the world fauna as a unit has necessitated many changes in classification, and many new species have been discovered. In this study, for the sake of clarity, the phylogenetic and taxonomic materials are presented in separate sections of the appropriate chapters. This arrangement allows the orderly presentation of each viewpoint and has the added advantage of permitting a convenient listing, in the taxonomic section, of references and distributional data pertinent to the whole study.

## TERMINOLOGY

Names for various parts of insects used throughout this paper are standard morphological designations unless otherwise explained. Wing venation is designated according to the Comstock-Needham system. The standard abbreviations for veins are as follows: $C$, costa; $Sc$, subcosta; $R$, radius; $M$, media; $Cu$, cubitus; $A$, anals; $J$, jugal. The abbreviations for cross-veins are: $ic$, intercostal; $r$, radial; $s$, sectorial; $r$-$m$, radio-medial; $m$, medial; $m$-$cu$, medio-cubital; $cu$, cubital; $cu$-$a$, cubito-anal; $a$, anal.

## CLARIFICATION OF CONCEPTS

As a preliminary, it is desirable to define or explain certain terms as they are used in this paper, and to outline certain general concepts fundamental to a biogeographic study based primarily on living forms. The items listed here concern only phylogeny and dispersal, and are applicable to Chapters 2 to 6. Other concepts dealing with the use of time factors in relation to these data are outlined in Chapter 7.

### Living Fossils

Clarification is believed desirable concerning use of the term, living fossils. It should be understood at the outset that in one sense every living species could be so designated. Each species goes back to antiquity in geologic time, in an uninterrupted antecedence of reproducing organisms. On this basis it could be said that every species is the same age. Yet when we examine all the species within a group we often notice that certain ones possess a combination of characters which are almost identical with those of an early ancestral type of the group. It is to these archaic species that the term, living fossil, is applied.

Recognition of a species as a living fossil depends on its retention of primitive characters in comparison with specializations which have evolved in other members of its group. As an example, let us consider the genus *Chimarra* (Chart 15). In studying the *aterrima* group, it becomes evident that *montana* is very like the ancestral form from which the group arose. From the standpoint of the *aterrima* group alone, *montana* could be considered a living fossil. In considering the entire genus, *moselyi* is conspicuous as being almost exactly what the prototype of the genus must have been, and could, for *Chimarra,* be called a living fossil. Going back further, from the standpoint of the entire subfamily Philopotaminae, we find that forms such as *Sortosa sisko* combine characters that we would expect to find in the progenitor of the subfamily; by almost any criteria, these forms could be called living fossils because they have persisted with apparently little change for at least 70 to 100 million years. In general, a species may be considered as a living fossil if it has the distinctive characters of some deduced ancestral type.

## Primitive, Generalized, and Specialized

Making the decision as to whether or not a particular species should be called a living fossil is much like deciding whether or not a particular condition is generalized or specialized. We say that the one-toed foot of the horse is specialized, whereas the five-toed foot of the bear is generalized; or that the flipper of the whale is a specialized foot. When compared with the fins from which they evolved, however, even five-toed feet are not generalized, but are highly specialized structures. "Generalized" and "specialized" are thus strictly comparative terms in relation to whatever standard is being used as a basis. The term "primitive" must be used in exactly the same fashion.

## Deducing Ancestral Types

The ancestral types designated as "deduced" or "postulated" represent the sum of the primitive characters of the progeny beyond a certain point in a phyletic line. Deducing the ancestral type of male genitalia for the Philopotamidae affords an example of how this summation is made. Referring to Chart 4, we see that the Paulianodinae possess male genitalia having an annular ninth segment (a primitive character) and fused claspers (a specialized character); the Philopotaminae possess male genitalia having a ninth segment reduced dorsally (a specialized character) and separate, simple, two-segmented claspers (a primitive character). Both the Paulianodinae and the Philopotaminae must have arisen from a common ancestor possessing male genitalia in which both characters were in the primitive condition, i.e., an annular ninth segment and separate, primitive claspers. No such form of Philopotamidae is known, and hence this deduced ancestor is simply an imaginary creation of our reasoning based on conditions found in living species of close kinship.

In many groups the species exhibiting connecting links between different characters are widely scattered geographically, as in the case of *Chimarra.* For this reason the deduction of ancestral types should be based on a detailed knowledge of the world fauna of the group under study. Good results may sometimes be obtained from a study of forms inhabiting a limited area, but ultimately these results need verification by a study of the larger fauna.

Even the known world fauna may fail to give enough evidence to unravel many problems. We frequently discover a peculiar structure which is so different from other known types that we are unable to visualize how it arose. In such cases it is impossible to be sure whether the structure evolved by an initial change in one character, followed by changes in another, and so on, or by gradual and simultaneous change in all the characters involved.

## Dispersal

The first major problem in biogeographic analysis is to establish the routes of dispersal of the various phyletic lines. Many methods and criteria for such determination have been suggested by different investigators (Ortman 1902, Adams 1902, Cain 1944, Darlington 1948), but most of these methods rely to some extent on statistical analysis. Although statistics may ultimately be of great value in testing biogeographic conclusions, they are unreliable as a basis of reasoning in the present qualitative approaches to a study of dispersal.

To my knowledge, the first successful attempt at solving this problem of deducing dispersal was made by Kinsey (1930, 1936) in his studies of the gall wasp genus *Cynips*. Kinsey first employed annectent series of species showing morphological progression of characters to establish a phylogenetic analysis of the species, then correlated the resulting family tree with geographic distribution to determine paths of dispersal. He found that in *Cynips* the primitive species of all lines were concentrated in southern Mexico and that chains of annectent species extended into areas to the north. Kinsey reasoned that this existing distribution pattern represented the actual dispersal pattern of the group. He concluded that the primitive Mexican species were essentially living fossils still persisting in or near their ancestral home, and that various lines of northward dispersal resulted ultimately in the specialized, more northern species now existing in North America and Europe.

The principle thus embodied is the one which has proved most tenable in these studies: in brief, the dispersal pattern of a group can best be deduced by an integration of detailed phylogenetic analysis and geographic distribution of its species. To this end, the more important tenets and limitations are listed here to assist the reader in following steps of reasoning used in the course of this paper:

1. *Origin* and *ancestor* are terms to be used definitively in phylogenetic reference. For example, we may speak of the origin of the *aterrima* group or the origin of the whole genus *Chimarra* (see Chart 15). The genus *Chimarra*, we must remember, *developed* in South America from a segregate of an Old World genus *Sortosa*. The ancestor of *Chimarra* may be traced back to the South American segregate after it had become isolated in South America, or to the original Old World population of *Sortosa*.

2. Other factors being equal, the larger and more widespread groups offer greater possibilities for the accurate diagnosis of paths of dispersal. This is especially true if (a) the total range of the group includes two or more continental areas or isolated areas on several continents, and (b) many branches of the group have given rise to a large number of species.

A group for which there is only limited available data affords little reliable information regarding dispersal. The sawfly family Blasticotomidae, for example, is known from only a single living European species and a Miocene fossil from Florissant, Colorado (Benson 1942). From this scant evidence it is impossible to know when or in what direction the dispersal of this family occurred.

3. In many instances several species, each restricted to a different area, trace directly back to a common ancestor. From the data obtainable in such cases it is impossible to ascertain the area occupied by the ancestor; it could have been within the range of any one of the daughter species, or possibly in some other area. Certain large genera, such as the sawfly genus *Dolerus*, contain chiefly species groups associated with such circumstances. Such genera have been a source of discouragement for many biogeographers, and doubts have arisen as to the feasibility of trying to use present distribution as a means of ascertaining past events. Many cool-adapted genera present comparable difficulties, which has been one reason for the scarcity of information regarding their origin.

4. If alternate steps of a phylogenetic series occur on different continents, it seems impossible to make any choice as to the place of origin of any one step, or the forms which actually dispersed. Similarly, if one group of species flourishes on one continent and its sister group on another, there is no evidence from these two groups alone as to the place of origin of their common ancestor. It could have been either place, or even another. Such a situation does indicate, however, that after the dispersal of the original ancestral form, each of the isolated sister populations evolved independently and the progeny of one never spread to, or became established in, the territory of the other. To solve such problems of origin it is necessary to obtain information from representatives of lower branches on the family tree.

5. Consecutive steps in a phylogenetic sequence occurring in the same area constitute the first indication that the sequence actually evolved in that

area. Even two such sequential steps give some indication of such development. The greater the number of such sympatric steps, the greater the likelihood that they occur in the original area of evolutionary development.

6. It must be remembered that many phyletic lines of which we have no knowledge could have evolved and become extinct. When we say that a certain line divided into many branches we refer to known branches, tacitly acknowledging that others could have existed but are now extinct, or that others exist but have not yet been collected and so are unknown.

chapter two

# THE EVOLUTION OF
# THE CADDISFLIES

The caddisfles comprise only a small order of insects, with an estimated 5,000 species, but they exhibit remarkable diversity in form and habits. The adults range from 1.5 to about 40 mm. in length. Some are slender-winged, trim, strong fliers; others are broad-winged, slow, and fluttery. The larvae are all wormlike but exhibit many differences in shape and type of sclerotized plates with which their anterior portions are armored. The habits of the larvae are the most interesting phenomena of the Trichoptera. Some of them build retreats or nets, others build portable cases of sand grains, sticks, or leaves, while a few are free-living. Habitat diversity among different species of caddisflies ranges from cold, swift, mountain torrents with maximum temperatures of 45° to 55° F. to sluggish rivers and lakes with temperatures in excess of 70°F.

In exploring the relationship between habitat preference and evolutionary development, the available phylogenetic evidence was reviewed. The family tree resulting from this survey embodies several innovations but seems to afford a good picture of the development of the order (Chart 1). Evolution of the family units within the order is apparent primarily in the structures of the larvae and pupae and many of their associated habits. Evolution of generic units within the families is apparent more often in adult structures. Early caddisfly evolution is, therefore, essentially the history of net-making and case-making by the aquatic larvae. From this it is apparent that the development of the entire order had its basis in changes of behavior pattern in different phyletic lines or columns. Morpholog-ical changes adaptive to the new behavior patterns must have followed rapidly.

In reconstructing the path of evolution in the Trichoptera this combination of comparative data from both morphology and behavior has been highly profitable. The two sets of data complement each other and allow definite conclusions to be drawn in one or two instances where direction of evolution is not strongly indicated by one set alone.

The life history of a typical caddisfly may be summarized rapidly. The female crawls into the water and lays eggs. These hatch into larvae which spin nets or retreats, or build portable cases, in which they live. The larvae feed on micro-organisms or other food as it is available, a few predaceous genera feeding chiefly on other insects. When mature, each larva spins a cocoon, or seals and fastens down its case, and pupates inside. The mature pupa has sharp mandibles which it uses to cut its way out of the cocoon or case. Then it swims to the surface of the water, climbs up on some object, and molts, the adult emerging and flying away. After mating, eggs are laid and the cycle is complete.

The caddisflies probably arose from an ancestor having net-veined wings and resembling an alder fly or megalopteron. This ancestor probably differed from the Megaloptera in having vein 1A fused for a short distance with $Cu_2$, as is the case now in the Mecoptera and Trichoptera. This ancestral form gave rise to the Mecoptera (which retained the netlike venation in general but lost $Cu_{1a}$ and the Trichoptera (which lost most of the cross-veins but retained $Cu_{1a}$, Fig. 23). Very likely, the Lepidoptera (moths and butterflies) arose from this same

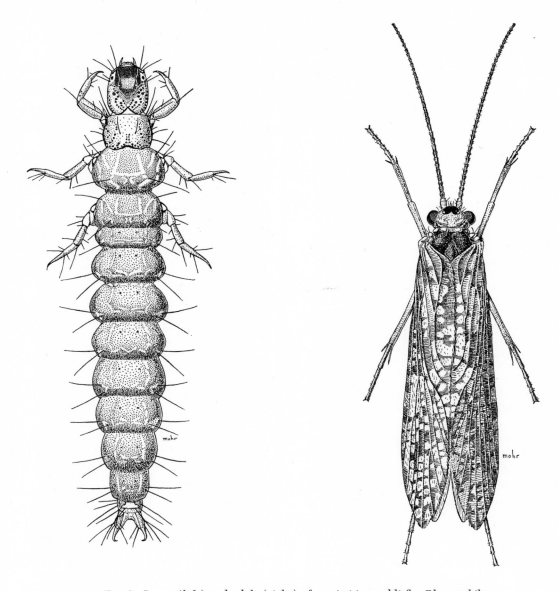

FIG. 1. Larva (left) and adult (right) of a primitive caddisfly, *Rhyacophila fenestra*. (From Illinois Natural History Survey.)

ancestor or from the line leading to the Trichoptera, although the exact relationships of the two orders is not known.

Unlike those of the Lepidoptera, the larvae of the Trichoptera lost their spiracles and thus became wholly dependent on the aquatic habitat. The first caddis larvae were probably agile and slender, much like those of *Hydropsyche* and *Polycentropus* (Fig. 2), living under rocks, and reacting much like their ancient relative, the hellgrammite *Corydalus*.

In tracing the phylogeny of the Trichoptera, I have assumed that they did arise from a megalopteroid-mecopteroid ancestor. Two groups of caddisflies, the primitive Philopotamidae and Rhyacophilidae, resemble such a postulated ancestor more than any others. They have the most complete wing venation found in the Trichoptera, ocelli, 5-segmented maxillary palps, unspecialized pupae, and active larvae with membranous meso- and metanotum and simple anal legs.

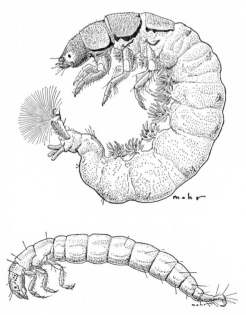

FIG. 2. Larva of *Hydropsyche simulans* (above) and *Polycentropus interruptus* (below). (From Illinois Natural History Survey.)

The predaceous Rhyacophilidae larvae are free-living and keep their footing in the running water by clinging to silken threads spun on the stones. The mature larva constructs a cocoon with a double covering—an outer shell of stones cemented to a rock, and suspended within this shell an inner container made entirely of silk. The larvae of the Philopotamidae construct silken nets under stones, living inside the nets, foraging around the openings and using the back part as a retreat. The mature larva builds a cocoon in the end of or outside the net, cemented to a stone or other object. The cocoon has an outer covering of rough materials embedded in webbing, and an inner lining made solely of silk; the inner and outer portions are not easily detached from each other.

Using these two families as a basis, it has been possible to trace a most interesting evolutionary development leading to many specialized types. In retrospect it seems certain that these families, the Philopotamidae and Rhyacophilidae, represent the bases of the two great divisions of the Trichoptera, the net-makers and the case-makers.

## PRIMITIVE CHARACTERS

The phylogeny of the caddisflies is based on the comparative morphology of adults, larvae, and

pupae, plus certain behavior patterns regarding net or case making. Deducing the phylogeny from one stage alone would give an entirely false view of the actual evolutionary development, because in some instances the larvae evolved faster than the adults, and vice versa.

In visualizing the phylogeny, it is necessary at all times to compare changes with respect to the initial ancestral form. For this purpose a goodly number of characters have been found useful, and the *primitive condition* of each is outlined below.

*Larva.* 1. Antennae short, situated at the edge of the capsule near the base of the mandible.

2. Propleurae with a distinct trochantin, one edge free and projecting (Fig. 3,*t*), appearing as a

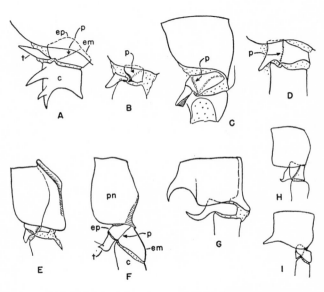

FIG. 3. Propleurae and trochantin of caddisfly larvae. *A, Stenopsyche; B, Sortosa; C, Psychomyia; D, Phylocentropus; E, Phryganea; F, Athripsodes; G, Anisocentropus; H, Sericostoma; I, Psilotreta. c,* coxa; *em,* pro-epimeron; *ep,* pro-episternum; *p,* pleural suture; *pn,* pronotum; *t,* trochantin.

scraper, the posterior edge articulating with the episternum by a membranous connection; and with episternum and epimeron separated by a shallow crease, the pleural suture (*p*).

3. Pronotum sclerotized, mesonotum and metanotum membranous, the latter each with three pairs of setae (Fig. 11A), the anterior, posterior, and anterolateral pairs (indicated by the numbers 1, 2, and 3, respectively, in the illustrations).

4. Anal legs (Fig. 9) separated on meson to

near base, each with an elongate lateral sclerite *s* and an apical claw *c*. The claw is joined to the leg by a long dorsal strap *d* bearing two long setae at the base (basal tuft, *b*), and by a ventral membrane in which is embedded a small sclerite or sole plate *v*. This plate bears a single seta and touches the base of the claw.

*Pupa*. Abdomen with no sclerotized processes at apex.

*Adult*. 1. Head with 5-segmented maxillary palps, 3-segmented labial palps in both sexes. Ocelli present.

2. Thorax with praescutum well delineated, the lateral sutures sometimes forming elongate warts. Mesoepisternal suture short but distinct.

3. Punctate areas or warts occur as follows: 2 dorsal pairs on the head (the posterior pair the larger), 2 pairs on the pronotum, a pair on the lateral sutures of the mesopraescutum, and a pair on the mesoscutellum.

4. Male genitalia with ninth segment complete nd ringlike; tenth tergite a simple lobe, but well fferentiated dorsad from ninth; and claspers 2-gmented, probably resembling Figure 30 in genl appearance.

## EVOLUTIONARY DEVELOPMENT

e first division of the Trichoptera was into two the fixed retreat or net makers, and the freely g types. These differing lines are shown in 1. Ancestor A had the terminal segment of ult maxillary palpus subdivided into many gs, its front wings retained cross-vein *m*, larva spun some sort of a fixed retreat. B had a solid terminal segment in the xillary palpus and the front wing had lost m. Its larva built no retreat but moved ely.

### The Fixed Retreat Division

cestor A there arose two major lines or e developing into the Philopotamidae, o the Hydropsychid-Psychomyiid com-ilopotamidae line changed very little; as did occur was chiefly in the de-the membranous, widened labium of adults and pupae of the primitive arkably similar to their deduced pro-

ychid-Psychomyiid line also changed

little at first, sclerotized appendages at the apex of the abdomen in the pupa being the chief development. The ancestral form with these characteristics in turn gave rise to two lines. The line leading to the Hydropsychidae preserved a primitive venation and 2-segmented claspers in the adult and a simple trochantin in the larva but became specialized in many other characters. These include loss of ocelli and mesonotal warts in the adult and the development of tergal plates on the meso- and metanotum, tufted gills, and a thick brush of hairs at the base of the dorsal strap of the claw in the larva (Fig. 2).

In the Psychomyiidae line the adult male claspers became 1-segmented but other characters remained primitive. An early offshoot representing this primitive condition is the family Stenopsychidae, especially the genus *Stenopsyche*, which still retains adult ocelli and the larval protrochantin (Fig. 3A). *Stenopsyche*, however, has become specialized in losing the mesoscutal warts and developing realignments of wing venation, the latter associated with stronger flight.

The line leading beyond the Stenopsychidae to the Psychomyiidae proper changed in important respects. In the larva the protrochantin fused solidly with the propleuron (Fig. 3, C, D). In the adults the mesoscutal warts moved close together on the meson, and the ocelli atrophied.

*Xiphocentron*, *Pseudostenopsyche*, and *Dipseudopsis*, belonging to the fixed retreat line, are difficult to place phylogenetically because their larvae are unknown. *Xiphocentron* is considered as constituting a distinctive family, Xiphocentronidae, because of its possession of specialized 1-segmented claspers and lack of ocelli, combined with what seems to be a very primitive condition of the praescutum (Ross 1949a). *Dipseudopsis* has been placed in a separate subfamily of the Psychomyiidae, primarily because of the structure of the male genitalia. This may not represent the true affinities of either genus, but must be considered as only tentative. *Pseudostenopsyche* is entirely enigmatic, although placed in the Stenopsychidae by Martynov (1926). Association of the larvae of these genera will undoubtedly provide more conclusive evidence regarding their exact place in the family tree.

In reviewing the fixed retreat line we find that it has evolved into four well-marked families, counting genera of doubtful placement. The initial family

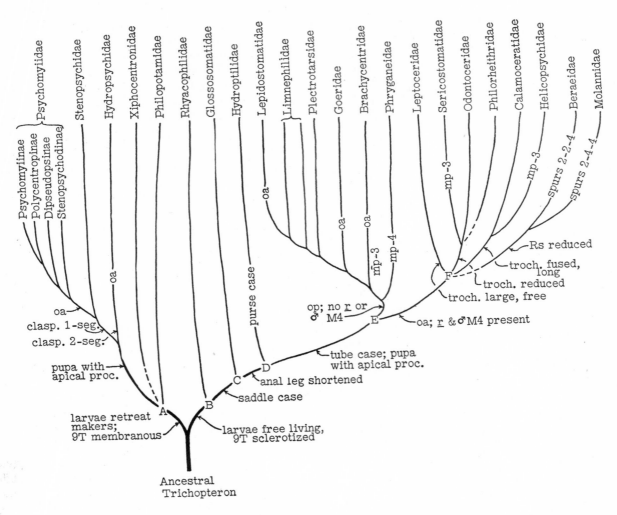

CHART 1. Phylogenetic diagram of the Trichoptera. *mp*, maxillary palpi of male; *oa*, ocelli absent; *op*, ocelli present.

lines must be of considerable age, for each has since given rise to a variety of forms, as follows:

*Philopotamidae.* Two subfamilies are known, one from only one genus (*Paulianodes*), the other from a large fauna treated in greater detail in Chapter 3.

*Hydropsychidae.* This very large and diverse family is divided into four subfamilies, tabulated here from primitive to most specialized.

A. Larval gills with apical branches only. Adult venation complete; male genitalia with distinct cerci. Strictly confined to cold regions or mountains ..................... **Arctopsychinae**

AA. Larval gills with both apical and subapical branches. Male genitalia without cerci.

B. Hind wing with apex of *Sc* free and distinct; front wing with no coupling device along lower edge of 1A. Primitive genera chiefly cool-adapted and montane... **Diplectroninae**

BB. Hind wing with apex of *Sc* fused with apex of $R_1$; front wing with lower edge of 1A having a coupling device.

C. Front wing with lower edge of 1A bearing a linear patch of stout bristles for attachment of hind wing. Primitive genera chiefly cool-adapted and montane......
.................. **Hydropsychinae**

CC. Front wing with lower edge of 1A having minute filelike roughening; the membrane anterior to it invaginated to form a pocket. Warm-adapted groups confined almost entirely to tropical and subtropical regions
.................. **Macronematinae**

**Stenopsychidae.** This family is represented by a single large genus confined to the mountainous regions of Asia.

**Psychomyiidae.** Tentatively, the family is being divided into four subfamilies: (1) the Dipseudopsinae (containing the tropical Old World genera *Protodipseudopsis* and *Dipseudopsis*) in which the mesoscutal warts are lacking; (2) the Stenopsychodinae, in which the mesoscutal warts are some distance apart; (3) the subfamily Psychomyiinae in which the mesoscutal warts practically touch on the the meson but in which the fore trochantin is well differentiated although solidly fused with the episternum (Fig. 3C); and (4) the subfamily Polycentropinae in which the adults are very similar to those of the Psychomyiinae but the larva has lost all trace of the suture between the trochantin and episternum of the front leg (Fig. 3D).

The subfamily Polycentropinae is a most interesting one. Its most primitive genus is *Phylocentropus* which has a distinct intercostal cross-vein in the front wing, complete venation, and very simple male genitalia. At least two branches or tribes have arisen, each from a primitive ancestor which must have been almost identical in major points with *Phylocentropus* as it occurs today. *Phylocentropus* and many forms of the tribe Polycentropini are cool-adapted and chiefly montane. Other tribes are more warm-adapted, but contain some montane elements.

### The Casemaker Division

The second main line of caddisfly development (Chart 1), starting with the Rhyacophilidae, had a much more unusual sequence. As previously noted, the Rhyacophilidae larvae are free-living. When mature, each larva constructs over itself a dome-like, rigid outer covering of small stones. By means of salivary secretion applied all around its edge, the covering is solidly cemented to some support. The larva then spins a completely fibrous inner cocoon cemented at each end to the outer stone cover, and pupates within it. If cut from its base, the inside bottom view looks like Fig. 4. Note its resemblance to the retreat-making Hydropsychidae cocoon, Fig. 5.

From the primeval Rhyacophilidae line there arose a line, the primeval Glossosomatidae, in which the larva constructed the outer covering of the cocoon precociously, probably in the first or second

instar, and carried it around on its back. Across the bottom it fabricated a strap, and walked around with its head and thoracic legs protruding from one side of the strap, and its anal legs from the other side, Fig. 6. The outer covering or case, which concealed the protruding parts from view above, was enlarged as the larva grew and increased in size. Presumably the ventral strap was periodically removed and replaced. When full grown, the larva removed the ventral strap, plastered the case to

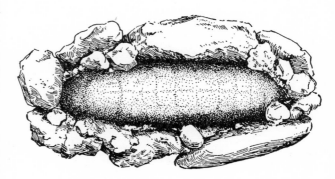

FIG. 4. Pupal case of *Rhyacophila*. (After Betten.)

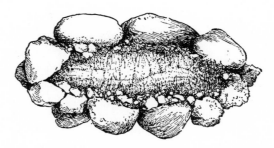

FIG. 5. Pupal case of *Hydropsyche*. (After Betten.)

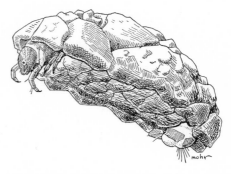

FIG. 6. Case and larva of *Glossosoma intermedium*. (From Illinois Natural History Survey.)

a rock, and constructed the fibrous inner cocoon within it. This pupal chamber is exactly like that of the Rhyacophilidae. This first step in the case-making story is illustrated beautifully by the family Glossosomatidae, the saddle casemakers. The effectiveness of their protective case is perhaps shown by the fact that Rhyacophilidae larvae remain under stones (at least in the daytime), whereas Glossosomatidae larvae in their cases wander about freely on exposed rock surfaces in the stream.

The next step is shown by the Hydroptilidae. In the primitive genera of this family the larva makes a case which is open at both ends, and the two ends of the larva may protrude from it as in the Glossosomatidae. The case is barrel-shaped or purse-shaped (Fig. 7). In *Hydroptila* and some

Fig. 7. Case and larva of *Ochrotrichia unio*. (From Illinois Natural History Survey.)

other genera the larva splits it along the venter and increases the size of each "valve" before recementing the ventral edges together. In his monumental treatise on the development and biology of the Hydroptilidae, Nielsen (1948) describes this activity for several genera. He offers evidence that indicates a marked advance in behavior pattern in comparison with the Glossosomatidae. The *Hydroptila* larva constructs the case chiefly from spun silk, with other material added to this in some species. Thus the spun matrix is now the base of the case, and other material is secondary. When the larva is full grown a second important difference is noted. It does not cut open the case and cement the edges down; it simply ties it securely at both ends to a support, and seals up each end before pupation. No evident fibrous inner cocoon is made, although some spinning is done inside the case to seal it up.

The final step in the casemaking evolution in the Trichoptera is the development of the "tube case," a descriptive term employed to distinguish this form from the saddle and purse case forms. The tubular case, the product of any of the so-called

true casemakers such as the Limnephilidae (Fig. 8), is made of a silken matrix and building materials such as stones or sticks. The posterior end, rather than being left open, is closed by a mesh webbing. Thus, only the anterior portion of the larva protrudes; the posterior end hooks firmly into the back part of the case. Preparatory to pupation, only the front end of the case is anchored down, but so firmly that the entire case is held rigid against its support.

The best morphological evidence to support this hypothesis of casemaking evolution is found in the

Fig. 8. Case and larva of *Limnephilus rhombicus*. (From Illinois Natural History Survey.)

structure of the larval anal claw. In free-living Rhyacophilidae the anal claw is of the primitive type (Fig. 9A, B) with *s* and *d* long and *v* ventral. In the Glossosomatidae (Fig. 9F, G) the saddle casemakers, *s* is still long, but *d* is shorter and amorphous; *v* has enlarged greatly but this may be only a side branch specialization within this family. In the Hydroptilidae (Fig. 9H, I)*s* is shorter, *d* is only a small plate, and *v* is mesal, situated beneath *s* and anterior to the claw. Up to this point the claw has been freely movable in an up-and-down direction. In the tube casemakers (Fig. 9J) *s* is still shorter and triangular, and *d* is a minute strap serving to connect the base of the claw rigidly to the top of *s*. Sclerite *v* is triangular and wedged between the posteroventral margin of *s* and the base of the claw. The claw, therefore, cannot move independently up and down, but only a little sideways. It seems admirably suited for anchoring the body inside a tight case.

There is another change which parallels the sclerotization changes of the anal leg. In the Rhyacophilidae the two anal legs are separate in their attachment and capable of independent movement (Fig. 9B). Gradually they fuse, until in the tube casemakers the anal legs have become a single unit composed of the two hooks embedded on the outside of two large, contiguous membranous pads (Fig. 10).

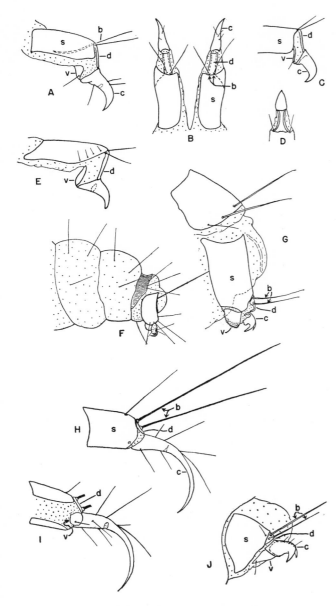

B. We may therefore conclude that in these species startling changes occurred in casemaking and larval evolution while the adults practically stood still, in an evolutionary sense. (See page 20 for further discussion.)

At this point it is desirable to discuss another peculiarity in the record. In all the Hydroptilidae studied to date, the first four instars build no case but are free-living and possess long anal claws much like those of *Rhyacophila* in general appearance. These Hydroptilidae are tiny insects less than 5 mm. in length, and their first four larval instars are exceedingly minute. The fifth instar larva does build a case, and it is in this instar that most of the larval growth occurs. Nielsen (1948) is of the opinion that this represents the first casemaking pattern, and that the young larvae are primeval in structure. Details of the anal claws of these young larvae, however, show that sclerite *d* is only a short piece joining the claw very closely with sclerite *s* (Fig. 9H, I). This is a condition more specialized for casemaking than that which occurs in the Glossosomatidae, in which even the young larvae make cases. It is my conclusion, therefore, that the free-

Fig. 9. Anal legs of caddisfly larvae. *A, B, Atopsyche; C, D, Sortosa; E, Stenopsyche; F, Agapetus; G. Glossosoma; H, I, Agraylea; J, Lepidostoma.* All lateral aspect except *B* and *D*, which are the dorsal aspect, and *I* which is the mesal aspect. Abbreviations: *b*, basal tuft, *c,* anal claw; *d,* dorsal plate; *s,* lateral sclerite; *v,* ventral sole plate.

Consulting Chart 1 again, it can be deduced that Ancestor E, the first tube casemaker, was remarkably similar to *Rhyacophila* in all important adult characters considered as primitive. From this it follows that the adults of Ancestors C and D were likewise little changed from the primitive Ancestor

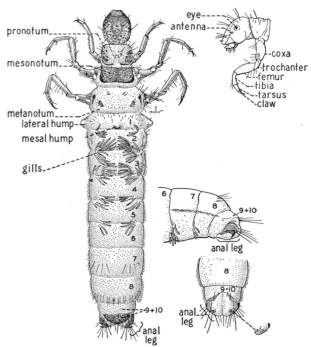

Fig. 10. Larva of *Limnephilus submonilifer.* (From Illinois Natural History Survey.)

living condition found in the young larvae of the Hydroptilidae is a specialized deviation from casemaking, evolved in parallel with minute size.

In spite of their great antiquity, the early branches on the casemaking line have not become as diversified as the tube casemakers. This is brought out in a brief synopsis of these groups.

### Free-Living Series

This series contains only one family, the Rhyacophilidae, which has two subfamilies: the Rhyacophilinae, adapted to cold and principally montane streams; and the Hydrobiosinae, which live in cool streams in subtropical and adjacent areas. These are the primitive descendants of Ancestor B in Chart 1, and are dealt with in greater detail in Chapter 4.

### Saddle Casemakers

Here, again, only a single compact family is known, the Glossosomatidae, representing the primitive descendants of Ancestor C. This family is mainly cool-adapted, with specialized forms in tropical areas. The family is treated in Chapter 5.

### Purse Casemakers

The members of this group are more diverse than the Glossosomatidae, although the known genera are all included in the one family Hydroptilidae. Most of the genera make barrel- or purse-shaped cases (Fig. 7), but a few, such as *Neotrichia* and *Mayatrichia*, make a cylindrical case sealed at one end, and thus resemble completely the tube-case of the higher forms. The adult structure of these latter genera, however, is so specialized and so like that in many other Hydroptilidae that the tube casemakers could not possibly have evolved from these tiny Hydroptilidae. It is evident that here is a most interesting case of parallel evolution in casemaking.

The adults of the Hydroptilidae range from primitive genera 5 or 6 mm. long to highly specialized forms only 1.5 mm. long. The large primitive forms, *Paleagapetus* and *Ptilocolepus*, resemble small rhyacophilids or glossosomatids. From the Glossosomatidae, the Hydroptilidae differ in having closely set median warts on the pronotum, and from the Rhyacophilidae they differ in having the ocelli absent or situated very close to the eyes. Two distinct subfamilies of Hydroptilidae can be delineated.

Front wing with $Cu_1$ branched; mesonotum convex, praescutum well marked and scutellum with a large oval wart; katepisternum with anterior suture present. Contains only the two small montane genera *Ptilocolepus* and *Paleagapetus*..........
.......................... **Ptilocolepinae**
Front wing with $Cu_1$ appearing unbranched; mesonotum flat, praescutum at most very faintly delineated, and scutellum with warty texture only along edges; katepisternum usually with anterior suture lacking. Contains a large number of genera including both cool-adapted and warm-adapted forms..........
.......................... **Hydroptilinae**

### Tube Casemakers

These are the decendants of Ancestor E, and comprise the most profuse development of any group of the caddisflies. Ancestor E itself must have been a very primitive caddisfly, differing from Ancestor B chiefly in the casemaking habit, the modified anal legs of the larva, and the presence of a pair of terminal processes on the abdomen of the pupa. The primitive characters of Ancestor E are no longer combined in any living family, but each of them may be found in some existing family. The adults of primitive genera of the Calamoceratidae and Odontoceridae have a venation as primitive as that of the Rhyacophilidae. The Phryganeidae and Limnephilidae have ocelli. The Calamoceratidae and Phryganeidae have larvae fully as primitive as those of the Rhyacophilidae except for the anal legs and claws.

There has been much difference of opinion regarding the relationships and the family groupings of this assemblage of caddisflies. In the following analysis I have attempted to correlate characters of both larvae and adults in such a way as to arrive at an orderly morphological sequence from the primitive Ancestor E to the various specialized types among the tube casemakers.

Ancestor E gave rise directly to two distinct lines. Members of one line retained the ocelli but lost $M_4$ in the male front wing, resulting in only the limnephilid line. Members of the other line lost the ocelli but preserved a complete wing venation in both sexes, giving rise to Ancestor F. From this latter prototype there arose three or four independent branches, although they may not have all developed simultaneously. In each of these branches certain genera retain combinations of primitive characters which appear to trace back directly to Ancestor F rather than to one of the sister branches.

On this basis, we must postulate that several peculiar characters have evolved independently in different lines, but this same circumstance arises with any arrangement thus far proposed.

*Limnephilid Line.* In this line the front wing lost $M_4$ in the male and cross-vein $r$ in both sexes; the maxillary palps of the male lost a segment; and the larva developed a short, curved, semimembranous horn between the two front legs, and a line-like furrow on the pronotum running anterior to the pleural suture (Fig. 3E). The most primitive family is the Phryganeidae. Its larva has an almost Rhyacophila-like thorax (as in Fig. 11A), in which the meso- and metanotum are membranous, and both have seta 1 and 2 single and seta 3 represented by an isolated cluster of a few setae called the *lateral cluster.*

From this primitive condition a simple series of steps can be traced which leads to the most specialized members of the line. The first step appears to have been the development of two pairs of sclerites occupying most of the mesonotum (Fig. 11C). The mesal pair of sclerites includes setae 1 and 2, the lateral pair only seta 3. Simultaneously the male maxillary palps became reduced to three segments. Typical of such a form is the family Brachycentridae, except that it has lost the adult ocelli.

The next step was the loss of $M_4$ in the female front wing. Apparently arising from this point in the line was the family Goeridae, which also has lost the ocelli.

Beyond the goerid branch, the larval antennae moved away from the margin of the head toward the eye. An existing form still showing this condition is the limnephilid genus *Pedomoecus* (Fig. 11C), although in other characters it is highly specialized. After this the two pairs of larval mesonotal plates consolidated into a single pair closely appressed on the meson (Fig. 10). The rest of the Limnephilidae exhibit this stage of development.

The family Lepidostomatidae would appear to be a specialized offshoot of the main group of Limnephilidae, because in the lepidostomatid larva the mesonotal plates are fused as in these Limnephilidae and the antenna has moved appreciably closer to the eye. The adult Lepidostomatidae, however, have preserved all the typical tibial spurs (2-4-4) whereas in *Pedomoecus* and the other Limnephilidae at least two spurs have been lost (minimum count 1-3-4). Until more information is available it

is necessary to choose between the view that the tibial spurs were lost independently in *Pedomoecus* and in the other Limnephilidae, and the view that the mesonotal lobes fused independently in the Lepidostomatidae and in the higher Limnephilidae. Incidental to this question it should be noted that very few of the primitive genera of Goeridae and Limnephilidae have been reared. If larvae and pupae of these were available, they could well provide information that would contribute toward a better understanding of evolutionary development within the limnephilid line.

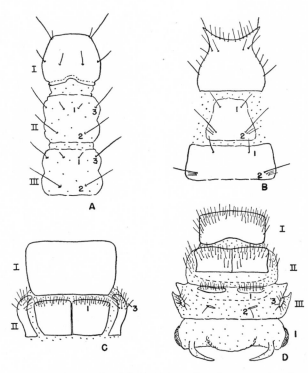

Fig. 11. Thorax of caddisfly larvae, dorsal aspect. A, *Rhyacophila*; B, *Anisocentropus*; C, *Pedomoecus*; D, *Sericostoma*. 1, 2, 3, dorsal setae or setal tufts.

The Australian family Plectrotarsidae undoubtedly belongs to the limnephilid line. The adult characters—ocelli present, $M_4$ lost in male front wing only, and spur formula 1-4-4 (Mosely & Kimmins 1953)—indicate that the family is a primitive offshoot of the branch leading to the Limnephilidae. The larva is unknown.

The Phryganeidae is a moderate-sized family, its members all cool-adapted, many montane.

The Limnephilidae is a large family, the primitive genera all cool-adapted and chiefly montane.

The Goeridae and Brachycentridae are small families, either cool-adapted or occurring in mountainous areas in warmer regions.

The members of the Lepidostomatidae are primarily inhabitants of springs or cool streams. A few are montane.

*Ancestor F.* In the second line arising from Ancestor E the adults lost the ocelli but retained $M_4$ in the front wing of both sexes. Judging by primitive genera arising from it, the larva was little if any different from that of Ancestor E, having seta 1 and 2 single on both mesonotum and metanotum, and seta 3 a cluster of setae on a short bar. As currently defined, at least eight families have arisen from Ancestor F. On the basis of larval characters, these eight families comprise four phyletic lines, but the exact relationship of one line to another is difficult to ascertain.

*Leptocerid Line.* In the primitive members of this line the larva has the fore trochantin large and well separated from the episternum (Fig. 3F), and setae 1 and 2 single. The adult wing venation, however, is considerably specialized by coalescence and atrophy of veins and cross-veins. This line contains only the family Leptoceridae. It contains two cool-adapted genera, *Athripsodes* (the most primitive in the family) and *Mystacides*. The remaining large number of genera are either warm-adapted, such as the tribe Triplectidina, or exhibit a remarkable breadth of ecological tolerance.

*Calamoceratid Line.* In this line the larva has become specialized primarily by a fusion of the fore trochantin with the mesepisternum to form a long curved process (Fig. 3G), and by a movement of the antenna to a point midway between the eye and the margin of the head. In adults of primitive genera the wings retain a full complement of veins. Two families developed from this line:

Larva with mesonotum having a single, central, semi-sclerotized shield not including the lateral cluster (Fig. 11B); case straight or curved; adult with male maxillary palp 5-segmented............... ...........................**Calamoceratidae**
Larva with mesonotum bearing four irregular plates, the posterior pair embracing the lateral cluster 3 (Fig. 12D); case shaped like a snail shell; adult with male maxillary palp 3-segmented.............. ...........................**Helicopsychidae**

The Calamoceratidae have one or two primitive, cool-adapted genera, but most of them are warm-adapted.

The Helicopsychidae are primarily warm-adapted, with a few species extending into cool temperate regions.

*Odontocerid Line.* The ancestral form of known existing genera of this group was relatively specialized, having the larval mesonotum nearly completely sclerotized and the metanotum with a linear sclerite in place of seta 1. The larval fore trochantin became smaller than in the Leptoceridae but of the same shape (Fig. 3I). This line gave rise to two distinct families:

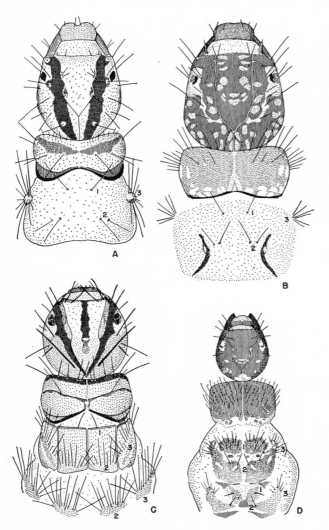

FIG. 12. Head and portion of thorax of caddisfly larvae, dorsal aspect. A, *Ptilostomis*; B, *Athripsodes*; C, *Brachycentrus*; D, *Helicopsyche*. A, B, head to mesonotum; C, D, head to metanotum. 1, 2, 3, dorsal setae or setal tufts.

A. Larval fore trochantin hooklike (Fig. 3H), projecting beyond outline of coxa; larval mentum and submentum large; larval gills single; adult with male maxillary palp 1 to 3-segmented, both sexes with $M_4$ lost in front wing . . . . . . . .
. . . . . . . . . . . . . . . . . . . . . . **Sericostomatidae**

AA. Larval fore trochantin without a hook (Fig. 3I), projecting little or not at all beyond outline of coxa; larval mentum and submentum reduced to small plates; larval gills tufted; adults of primitive genera with $M_4$ present in front wing and male maxillary palp 5-segmented . . . . . . . . . . .
. . . . . . . . . . . . . . . . . . . . . . . **Odontoceridae**

Primitive genera of both families are cool-adapted and montane. Specialized genera, especially of the Odontoceridae, are chiefly tropical in distribution.

Based on adult characters outlined by Mosley and Kimmins (1953) the family Philorheithridae belongs to this phyletic line and is a close relative of the Odontoceridae. It has a similar case and an affinity for swift water.

*Molannid Line.* This small group must have started from a very primitive ancestral type, the adult front wings having M 4-branched, and the larva having a primitive setal arrangement and little sclerotization on the meso- and metanotum. In adults of the most primitive known genera the branches of R are either reduced or partially coalesced with each other or with $M_1$. In their larvae the fore trochantin is small, somewhat as in the Odontoceridae (Fig. 3I). Only two families are known, the Molannidae with an adult leg spur count of 2-4-4, and the Beraeidae with an adult leg spur count of 2-2-4. Both families are chiefly cool-adapted.

*Groups of doubtful position.* The foregoing arrangement is based entirely on those genera for which larvae are known. Several families and genera are difficult to place because their larvae are unknown. The Oriental Limnocentropodidae, for example, may represent a branch arising from the foot of the limnephilid line because the adults have ocelli and 5-segmented male maxillary palps. The larvae, however, appear to be highly specialized (Tsuda 1936), and may indicate that the Limnocentropodidae belong to a separate line arising from or near Ancestor E.

The New Zealand family Philanisidae and the Australian family Helicophidae are likewise difficult to place in the absence of larvae. On the basis of adult characters both could well be primitive offshoots of the branch leading to the Sericostomatidae. It is, however, believed to be unwise to make definite assertions regarding these particular forms without benefit of larval evidence.

## Evidence from Internal Characters

The foregoing reconstruction of the evolutionary development of the Trichoptera is based entirely on external characters. There is no doubt a great deal of evidence to be found in the internal structures of both larvae and adults. The range of internal structures in the adults is well depicted by Deoras (1944-45), who illustrated the principal organs for eight species representing six families. Deoras points out that the different organic systems have not evolved synchronously. Such a scattered sampling gives more information regarding family differences than regarding phylogenetic affinities, yet does show that much valuable data may be obtained by the study of these organs. In the larvae, I have observed striking differences of the intestinal tract among members of a few families, but to my knowledge no one has yet published a comparative account of these organs throughout the order.

An interesting paper by Pryor (1951) shows the homologies of the musculature of the anal legs of larvae belonging to several representatives of the orders Megaloptera and Trichoptera. Data from Pryor's studies fit well into the hypothesis that (1) the Trichoptera arose from a Megaloptera-like ancestor, (2) the families Rhyacophilidae and Philopotamidae are extremely primitive families, (3) the Psychomyiidae represent the highly specialized end of their phyletic line, and (4) the casemakers arose from a *Rhyacophila*-like ancestor.

## HABITS OF THE ANCESTRAL TRICHOPTERON

It was assumed earlier in this discussion that the larva of the ancestral trichopteron was much like that of the Philopotamidae. Consulting Chart 1, it is pertinent to note that the descendants of Ancestor A are all retreat makers, and all have precisely the same type of anal leg. Of the descendants of Ancestor B, a few very early forms have this type of anal leg, but in later forms it became progressively modified with the development of casemaking. In the free-living forms (spinning only ground lines of silk), the philopotamoid claw occurs only in the Hydrobiosinae, being modified to some extent in the Rhyacophilinae.

From this it would appear that the philopotamoid claw (Fig. 9C) was so well adapted for life in retreats that in the entire large evolutionary development of the retreat makers, no modification of these basic structures became established. On the other hand, modification of the dorsal strap and other sclerites occurred, at least to some extent, with all other types of habit. Because the philopotamoid claw occurs at the base of both main lines of the Trichoptera, we can infer that the ancestral trichop-

rise to a caddisfly making a portable case. In other words, the caddisfly case is not a modified retreat but a specialization of the outer covering of the cocoon. Corroboration is found in the fact that we know of no instance in which a retreat maker has given rise directly to a form making a portable abode.

## HABITAT OF THE ANCESTRAL TRICHOPTERON

In the family tree of the Trichoptera delineated in Chart 2, families and lesser groups containing

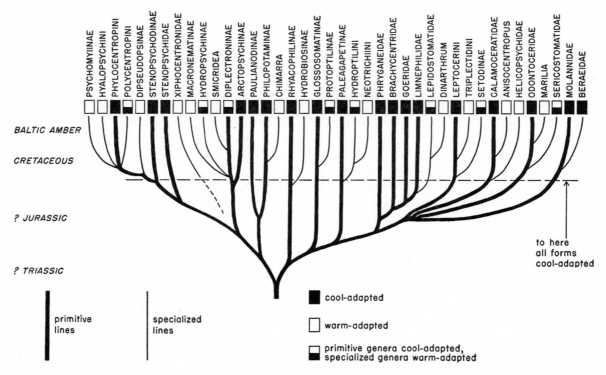

CHART 2. Phylogenetic diagram of the Trichoptera showing coincidence of primitive lines with cool-adapted habitat.

teron also possessed such a claw, and was a retreat maker. Had it been otherwise we would expect that either (1) the base of the casemaker line would have had some other type of claw, or (2) in the retreat-maker line a different type of claw would have evolved, better suited to retreat habitation.

This brings us to the interesting conclusion that some retreat maker lost its retreat-making habit, and only after this change had occurred did it give

primarily primitive genera are represented by a heavy line. Above each taxonomic unit is a box representing the general ecological affinities of the unit. A black box indicates that the group immediately below is chiefly or entirely cool-adapted; a white box indicates that the group is warm-adapted; and a half black-half white box indicates that the primitive genera of that group are cool-adapted, the more specialized genera warm-adapted.

THE EVOLUTION OF THE CADDISFLIES

The scale of temperature adaptation is acknowledgedly arbitrary. Cool-adapted groups typically include those living in areas with regular periods of freezing weather and in streams which are cool for the entire year. On the basis of unfortunately few recordings, there seems to be a significant change in caddisfly fauna in the neighborhood of a maximum water temperature of 65° to 68° F. This point also corresponds to the high end of the optimum range for the cooler-adapted species of trout (Davis 1953, Needham 1938). For the present, therefore, those streams are considered cool that have temperatures not exceeding 68° F. except perhaps for rare periods of only a few hours. Such conditions also occur at high elevations in equatorial regions where streams are cooled throughout the year by snow melt water. This would apply especially to areas such as New Guinea, Northern India, and the Andes, all of which have glaciers or continuously snow-capped mountains.

A careful perusal of Chart 2 indicates that primitiveness coincides to a remarkable extent with cool-adaptation. Of the 18 primitive (heavy) lines, 17 are cool-adapted and one has primitive genera which are cool-adapted. *Not one is warm-adapted.* The warm-adapted lines represent specialized offshoots from cool-adapted primitive lines.

There are two current views concerning these phenomena. Proponents of one view believe that within a given habitat specialized forms arise which are better suited for life in the habitat than the primitive forms, and as a result the specialized forms crowd the primitive ones out of the ancestral habitat into peripheral areas. In the case of the Trichoptera this infers that the specialized groups occupy the ancestral habitat—in this case, the warm-water habitat—and that they have crowded the primitive forms into cool-water habitats.

Proponents of the other view consider that the primitive forms remain in the ancestral habitat, and that specialization comes about through adaptation of a group to a new and therefore specialized habitat. Thus, if a population of a primitive group becomes isolated in an area which later changes in ecological characteristics, that population will tend to change (i.e., become specialized) in response to changing selection pressures exerted by the environment. In the case of the Trichoptera this implies that the primitive forms are in the ancestral habitat, in this case the cool-water habitat, and that the specialized forms represent groups which have become adapted to conditions different from the ancestral. According to this view, then, the Trichoptera originated in cool water and later some forms became specialized to live in warmer water.

In attempting to judge which interpretation is correct, three points offer evidence.

1. The terms *warm* and *cool* have been employed for caddisfly habitats because these terms describe phenomena most obvious to the human observer. It is doubtful, however, if the actual temperature as such is of paramount importance to the caddis larva. More likely the important factor is dissolved oxygen, because in water, respiration is one of the most critical adaptive features. Cool water (other things being equal) has a higher oxygen tension than warm water, and presumably would be better suited for an organism having only the minimum adaptation for aquatic life. To live in warmer water an organism would theoretically require specializations resulting in its ability to respire successfully in the presence of a lower oxygen tension. This would imply that warmer water groups would be specialized rather than primitive in physiological adjustments. It seems logical, therefore, to suppose that the earlier, primitive forms existed in the habitats more ideally suited for aquatic life, that is, in cool running water.

2. The theoretical selection pressures outlined by Simpson (1944) support the second view. These selection pressures retard change in a species which remains in the same environment and accelerate change in a species which comes within the influence of a changing environment.

3. It seems completely unlikely that an aggregate of 18 primitive groups would evolve in warm water, and that specialized groups would arise and crowd *every one* of these primitive groups into a cool-water habitat.

These three items seem to provide convincing arguments in favor of the second view. I am therefore assuming that the primitive caddisflies were cool-adapted forms living in running streams. Adaptation to warmer, slower waters was a later specialization dependent on the development of physiological characteristics facilitating more efficient utilization of oxygen.

Referring again to Chart 2, it is apparent that all main lines of the Trichoptera differentiated while the group was still entirely cool-adapted. The only possible exception seems to be the warm-adapted family Xiphocentronidae, but this family is represented today by only a single, highly specialized genus. The line may well have begun as a cool-adapted line similar to those giving rise to the Hydropsychidae and Psychomyiidae, but it differed in its later history in that the primitive forms of the Xiphocentronidae have not persisted to the present.

This period of group differentiation corresponds to the evolutionary diversification of retreat and case making, which must have occurred also within the cool-water habitat. According to this reasoning, the divergence of structure and behavior between the various phyletic lines of caddisflies progressed concurrently with competition within the cool stream environment. It was not until structural, behavioristic, and ecological specializations resulted in relatively advanced types of caddisfly larvae that any of the Trichoptera appear to have become successful denizens of warmer water.

This reasoning is substantiated by a consideration of the adults. On page 13 it was pointed out that the adults seem to have changed scarcely at all while the larvae were evolving casemaking habits at a relatively rapid rate. Again applying Simpson's ideas of selection pressures, it is logical to assume that the adults were static because *they remained in virtually the same environment* during this entire evolutionary period. That environment would be the shaded banks of cool, woodland streams, where today we find the adults of primitive families disporting themselves in very much the same manner as they probably did eons ago.

## ORIGIN OF THE ORDER

The origin of the Trichoptera is poorly documented in the fossil record. The earliest known fossils that are indubitably Trichoptera, as known today, occur in the Upper Triassic and Lower Jurassic periods. Several wings are known from strata occurring throughout this period, but all are primitive in venation and show little definite progression in type from early to late strata.

Certain Permian forms described in the order Paramecoptera could be similar to the ancestral Mecoptera-like form from which the Trichoptera presumably evolved. Such a form is *Belmontia mitchelli* Tillyard (Fig. 13) from the Upper Permian of New South Wales, Australia. It is even possible that this form is very similar to an ancestor which could have given rise to the Mecoptera in one direction and the Trichoptera in another.

From the standpoint of wings, the most conspicuous differences between the two orders are that the Mecoptera have $Cu_1$ unbranched, and have many cross-veins, whereas the Trichoptera have $Cu_1$ branched and few cross-veins. Tillyard (1933, p. 69) expresses the opinion that the extra branch of $Cu_1$ in the Trichoptera actually represents a transfer of a posterior branch of $M_4$ from its parent vein to $Cu_1$. While this is a possibility it is far from demonstrated by fossil evidence. It is just as logical to suggest that in the Mecoptera the anterior branch of $Cu_1$ became associated with $M_4$ and then detached from $Cu_1$. If this latter were the case, then *Belmontia* could readily be the common ancestor of the Mecoptera and Trichoptera, or a little-changed descendant of such an ancestor, for *Belmontia* combines a branched $Cu_1$ and a large number of cross-veins (Fig. 13). If a form arising from such an ancestor lost a few cross-veins and a branch each of $R_3$ and $M_4$, but retained the branch of $Cu_1$, it would be well on its way to becoming a typical caddisfly.

This conjecture and many others in the literature are greatly undermined by lack of information on body sclerites of the adults and structure and habits of the larvae. We must rely heavily on these structures and habits in classifying the living forms, frequently on differential evolution between adult and larva. There is every reason to suppose that the same structures are needed to deduce the correct affinities of the fossil forms now known in the main by only disassociated wings.

I believe that it is the better course simply to say that there are known from Permian strata a moderate number of wings representing species which could have given rise to the Trichoptera. Since we infer that the first ancestral caddisfly to become truly aquatic did so in cool, running water, we may also infer that it evolved from an ancestral form living near or at such a situation. Tillyard, in his fascinating account of the evolution of the Mecoptera (1933), gives a pertinent comment on the habitat of one of the primitive Mecoptera of Australia (italicization mine):

The account shows how the two recent Australian families Choristidae and Nannochoristidae are descended in an unbroken line from the Upper Permian Mecopterous fauna of the Newcastle coal-measures, New South Wales. I should like to add here the interesting observation that in April it is possible to capture specimens of *Chorista australis* Klug at Belmont or Warner's Bay, where, at a depth of only two or three feet, lie the actual Upper Permian rocks in which the genus *Permochorista* occurs. When one recalls that *Chorista* has a yearly life-cycle, that it is a weak, defenseless insect unfitted to compete with vigorous modern forms, and that its life-history is such that *it is of necessity confined to cool glades* where autumn dews are abundant, one can only marvel at its persistence through so many millions of years with such slight changes in form and venation.

Perhaps *Belmontia* or some other primitive premecopteron was similarly a dweller in cool glades by a rapid stream, and in this setting the first ancestral caddisfly became a stream dweller.

It is of unusual importance to note that the persistence of the Trichoptera, as well as of Tillyard's *Chorista*, indicates the uninterrupted existence of cool glades and cool streams from Permian times to the present. These conditions need not always have been in the same place; if they were not, corridors of similar conditions must have been provided for the dispersal of the cool-adapted groups from one area to another.

### The First Caddisflies

From the Upper Triassic of Queensland, primitive forms are described which may be true caddisflies. These have been placed by Tillyard (1917) in the family Mesopsychidae, including the two genera *Mesopsyche* Tillyard (Fig. 14) and *Triassopsyche* Tillyard. Both are known only from front wings. The branches of Rs and M are each reduced to four branches, and in *Mesopsyche* Cu₁ is definitely branched. The anal veins are looped together in both genera. These characteristics are trichopterous. There are, however, additional cross-veins in the

→

FIG. 13. Front wing of *Belmontia michelli* (Upper Permian). (After Tillyard.)

FIG. 14. Front wing of *Mesopsyche triareolata* (Upper Triassic). (After Tillyard.)

FIG. 15. Front wing of *Necrotaulius furcatus* (Lower Jurassic). (After Tillyard.)

FIG. 16. Front wing of *Necrotaulius maculatus* (Lower Jurassic). (After Handlirsch.)

FIG. 17. Front wing of *Necrotaulius stigmaticus* (Lower Jurassic). (After Tillyard.)

FIG. 18. Front wing of a primitive living caddisfly, *Paleagapetus celsus*.

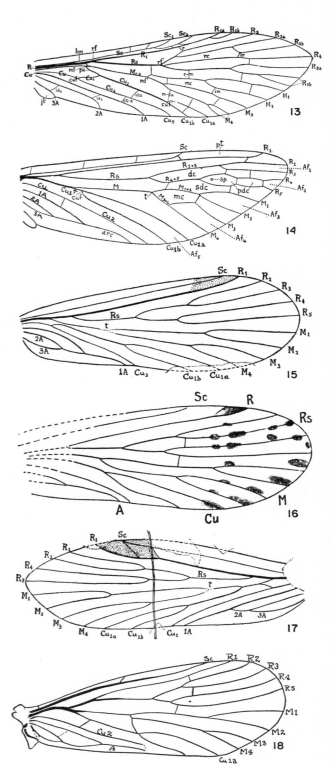

radiomedial area, which indicate a condition more primitive than any found in existing Trichoptera. There seems little doubt that these forms are off-shoots from the line leading directly to the typical Trichoptera.

From the Upper Triassic (Rhaetic) and Lower Jurassic (Lower and Upper Liassic) of England and Germany there have been described about 20 species, placed in the family Necrotauliidae, which are

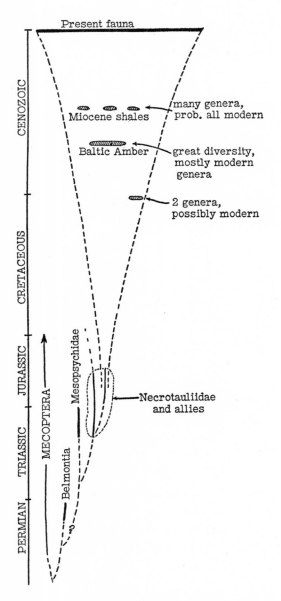

CHART 3. Résumé of known geological history of the Trichoptera and some of their immediate allies.

indubitably true Trichoptera as defined by living forms. Their front wings are from 3.5 to 6 mm. long. In general there is a striking resemblance between some of the fossil necrotauliid wings (Figs. 15-17) and wings of living *Paleagapetus* or *Rhyacophila* (Fig. 18). Lower Jurassic species such as *Necrotaulius furcatus* (Giebel) (Fig. 15) are more primitive than any living caddisflies in having the bases of M and $Cu_1$ separate. Other species from Lower Jurassic and most of the species from middle Jurassic appear to have the bases of M and $Cu_1$ fused (Fig. 17) as in the front wings of present-day species. A good example is Handlirsch's figure of *Necrotaulius intermedius* Handl. This character cannot be seen on most of the known illustrated Rhaetic specimens.

The wings of the Jurassic caddisflies give little indication of the relationship of these early forms to the phylogenetic arrangement outlined in Chart 1. These wings resemble primitive types, perhaps most suggestive of Philopotamidae or Rhyacophilidae, but that of *Necrotaulius intermedius* has an intercubital cross-vein and might be a relative of Ancestor E. All the wings which postively are hind wings have M only 3-branched as in modern forms. There is a possibility that the specimen of *Necrotaulius maior* Handlirsch is a hind wing, and it has M 4-branched. This condition would be reminiscent of the Recent genera *Paulianodes* and *Sortosa,* in which M in the hind wing is 4-branched in an occasional specimen.

It is probable that species of the Necrotauliidae represent one or more of the existing primitive caddisfly groups, and that they were cool-adapted. Certainly they were on the main line of typical caddisfly evolution. These forms give no indication that highly specialized lines developed in any of the known Necrotauliidae, but give every indication that the primitive Trichoptera became well established during Jurassic time.

From the Cretaceous, collectors have secured only a few caddisfly fossils. The specimens are difficult to place phylogenetically because only characters of venation are distinct. There is no doubt, however, that they either belong to or are very closely related to two existing genera, both in the Psychomyiidae.

Two extensive series of Cenozoic fossils have been studied, one from the Baltic amber of Germany, the other from the Miocene shales of western

North America. The Baltic amber specimens are unusual in that characters of head, legs, and genitalia are preserved with unusual clarity; hence, it is possible to ascertain the exact relationships of many components of this fauna. In it are found most of the families known today. The great bulk of the Baltic amber species belong to existing genera, and some are little different from existing species. The Baltic amber fauna is essentially a modern one. Conversely, we can say that our recent fauna has changed little since Baltic amber time except for increase in the number of species.

The fossils of the Miocene shales consist chiefly of wing impressions, hence afford little data for more than approximate phylogenetic placement. What data can be secured complements that from the Baltic amber.

The total fossil record indicates that a well-developed caddisfly fauna evolved after Jurassic and before mid-Tertiary time, and that in general this same type of fauna has persisted since. There is no fossil record to indicate where or how the pre-Eocene forms developed, or the details of their subsequent evolution. For this information it is necessary to turn to an analysis of phylogenetic and biogeographic data.

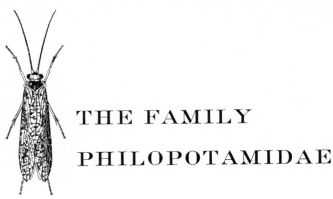

chapter three

# THE FAMILY PHILOPOTAMIDAE

## EVOLUTION AND DISPERSAL

The Philopotamidae are world-wide in distribution, and are abundant in rapid, clear streams from subarctic to tropical areas. The larvae make elongate saclike nets under stones, and apparently have uniform habits throughout the family. They are also remarkably similar in general structure, differing chiefly in head characters. The pupae of all genera are similar, in general, but have significant differences in the mandibles.

The adults vary considerably in size and shape. The smallest are 3 or 4 mm. long and drab in color; the largest attain a length of 20 mm. and may be speckled with brown and golden flecks. Some of the tropical species of *Chimarra* are gaudy red or yellow and black creatures, and may have brightly patterned wings. These external features offer little aid in grouping the species into natural units. The best criteria for this have proven to be differences in wing venation and male genitalia.

As was first pointed out by Ulmer (1930), the Philopotamidae contain three principal groups, based on the shape of the anal veins in the hind wing:

The primitive complex, whose members have all three anal veins present (Fig. 19), including a few with the second (2A) represented by only a stub;

The *Chimarra* complex, in which 2A is curved up and fused with 1A to form a loop at the base of 1A (Fig. 21); and

The *Wormaldia* complex, in which all trace of 2A has disappeared, so that the anal veins give the appearance of a divergent fork (Fig. 20).

The venation of both front and hind wings of the primitive complex agrees so perfectly with the ancestral type for the order that the group obviously contains the primitive elements of the Philopotamidae.

Further evidence of this primitive condition is found in a peculiar feature of the hind wing. Normally in Trichoptera the hind wing has media 3-branched, but in some specimens of *Sortosa* and the sole known male of *Paulianodes* this vein is 4-branched. Media is primitively 4-branched in the caddisfly front wing. The early Trichoptera certainly had a stage in which this condition was typical of the hind wing also. It may be that the specimens of *Paulianodes* and *Sortosa* noted are relics of this condition, or throwbacks to it. Except in the case of one wing of doubtful identity, the Jurassic fossils of hind wings have media 3-branched; hence there is a possibility that the ancestral philopotamid line is at least as old as these fossils.

The male genitalia in the primitive complex represent two types. In one the ninth segment is distinct dorsally and the tenth tergite is set off from it sharply by a membranous division, and the claspers are fused into a single, highly modified structure (Fig. 22). This type occurs only in the genus *Paulianodes*. In the second type the ninth and tenth tergites are fused and the tenth is more or less recessed into the ninth; the claspers are separate and 2-segmented, evidently of a primitive type. This second type occurs in many members of the *Sortosa* complex. Since one type is specialized in one character and primitive in the other, whereas the other type is primitive in the first character and specialized in the second, neither could have evolved from the other. Both must have arisen from an earlier form primitive in both characters, that is, with the ninth and tenth segments separate, and the claspers separate and 2-segmented. Such a form has never been found, but may be postulated as a hypothetical type resembling the ancestor of the Philopotamidae.

It is clear from the above evidence that at some early date the ancestral philopotamid gave rise to two lines, one evolving into *Paulianodes* and the other into the *Sortosa* complex.

*Paulianodes* is known from one species, *tsaratananae*, collected only in Madagascar. It is a curious combination of primitive and specialized characters, and undoubtedly has had a most interesting history since it began its own evolutionary path.

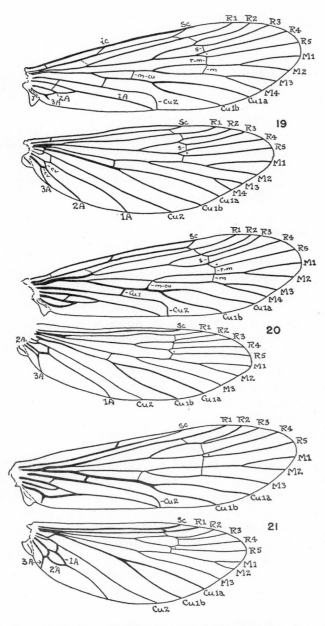

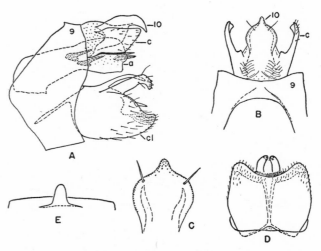

FIG. 22. Male genitalia of *Paulianodes tsaratananae*. A, lateral aspect; B, dorsal aspect; C, enlarged view of tenth tergite; D, ventral aspect of claspers; E, apex of seventh sternite; a, aedeagus; c, cercus; cl, clasper.

FIGS. 19-21. Front and hind wings of Philopotamidae. 19, *Paulianodes tsaratananae*; 20, *Wormaldia arizonensis*; 21, *Chimarra betteni*.

But we have only one species from one place as evidence of what took place in more than a hundred million years. This interesting course can not be followed further until more data are available.

### The *Sortosa* Complex

The second line of the primitive complex developed into *Sortosa* and its allies. This aggregation contains nearly 50 species presenting considerable diversification in characteristics of the male genitalia. These species form nine fairly homogeneous groups, each group obviously distinct from its nearest relative on the basis of one or more diagnostic characters. In each group some or all of the included species have wings that are practically identical with the prototype of the order (Fig. 23), indicating the primitive nature of each group. Noteworthy wing characters include a complete set of veins and cells $R_2$ and $R_4$ beginning at or before

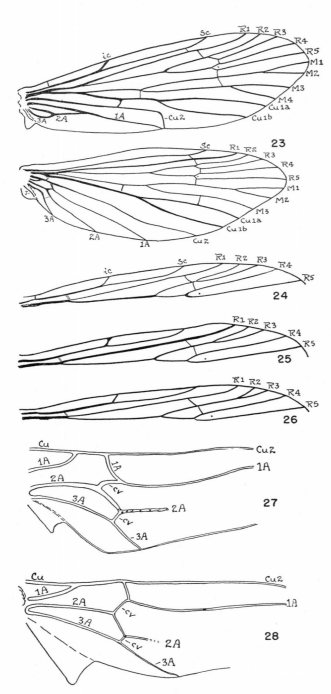

FIGS. 23-28. Wings of Philopotamidae. 23, front and hind wings of *Sortosa stenocerca*; 24, 25, 26, radial region of front wing of *Sortosa dorca* showing variation of fork $R_{2+3}$; 27, anal region of front wing of *Sortosa forcipata*; 28, anal region of front wing of *Sortosa urceola*.

the sectorial cross-vein *s*. In several groups the claspers of the male genitalia are simple and 2-segmented.

The segregates made on morphological grounds are supported to a remarkable degree by the geographic distribution of their included species. In the case of eight of the nine groups, each group occurs on only one continent. Species of the ninth group occur on two neighboring continents, Asia and North America.

The salient characters of each group are listed below.

1. Subgenus *Hydrobiosella*: Confined to Australia and New Zealand. Contains 9 species having varied genitalic structure. In all species but one, cells $R_2$ and $R_4$ begin at or before *s* (Fig. 23), and the apex of the tenth tergite is undivided (Fig. 42). The cercus is either small or apparently absent. The Australian species *cognata* is the sole exception. Its chief difference is that cell $R_2$ begins slightly beyond *s*, but this species is so similar to others of the subgenus, on the basis of genitalic characters, that it obviously belongs with them.

2. Subgenus *Sisko*: Confined to eastern and western montane areas of North America. Contains only 1 species, *sisko*, having wing venation similar to *Hydrobiosella*. The genitalia are very simple (Fig. 30). The tenth tergite is undivided, and the cerci are finger-like and of moderate length. The seventh sternite is slightly produced into a wide but short projection.

3. Subgenus *Fumonta*: Confined to the eastern montane area of North America. Contains only 1 species, *major* with venation essentially as in *Hydrobiosella*. The genitalia (Fig. 29) have the tenth tergite divided into a pair of hooklike side pieces; the cerci are broad and project dorsad.

4. Subgenus *Thylakion*: Confined to South Africa. Contains only 2 species, differing from the first three subgenera in several points. The front and hind wings have cell $R_2$ beginning just beyond *s*. The hind wings have 2A represented only by a short stub, although otherwise the anal veins exhibit the primitive condition (Figs. 27, 28). The tenth tergite bears a pair of lateral processes, each arising *below* the insertion of the elongate cercus (Fig. 35).

If we compare the other groups in which the anal venation of the hind wing is primitive, some interesting similarities and differences are apparent.

5. Subgenus *Sortosa*: Confined to southern South America. Contains three species remarkably similar to *Hydrobiosella* even in minute points of venation; in the male genitalia the apex of the tenth tergite is entire and the cerci are elongate; the claspers are unusually short and in one species are highly modified (Fig. 38).

6. Subgenus *Kisaura*: Contains several Asiatic forms. The species in this group have such a distinctive type of genitalia (Figs. 47-49) that there is no doubt of the homogeneity of the group. The tenth tergite has a pair of long lateral rods which lie *between the cerci and the* entirely membranous, narrow, but entire *tenth tergite;* the claspers have the apical segment pointed dorsad, with a curious, sclerotized, hinge-like piece at the base. In venation the group differs from *Sortosa* only in having cell $R_2$ variable (Figs. 31-33); in some species vein $R_2$ is completely gone.

7. Subgenus *Dolophilodes*: Widespread in Asia and North America. Contains about 10 species, all similar to the primitive *Sortosa* type except for two differences: in most species $R_{2+3}$ forks much beyond *s* (Fig. 26), and the apex of the tenth tergite is divided into a pair of lobes, small in most species (Fig. 57) but large in *dorca* (Fig. 62). The claspers and the anal veins are simple.

8. *Philopotamus*: Confined to Europe. Contains about 10 species characterized by a curious secondary apical segment on the clasper arising near and lying beneath the normal, larger, true apical segment (Fig. 50). The venation is primitive except in one respect: $R_{2+3}$ branches either near *s*, much as in *Sortosa dorca,* or much beyond it as in some species of *Dolophilodes* (see Figs. 24-26). In addition to the curious process of the clasper, the male genitalia have an extra pair of lobes arising from the extreme lateral base of the tenth tergite, so that the cercus is between the process and the tenth tergite, exactly as in *Thylakion,* and the reverse of *Kisaura.*

9. *Protarra*: Confined to South America. Contains four species forming a closely knit unit. In the hind wings all the anal veins are present, although 2A is reduced to a short stub (Fig. 104) resembling the condition in *Thylakion*. In the male genitalia the tenth tergite is of a primitive type (Figs. 105-107). Two other characters are unusual specializations. In the front wings $M_4$ is atrophied, and in the male genitalia the claspers are 1-segmented.

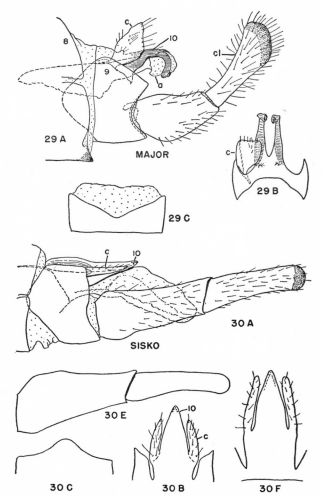

FIG. 29. Male genitalia of *Sortosa* (*Fumonta*) *major. A,* lateral aspect; *B,* dorsal aspect; *C,* dorsal aspect of eighth tergite. *a,* aedeagus; *c,* cercus; *cl,* clasper.

FIG. 30. Male genitalia of *Sortosa* (*Sisko*) *sisko. A,* lateral aspect; *B,* dorsal aspect; *C,* apex of seventh sternite; *A-C,* specimen from Oregon. *E, F,* clasper and tenth tergite, respectively, showing variation in specimen from North Carolina. Abbreviations as for Figure 29.

A survey of these nine species groups shows that some are very similar but that others have unusually distinctive attributes. All, however, are either virtually identical with, or only simple modifications of, the primitive ancestral type of the family. Genitalic structures suggest that the *Thylakion-Philopotamus* pair may be branches of the same line, but there is little evidence to support combinations of other groups into discrete sets. The most reasonable explanation for this situation seems to be that almost all of these groups arose directly from a common ancestral form having primitive wings and primitive claspers. This form will be called the *Sortosa* Ancestor.

It is practically certain that four of these groups must have arisen from the *Sortosa* Ancestor because they are almost identical with what the ancestor must have been. These are *Sortosa, Hydrobiosella, Fumonta* and *Sisko*. The others may have arisen either separately from this ancestor or as a single line with a tendency for the branching of $R_{2+3}$ to occur closer to the wing edge. Although the second alternative may seem more likely it is not a necessary postulate because it involves a parallelism common in widely scattered families of the order. If the second alternative did occur, then the line developed into at least two branches very soon—the *Thylakion-Philopotamus* branch and the

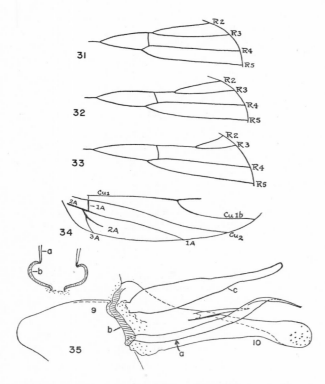

FIGS. 31-33. Radial sector of front wing of *Sortosa* subgenus *Kisaura.* 31, *Sortosa* sp. A; 32, *Sortosa pectinata;* 33, *Sortosa obrussa.*

FIG. 34. Posterior portion of hind wing of *Sortosa uncinata.*

FIG. 35. Dorsal portion of male genitalia of *Sortosa urceola,* with dorsal aspect of certain parts in upper left inset. *a,* lateral process arising below cercus; *b,* basal sclerotized strip; *c,* cercus.

*Dolophilodes-Kisaura* branch. The origin of *Dolophilodes* is nebulous. Its male genitalia are so primitive that it must have arisen from either the *Sortosa* Ancestor or some simple line little changed from the ancestral form.

There seems little doubt that *Protarra* evolved in South America either directly from the *Sortosa* Ancestor or from the same stock as the South American subgenus *Sortosa*. There is every indication also that *Protarra* represents an early stage in the development of the genus *Chimarra*. For this reason *Protarra* is treated as a member of the *Chimarra* complex.

These relationships are shown in Chart 24 as the branches arising from the *Sortosa* Ancestor. It is unfortunate that larvae and pupae are unknown for many of these groups. When known they should add materially to our understanding of the relationships of these early branches.

In spite of acknowledged deficiencies in our information about *Sortosa* and its allies, there is enough evidence to show that the group arose from an early ancestor which succeeded in spreading to almost all parts of the globe. It is of little moment whether this spread was by one species, in relays of several closely related species, or whether it reached all parts of the world simultaneously. The important facts are that the early primitive ancestor reached these many areas, the populations in many became cut off as separated units, and each such unit developed along an independent path. The phylogenetic evidence indicates that the progenitor of *Thylakion* reached Africa after the more primitive *Thylakion-Philopotamus* line arose.

Of the units we have studied to this point, only one shows evidence of reversals of distribution. Seven of the phyletic lines have changed so little that they must be considered at most as subgenera of *Sortosa: Hydrobiosella, Sisko, Fumonta, Thylakion, Kisaura, Dolophilodes* and *Sortosa* itself. One line has developed differences of greater magnitude and may be classed as a genus: *Philopotamus*.

The other two major complexes of the Philopotamidae (*Chimarra* and *Wormaldia,* outlined at the beginning of this section) are without doubt lines which arose either directly from the *Sortosa* Ancestor or from some primitive line which came from it. The *Wormaldia* complex seems to have originated in North America, and could possibly be a branch from near the base of the *Sisko* line. The

*Chimarra* complex gives every indication of a South American origin, and probably arose from the base of the restricted *Sortosa* line, possibly through an intermediate step much like *Protarra*. Data to support these conclusions are contained primarily in these groups, and will be discussed in the treatment of each complex.

When these genera are added to Chart 4, it is even more evident that the *Sortosa* Ancestor gave rise almost directly to virtually all of the existing forms of the Philopotamidae.

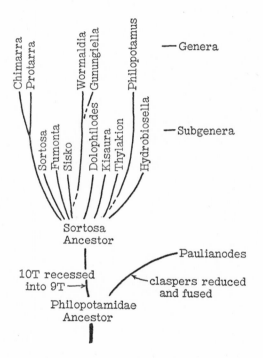

CHART 4. Phylogenetic diagram of the genera and subgenera of the Philopotamidae.

A detailed examination of the various genera and subgenera of the family contributes important material to an understanding of the time scale involved in this family. It is pertinent to follow this avenue next.

### The Genus *Sortosa*

It is difficult to discuss the evolution of *Sortosa*, its subgenera, and the genera which arose from it, in a strictly taxonomic order. Therefore, they are treated, instead, in the sequence and combination which serve best to elucidate the course of morpho-

genesis and geographic peregrination that have resulted in the fauna of today.

*Subgenera Fumonta and Sisko.* Each of these distinctive lines is known from only a single species of restricted distribution. Each has probably been where it is now found for a considerable length of geologic time, but the duration must be deduced or surmised later on evidence from other groups.

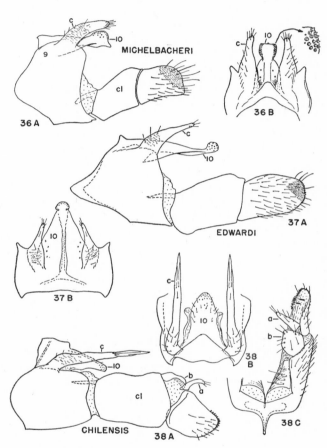

FIGS. 36-38. Male genitalia of *Sortosa* subgenus *Sortosa*. A, lateral aspect; B, dorsal aspect; C, ventral aspect. *a, b,* added dorsal sclerites between segments of clasper; *c,* cercus; *cl,* clasper.

*Subgenus Sortosa.* Only three species are known in this subgenus; they form two distinctive groups. The bent and imbricate base of the cercus and the short, deep clasper segments (Figs. 36-38) attest the phyletic unity of all three species. One group, including *michelbacheri* and *edwardi,* has become specialized in the structure of the tenth tergite, which is knobbed and crestlike at the apex (Figs.

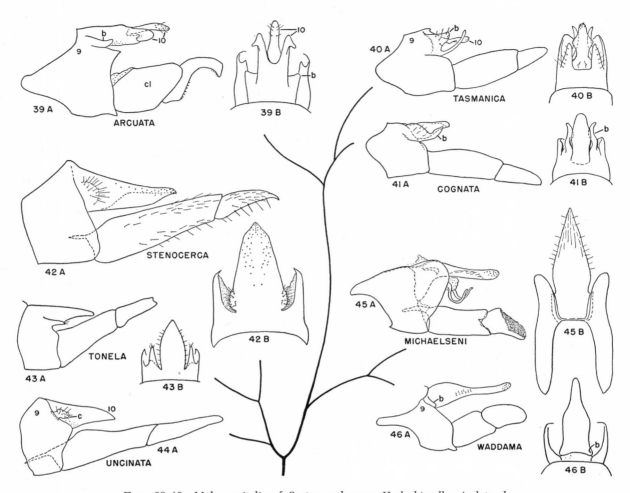

FIGS. 39-46. Male genitalia of *Sortosa* subgenus *Hydrobiosella*. A, lateral aspect; B, dorsal aspect. *b,* basal ridge or process of tenth tergite; *c,* cercus; *cl,* clasper. (Figs. 39-41, 43, and 46 modified from Kimmins.)

36, 37). In the other group, containing only *chilensis*, the tenth tergite is simple, but each clasper has two dorsal sclerites between the first and second segments (Fig. 38). It is likely that both groups arose from an ancestral form with both tenth tergite and clasper simple, an ancestor which would have looked extremely similar to a member of the subgenus *Dolophilodes*.

All three known species of the subgenus *Sortosa* are from Chile, so it is logical to suppose that the subgenus arose from a South American segregate of a very primitive line of *Sortosa*.

*Subgenus Hydrobiosella.* This subgenus contains two well-marked species groups. One consists of the species *uncinata* from New Caledonia, in which the base of 3A and the apex of 2A are

atrophied in the hind wing (Fig. 34) and the male genitalia have distinct but small cerci (Fig. 44). In the other group (including all the other Australasian species) the anal veins are essentially complete in the hind wing, but the cerci are either reduced to setose convexities at the base of the tenth tergite (Fig. 42) or not evident. In the latter case general areas normally occupied by the cerci have developed into projections of one sort or another.

The simplicity and general similarity of the male genitalia of *uncinata, stenocerca, tonela, and waddama* (Figs. 42, 43, 44, 46) suggest that these are all closely allied and form the primitive nucleus of *Hydrobiosella* (Chart 5). The primitive form (Ancestor 1) would have combined the primitive characters of all the descendants, and would have possessed short cerci (as in *uncinata*) and a complete set of anal veins (as in the other three species).

The problem of resolving the exact relationships of these species proved difficult on morphological grounds alone. On a strictly empirical basis, it might appear that *uncinata* represented one branch of the subgenus and all other species another branch. The male genitalia of *uncinata* and *stenocerca* are sufficiently similar, however, to suggest the possibility that these two species belong to a discrete branch as opposed to one consisting of Australian species. If this were true one would expect the New Zealand species *tonela* to belong to the *stenocerca* branch. A comparison of genitalic structures in the group offers as much evidence for this view as against it.

This second explanation brings into harmony both morphological and geographic data and it is the one I believe to be correct after summing up the evidence. The resultant arrangement is shown in Chart 5.

This reasoning leads to the following explanation of the evolution of *Hydrobiosella*. The original ancestral form gave rise to two lines, one on the New Caledonia–New Zealand chain and one on the Australian mainland. The former line changed little at first, but in the Australian line the cerci or the anatomical area they occupied developed into a shoulder-like projection (*b* in Figs. 39-46).

The New Caledonia–New Zealand line next gave rise to a New Caledonian branch and a New Zealand branch. The New Caledonian branch retained the distinct cerci but lost the tip of vein 2A in the hind wing (Fig. 34) and evolved into the species *uncinata*. In the New Zealand branch (Ancestor 2 in Chart 5) the cerci became reduced (Figs. 42, 43) but the anal veins of the hind wing were preserved intact. This line evolved into *stenocerca* and *tonela*.

The Australian form (Ancestor 3 in Chart 5) divided first into two lines. One (Ancestor 5) preserved the basal ridge of the tenth tergite and developed a long, ventral sclerotized process at the base of the aedeagus; this line is represented today by two species, *waddama* and *michaelseni* (Figs. 45, 46). The other line developed projections on the tenth tergite, presumably from the basal ridges. This second line (Ancestor 4) again divided, pre-

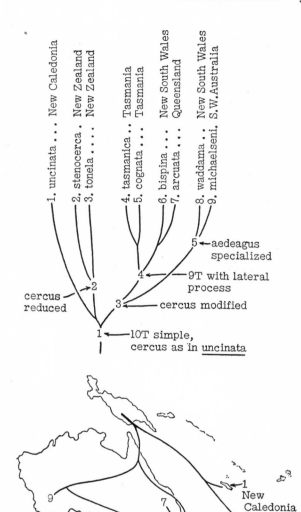

CHART 5. Phylogenetic diagram of *Sortosa* subgenus *Hydrobiosella*, and (below) the same superimposed on the known distribution.

sumably one branch becoming isolated on Tasmania, the other branch being the mainland population. The Tasmanian line is known from two species, *cognata* with a fairly simple lateral process on the tenth tergite (Fig. 41), and *tasmanica* with a clawlike process that is obviously a striking but simple modification of that in *cognata* (Fig. 40). The mainland form developed several conspicuous differences in claspers and tenth tergite (Fig. 39), and is known now by *arcuata* and *bispina,* a pair of closely related sister species.

The morphological and geographic data form a sufficiently cohesive whole so that the following sequence of events is suggested. Ancestor 1 of Chart 5 was undoubtedly widespread over an early land mass which included both Australia and an arc comparable in position with the New Caledonia–New Zealand chain of today. This arc became disconnected from Australia, and at a later date broke up into individual islands. This is indicated in our data by the occurrence of archaic characters in species now occupying distant island members of

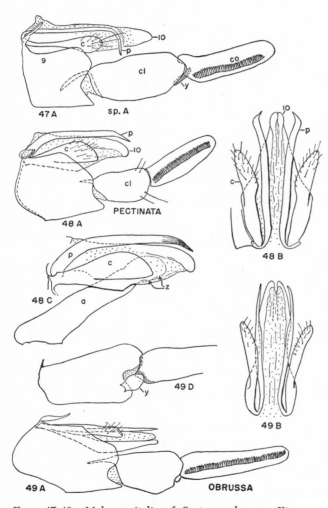

FIGS. 47-49. Male genitalia of *Sortosa* subgenus *Kisaura.* A, lateral aspect; B, dorsal aspect; C, enlarged portion of lateral aspect; D, mesal aspect of clasper. *a,* aedeagus; *c,* cercus; *cl,* clasper; *co,* comb; *p,* process mesad of cercus; *y,* articulation process of clasper; *z,* area of fusion of aedeagus and tenth tergite.

the old arc. The Australian population of Ancestor 1 developed into Ancestor 3. From this point there are multiple possibilities regarding dispersal. Ancestor 3 may have spread over both eastern and western Australia, then the middle of the continent became arid and divided the population into two parts. If this was the case, the eastern population evolved into Ancestor 4, which spread to Tasmania. Tasmania became separated from the mainland; its population of Ancestor 4 evolved into *cognata* and *tasmanica,* the mainland population evolved into *bispina* and *arcuata.* In the meantime the west Australia segregate of Ancestor 3 evolved into Ancestor 5. After Tasmania was separated from the mainland, conditions in the center of the continent became more humid so that Ancestor 5 was able to spread back to eastern Australia. The center of the continent again became arid, dividing Ancestor 5 into a western and an eastern segregate resulting in the two species known today.

It is equally possible that the evolution of all the early Australian forms occurred in the eastern part of the continent. In this case *michaelseni* arose from the westward spread of Ancestor 5, with the subsequent isolation and independent evolution of an eastern and a western segregate of the ancestral type. At the present moment there appears to be no way to test the applicability of either premise.

*Subgenus Kisaura.* As pointed out earlier, *Kisaura* probably arose directly from an Asiatic segregate of the *Sortosa* Ancestor. In this Asiatic segregate slender processes developed between the tenth tergite and the cerci. The segregate evolved into *Kisaura,* with highly modified claspers and lobes of the tenth tergite but still retained the central part of the tenth tergite in membranous form. As a matter of fact, the membranous sides of the central part of the tenth tergite have curled around the apex of the aedeagus, and these two pieces, sheath and aedeagus, are actually fused at a point on the venter designated as *z* in Fig. 48C. The lateral membranous area extends below the level of the cerci in some species (Fig. 48) so that at first glance each cercus seems to have three points of basal attachment. The highly modified features of the claspers are the development of a row of black, stout teeth (*co*) on the mesal margin of the apical segment, forming a regular comb (Fig. 47); and a small plate (*y*) presumably aiding in articulation, between the two segments (Fig. 49D). In repose, the apical segment of the clasper is often held straight up, at right angles to the basal segment (see Tsuda 1939, Fig. 2). There are no known species which show the stages involved in the development of this highly modified form from its more primitive ancestor.

At present about eight species of *Kisaura* are known, including several undescribed species collected in Burma by Dr. René Malaise and awaiting description by Mr. D. E. Kimmins. The species of *Kisaura* divide into two major groups, a slightly more primitive one from Burma (Fig. 47) embracing several species in which the basal segment of the clasper is longer than the apical segment, and a more specialized group from southeast China, Formosa, Japan, and Siberia in which the basal segment of the clasper is shorter than the apical segment. Of this eastern group four species are known. In *pectinata* (known from southeastern China) and *obrussa* (known from neighboring Formosa) the lateral processes are the same length as the median lobe of the tenth tergite (Fig. 48). In *aurascens* (from South Ussuri in Siberia) and *kisoensis* (from Japan) the lateral processes are much longer.

The family tree in Chart 6 suggests that *Kisaura,* as defined today, originated in eastern Asia and has been restricted to it since. Successive steps in speciation led to the formation of a Burma segregate and a more eastern segregate, which developed into the species we know today. The phylogenetic pattern, shown in Chart 6, indicates two dispersal possibilities for the *aurascens* line: it may have spread from southern China, through Formosa, to Japan and southeastern Siberia (Route 1 in Chart 6) or its main spread may have occurred on the continent with independent dispersals to Formosa and Japan (Route 2 in Chart 6). The extremely scant records from this part of the world point to the great need for more material to investigate the biogeographic picture.

*Subgenus Dolophilodes.* At present, ten of the eleven described species belonging to *Dolophilodes* have been studied (Chart 7). One of the species, *dorca,* is unique in many characters, and forms a distinctive subgroup. In it the tenth tergite (Fig. 62) is divided almost to the base to form a pair of large lateral lobes bearing typical minute sensillae. The venation is characterized by the same type of variability as is found in *Philopotamus*—cell $R_2$ is either long, as in primitive *Sortosa,* or it may be

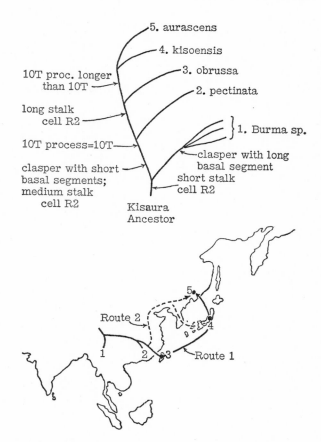

CHART 6. Phylogenetic diagram of *Sortosa* subgenus *Kisaura,* and (below) the same superimposed on the known distribution.

short due to the migration of fork $R_{2+3}$ toward the wing margin. In the remaining species the male tenth tergite is much simpler (Fig. 57) but cell $R_2$ is always short. Adding together primitive characters persisting in different species, it is plain that the ancestor for the subgenus combined a long cell $R_2$ with a tenth tergite which was only slightly incised. The simplicity of the genitalia coupled with the primitive condition of the wings indicates that the progenitor of *Dolophilodes* arose fairly directly from the *Sortosa* Ancestor.

The species *dorca* occurs only in the western montane region of North America and is an early offshoot of the *Dolophilodes* stem. Its affinity to the other members of the subgenus is demonstrated by the possession of a large, ovate, somewhat amorphous and almost entirely membranous aedeagus. This type is found only in *Dolophilodes.*

The other species belong to the *distincta* complex. A phylogenetic analysis of its known species demonstrates the existence of four groups, all based on characteristics of the male genitalia. A survey of these characteristics indicates that all these groups arose from a form in which the claspers had a moderately long basal segment, and both segments were flat and ribbon-like; the cerci were finger-like; and the tenth tergite had no lateral processes, but was incised at the apex to produce a pair of short, rounded lobes. Such a form is repre-

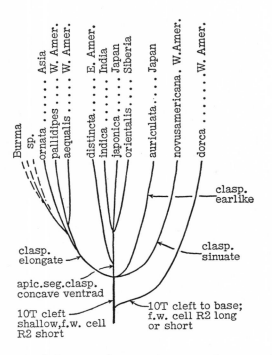

CHART 7. Phylogenetic diagram of *Sortosa* subgenus *Dolophilodes.*

sented in living forms by species such as *distincta.* From this deduced ancestor the four groups deviated as outlined below.

*Distincta Group.* Little change, but apical segment of clasper has concave ventral margin (Fig. 59). Contains four species: *distincta* in eastern North America; and three Asiatic species, *japonica* (Japan), *indica* (Punjab, India), and *orientalis* (South Ussuri District, Siberia). The North American species *distincta* is a hill-country species, and is unusual in that the species develops through the winter. At this season the females are wingless, each pair of wings represented by minute pads.

*Aequalis Group.* Again little change, but with the apical segment of the clasper longer and parallel-sided (Fig. 58). Contains *aequalis* and *pallidipes,* both in western North America; *ornata* in China and Siberia; and some undescribed species from Burma.

*Novusamericana Group.* In it the clasper is highly modified, contorted and excavated as in Fig. 61; otherwise primitive. Contains only one species, *novusamericana,* from western North America.

*Auriculata Group.* The apical segment of the clasper is very short, the tenth tergite has the pair of apical lobes unusually well set off from the base, and the cerci are enlarged and modified in shape (Fig. 60). Contains only *auriculata* from Japan.

It is difficult to be certain of the exact relationships of these four groups one to another. Each gives the impression of having evolved directly from the same ancestral form, and each has achieved varying degrees of specialization from it. The *auriculata* group has diverged the most, the *novusamericana* group the next, and the *aequalis* and *distincta* groups the least. Such an arrangement is shown in Chart 7.

The dispersal pattern is likewise difficult to determine exactly. Certain features, however, stand out with clarity:

The ancestor of the *distincta* group spread across Asia and North America. Its range was subsequently broken up and today species exist in both areas. It is interesting to note that the American segregate is known from only one species restricted to eastern North America.

The ancestor of the *aequalis* group also spread between Asia and North America, but apparently only into western North America.

The ancestor of *Dolophilodes* itself probably was also widespread, or had early species which became intercontinental in distribution.

Because virtually all of the species trace back directly to an intercontinental ancestor, it is impossible to deduce which continent was the original home of the ancestral forms. All that can be said is that either Asia or North America was the starting point.

No species of the group has been found in Europe. This would seem to be a function of the true montane nature of all but the eastern North American species *distincta.* It would seem that the group arose in Asia as a montane form and that after its origin there was no suitable humid montane avenue leading from eastern Asia into Europe. Otherwise we would expect to find survivors of the group somewhere in Europe, because in Asia and America *Dolophilodes* occurs with, and is ecologically dominant over, montane species of *Wormaldia* and *Glossosoma*, which thrive in Europe.

*Subgenus Thylakion.* The fact that *Thylakion* and *Philopotamus* have exactly the same type of lateral process on the tenth tergite suggests strongly that both arose from a common ancestor which developed such a process. This ancestral form must have been primitive in all other characters, as both offspring groups are today. It is reasonable to suppose that this ancestor was a geographic segregate of the *Sortosa* Ancestor.

*Thylakion* is restricted to Africa and *Philopotamus* to Europe. It is possible that the common ancestor was a European segregate of the *Sortosa* Ancestor. The European segregate could have developed these lateral processes, then spread into Africa. The dispersal route could have become untenable and there would have resulted a European segregate which could have evolved into *Philopotamus* and an African segregate that could have evolved into *Thylakion*.

Only two species of *Thylakion* are known, both from South Africa. Regardless of when the progenitor of *Thylakion* spread to this region, the record indicates that it developed into this distinctive group and never spread again to other parts of the world.

### The Genus *Philopotamus*

The ancestor of *Philopotamus* was probably very similar to *Thylakion,* but with simpler lateral processes on the tenth tergite. The principal specializations added were the accessory second apical segment of the claspers and the moving of fork $R_{2+3}$ toward the wing margin. This latter is not a fixed character in all members of the genus, the fork still occurring near cross-vein *s* in some species. All the species in the genus are remarkably similar in general structure, differing in details of individual parts. The immediate ancestor of the known living forms probably had a simple, pointed aedeagal strap as in *flavidus* (Fig. 51C) and a slightly bilobed tenth tergite as in *perversus* (Fig. 56B). In the *amphilectus-flavidus* line, the lobes of the tenth tergite

folded in over the meson (Figs. 51, 53), and the apical segment of the clasper became more pointed, but the aedeagus remained primitive. In the *perversus-ludificatus* line the ventral strap of the aedeagus became angled or hooked (Fig. 56C) and various other modifications occurred as outlined in Chart 8.

The entire genus is apparently confined to Europe. Within this area, three species (*variegatus, montanus,* and *ludificatus*) are widespread, whereas the others are known from only small ranges. One species (*tenuis*) is known only from Caucasia, two from Portugal (*perversus* and *amphilectus*), one from the Isle of Guernsey (*insularis*) and two from Corsica (*flavidus* and *corsicanus*). This is most readily explained on the assumption that the genus has been successively widespread over at least southern Europe, then restricted to isolated areas. This cycle has probably occurred at least three or four times since the *Philopotamus* prototype evolved. The result has been the development of species in the different isolated areas, and some of these have apparently been extremely restricted in distribution ever since. The two species on Corsica may have been cut off by a sea barrier ever since speciation occurred, isolation being thus retained.

In the case of the Portugal species some other explanation is necessary. It seems certain that these species have developed a very narrow ecological tolerance, much narrower and therefore more restrictive than that of *variegatus* and other widespread forms. It would seem, therefore, that since the speciation of *amphilectus,* the Portuguese mountains have been connected with the rest of the European ranges by ecological bands which allowed *variegatus* to spread from central Europe into Portugal, but did not permit *amphilectus* and other species to spread from Portugal back to other parts of Europe.

Perhaps this phenomenon also explains the restriction of the Corsican and Caucasian species. More detailed knowledge of the fauna of this area is needed in order to make a sound appraisal. As with other groups, the extremely meager records from the Balkan areas and Eastern Europe are a greater handicap in drawing extensive conclusions.

### The Genus *Ulmerodina*

From the Baltic amber material, Ulmer (1912) has described a most enigmatic species *impar* for

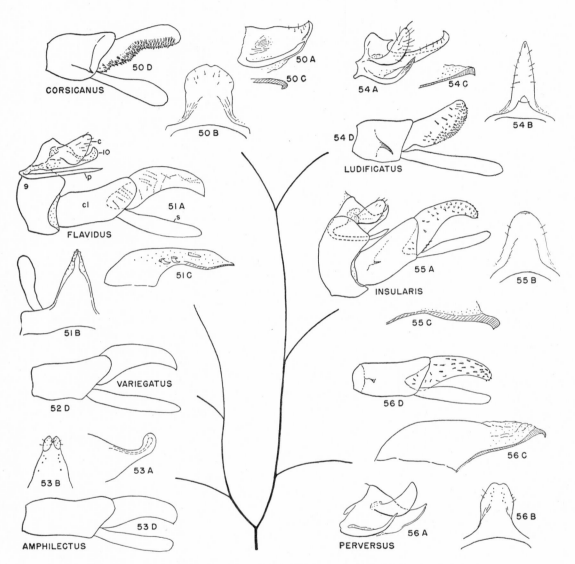

Figs. 50-56. Male genitalia of *Philopotamus*. *A*, lateral aspect of entire capsule or of tenth tergite (cercus omitted in Fig. 50); *B*, dorsal aspect; *C*, aedeagus, lateral aspect of whole of apex; *D*, clasper, lateral aspect but in some with mesal spines superimposed. *c*, cercus; *cl*, clasper; *p*, lateral process of tenth tergite; *s*, ventral secondary apical segment of clasper.

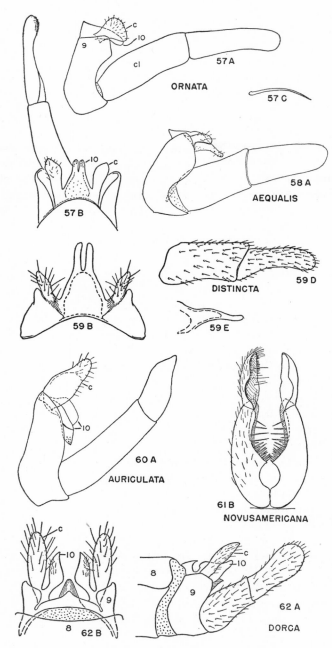

FIGS. 57-62. Male genitalia of *Sortosa* subgenus *Dolophilodes*. A, lateral aspect; B, dorsal aspect; C, internal spine of aedeagus; D, clasper, lateral aspect; E, tenth tergite, lateral aspect. c, cercus; cl, clasper.

which a new genus, *Ulmerodina*, is erected in this paper (see p. 60). Ulmer has given excellent illustrations of the head, wings, and certain parts of the male genitalia. On the basis of the presence of ocelli, shape and proportions of the maxillary palps,

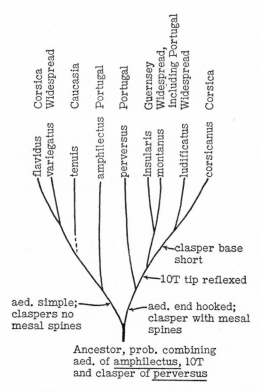

CHART 8. Phylogenetic diagram of the genus *Philopotamus*.

and certain features of the wing (hind wing with complete anal veins, front wing with $M_{3+4}$ branching just beyond *m*) there seems no doubt that *Ulmerodina* is a primitive genus of the Philopotamidae. The male claspers, however, appear to be composed of a single, elongate segment (Fig. 63). If this is really the true condition of the species, it would imply a possible similarity with either a very primitive *Protarra*, more primitive than any known because *Ulmerodina* has $M_4$ in the front wing and complete anal veins in the hind wing, both lost or modified in known *Protarra*; an early stage in the development of *Paulianodes*, before

FIG. 63. Male genitalia of *Ulmerodina impar*. A, lateral aspect of claspers (right) and cercus (left). (After Ulmer.)

the claspers fused with each other on the meson; or an extinct separate Eurasian or European line which arose from *Sortosa*, in which the two segments of the clasper became united.

Without knowledge of additional structures there seems to be no possibility of choosing between these three alternatives. Either the second or third seems more plausible on the basis of distribution. There is, however, always the possibility that the clasper is really 2-segmented, in which case *Ulmerodina* might prove to be a European species of some group such as *Kisaura* which is now known only from Asia.

This completes a survey of the *Sortosa* complex, those groups which have preserved a primitive anal venation in the hind wing and have primitive claspers. Next we shall examine the other two large complexes in the group, the *Wormaldia* complex and the *Chimarra* complex.

## The *Wormaldia* Complex

The group of species considered as the *Wormaldia* complex is characterized by the shape of the anal cells of the hind wing. From the basal group of cells only two veins project, these two connected at the base by a straight cross-piece, and diverging toward the wing margin, as in Fig. 20. This condition is a simple derivative of the *Sortosa* wing resulting from the atrophy of the projecting portion of 2A. This process occurs to some degree in several lines of the *Sortosa* complex (*Thylakion* and *Hydrobiosella*) where 2A is reduced to a small stub. In every other respect the wings of primitive *Wormaldia* species are exactly like those in primitive species of *Sortosa*.

A survey of the *Wormaldia* complex shows that the male genitalia of many species and groups are of a very primitive type. The claspers (Fig. 64) are simple and 2-segmented, the cerci are finger-like, and the tenth tergite is triangular (Fig. 68), without lateral processes, and with an irregular group of sensillae around the apex. This is essentially the type found in *Sisko* (Fig. 30), and it is undoubtedly from some such simple segregate of *Sortosa* that *Wormaldia* arose.

It is certain, therefore, that *Wormaldia* is another phyletic line which evolved directly, or fairly so, from the *Sortosa* Ancestor, changing primarily in the reorientation of the anal veins in the hind wing.

## The Genus *Wormaldia*

The existing species of *Wormaldia* present a great number of differences in shape of claspers, cerci, tenth tergite, various incisions and processes on the eighth tergite, and processes of the seventh, eighth, and ninth sternites. Employing these characters, it is possible to group the species into phylogenetic units exhibiting various degrees of specialization. The species *anilla, occidea, endonima,* and *dorsata* (Figs. 64, 65, 70, 71) form a group primitive in many respects. More specialized types include *dampfi* with recurved tenth tergite (Fig. 72); *planae* and *esperonis,* with lateral flanges on the tenth tergite (Figs. 75, 76); *arizonensis,* with ear-like cerci (Fig. 74); and *thyria* and *hamata,* with an elongate, hoodlike eighth tergite (Figs. 68, 69). The most distinctive group contains *mohri, montana,* and *kisoensis,* in which both the eighth and tenth tergites are unusually modified (Figs. 93-95) and the wings have developed a very small discal cell and have the apexes of veins $R_1$ and $R_2$ fused in the hind wing (Fig. 87).

On further analysis it is evident that none of these specialized groups arose from each other. Instead, practically every group appears to have evolved directly from the ancestral prototype. This is exactly the situation which prevails with *Sortosa*. These groups of *Wormaldia* are here tabulated.

*Anilla Group.* This entirely Nearctic group (Chart 9) is one of the most primitive in the genus. In it the tenth tergite is triangular, rounded at its tip; the cerci are finger-like; the claspers are simple and leaflike. The sternites have either no processes (*anilla*) or broad, short ones on seventh or eighth segments. The wings are primitive for the genus; that is, all branches are present and the anal cells of the hind wing are as in Fig. 20. Two Nearctic species, *anilla* (Fig. 64) and *cruzensis,* are especially simple in all characters, including the non-produced seventh and eighth sternites.

The species *occidea* has broad mesal projections or flaps on the seventh sternite (Fig. 65B) and differs in little more than this detail from the primitive *anilla.* Apparent offshoots from an *occidea*-like ancestor are two small complexes:

The *thyria-hamata* complex, in which the eighth tergite is produced into a hood (Figs. 68, 69), and the front wing has lost $M_4$; and

The *strota-shawnee* complex, in which both wings

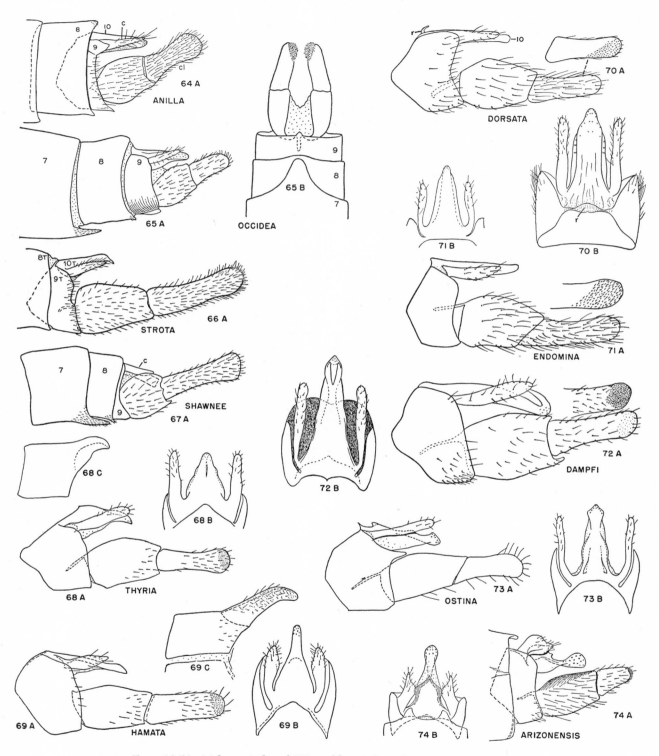

FIGS. 64-74. Male genitalia of *Wormaldia*. *A*, lateral aspect; *B*, dorsal aspect; *C*, eighth tergite, lateral aspect; mesal aspect of apex of clasper shown in inset in Figs. 70A, 71A, and 72A. *c*, cercus; *cl*, clasper; *r*, dorsal transverse ridge.

have lost R$_2$. In *shawnee* the apical segment of the clasper is elongate (Fig. 67).

Two intriguing species, *endonima* and *dorsata*, have been collected in Mexico. They are very similar to *anilla*, but in them the tenth tergite is elongate and parallel-sided nearly to the tip (Figs. 70, 71). In *dorsata* the male eighth sternite is barely produced, in *endonima* it forms a definite but short

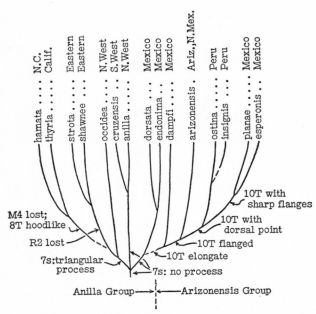

CHART 9. Phylogenetic diagram of the *Wormaldia anilla* and *arizonensis* groups.

wide process. From the extreme similarity of the two in other characters, one would conclude that the two are truly sister species. This leads to the assumption that the projection on the male seventh sternite arose independently in *endonima* and in *occidea* and its allies.

The most intriguing bit of speculation about *endonima* and *dorsata* is the possibility that they are surviving relics of a simple type which was the ancestor of the following group. There seems to be every logical ground for such an assumption, on the basis of both morphology and distribution (see Chart 9). If true, it indicates that almost all of the American species of *Wormaldia* evolved from a single ancestor, that the resulting line has never spread into Asia, and that species representing almost every step in the evolution of the group are still living.

*Arizonensis Group.* This appears to be a heterogeneous assemblage of species (Chart 9) having no more in common than a lengthened tenth tergite which has some sort of widening near the middle and is narrowed before its tip. Yet if studied in detail, the species show a logical evolutionary development along several lines which form a cohesive, pectinate unit. The ancestral form of the group could have arisen with little change from a form like *endonima*, by changes involving only a slight elongation of the tenth tergite and a narrowing of this structure just before the tip, and the development of slight lateral flanges near the middle of the tergite. Such an ancestral form would have looked like *dampfi* without its apical hook on the tenth tergite, or perhaps even more like the Peruvian *ostina*. From this ancestral form two lines developed. In one, represented by *dampfi*, the apex on the tenth tergite became recurved but only a suggestion of the lateral flanges remained (Fig. 72).

In the other line the tenth tergite was characterized by a development of the lateral flanges and by some elaboration of its apex. The first step in this process is probably represented by *arizonensis* (Fig. 74). Although its tenth tergite has remained primitive, its cerci have become short and somewhat auriculate. In the next evolutionary step, represented by *ostina* (Fig. 73), the apex of the tenth tergite became somewhat quadrangular. In the final step shown by the record the tenth tergite evolved two new structures— an ornate, notched apex and sharp, flaring lateral flanges. This last step is illustrated by *planae* (Fig. 75) and *esperonis* (Fig. 76).

*Copiosa Group.* This and the two following groups (Chart 10) are entirely European in distribution. The *copiosa* group has a full wing venation and very primitive genitalia (Fig. 77). It has two specialized features. The cercus is unusually large and the eighth tergite is produced into a short hood which extends over the base of the ninth and tenth tergites. The group contains only a single known species, *copiosa*, which is essentially as primitive as *anilla* and which unquestionably evolved from the same primitive ancestor of the genus.

*Pulla Group.* This is another small group primitive in having a full wing venation. The male genitalia are primitive in most characters, but the cerci are fused solidly to the sides of the ninth segment

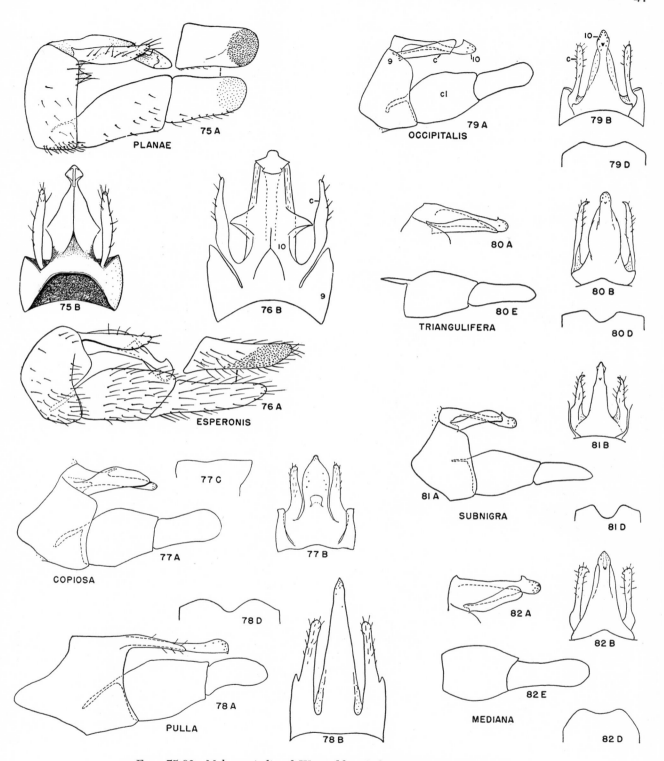

FIGS. 75-82.  Male genitalia of *Wormaldia*. *A*, lateral aspect; *B*, dorsal aspect; *C*, eighth tergite, lateral aspect; *D*, eighth tergite; dorsal aspect. *c*, cercus; *cl*, clasper.

(Fig. 78). The group contains only *pulla*, widespread in Europe, and *corvina* from Portugal. This is another simple derivative of the ancestral form of the genus.

*Occipitalis Group.* The front wings of this European group have lost M₄, and in the male genitalia the tenth tergite has developed a short preapical point. Otherwise this group is little specialized, indicating that it is a simple derivative of the ancestral form of the genus. Five species of the group are known, separated only by slight differences in the male genitalia. The two most primitive species are probably *occipitalis* and *mediana*, in

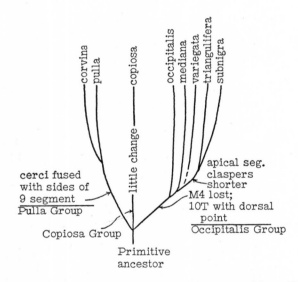

CHART 10. Phylogenetic diagram of the *Wormaldia pulla, copiosa,* and *occipitalis* groups.

which the apical segment of the clasper is fairly long (Figs. 79, 82) as in *copiosa;* in the more specialized species such as *triangulifera* and *subnigra* the apical segment is shorter (Figs. 80, 81). Aside from these and other equally slight differences, the members of the group form a remarkably homogeneous assemblage.

. . . .

In Europe there exists today in the form of the three preceding groups all the elements necessary to explain the ancestry and evolution of its *Wormaldia* fauna. The fossil species known from the Baltic amber of Europe, however, do not fit anywhere in this scheme. This point will be discussed later (see p. 46).

. . . .

*Moesta Group.* There are four species (Chart 11) which have very simple male genitalia and primitive or only simply modified wing venation, but which have a curious, long, tonguelike process on the seventh sternite, and sometimes also on the eighth (Fig. 83). The four species are *moesta* (eastern North America), *gabriella* (western North America), *chinensis* (China), and *relicta* (India

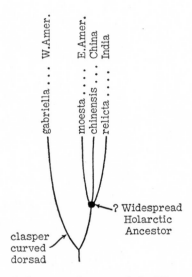

CHART 11. Phylogenetic diagram of the *Wormaldia moesta* group.

and Burma). *Moesta* has R₂ present in both wings, but in the other species R₂ has been lost. The venation and male genitalia indicate that the group is a direct derivative of the ancestral form of the genus, but where it arose is difficult to say.

The claspers of *moesta, chinensis,* and *relicta* (Fig. 83A) are extremely similar to each other and to the primitive type found in *anilla.* Those of *gabriella* are curved up at the apex (Fig. 84) and appear quite different from those of the other three. It is quite possible, therefore, that *gabriella* represents one line of the group, the other three another line. If this is the case, it would be necessary to suppose that *gabriella* has remained isolated in the Rocky Mountain system while the *moesta-relicta* ancestor was widespread between Asia and North America. There are other cases suggestive of this same point, and they will be mentioned from time to time as the involved species are discussed.

*Kyana Group.* In Africa and Madagascar two species occur in which the male genitalia are of pe-

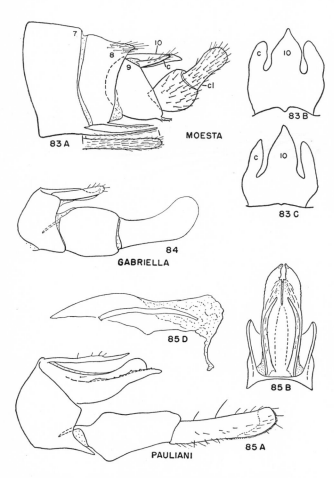

FIGS. 83-85. Male genitalia of *Wormaldia. A,* lateral aspect; *B, C,* dorsal aspect; *D,* aedeagus, lateral aspect. 83*B,* sketch of type of *Dolophilus breviatus;* 83*C,* sketch of type of *moesta. c,* cercus; *cl,* clasper.

*Montana Group* (Subgenus *Doloclanes*). One of the best-marked groups of *Wormaldia* occurs chiefly in Asia. This is the *montana* group (Chart 12), formerly described by Banks as the genus *Doloclanes*. In the hind wing the tips of $R_1$ and $R_2$ are fused (Fig. 87) and in the male, processes of moderate length occur on sternites 7 and 8 (Fig. 91A). Judging from the simple front wing venation and male genitalia in *alticola,* the group arose from a species very similar to the ancestral type of *Wormaldia.* Nine species are known to date, and these indicate the evolutionary lines shown in Chart 12.

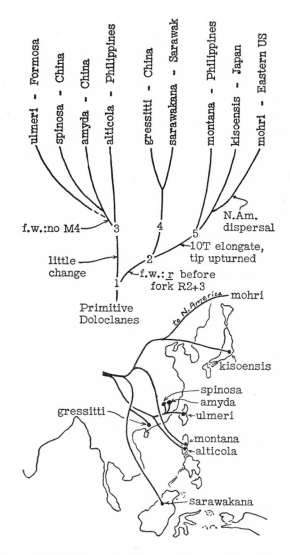

CHART 12. Phylogenetic diagram of *Wormaldia* subgenus *Doloclanes* and (below) the same superimposed on the known distribution.

culiar appearance (Fig. 85). The cerci are elongate and slender, arising almost at the basal edge of the segment, and the tenth tergite is crested. The wing venation is complete and simple. The two species involved have been collected from only a small area, *kyana* from Ruwenzori District in Africa, *pauliani* from Madagascar. The group probably arose from a form very similar to the ancestor for the genus, which had spread into and become isolated in Africa. Somewhere in Africa this segregate developed into a species very similar to the two existing species, then spread from continental Africa to Madagascar or *vice versa,* as the case may be. The one certain fact is that the African and Madagascan species have not become unduly different since this dispersal and their subsequent isolation and speciation.

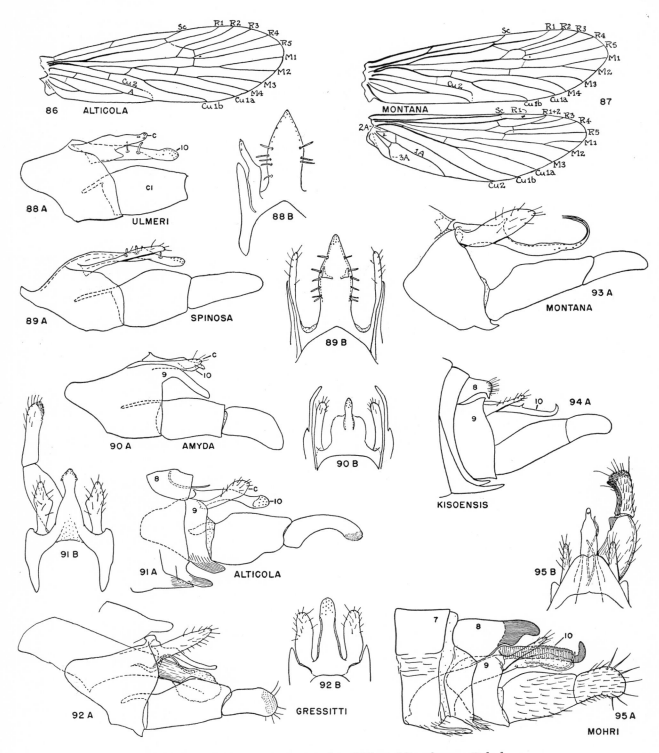

FIGS. 86-95. Wings and male genitalia of *Wormaldia* subgenus *Doloclanes*. 83, front wing; 84, front and hind wings; 85-92, genitalia. *A*, lateral aspect; *B*, dorsal aspect. *c*, cercus; *cl*, claspers. (Fig. 94A after Tsuda.)

The first typical member of the *montana* group (Ancestor 1 in Chart 12) gave rise to two lines. The one leading to Ancestor 3 changed little and in turn gave rise to the *alticola* and *amyda* branches. In the *alticola* branch, represented only by *alticola*, the front wing retained all its veins. In the other branch, represented by *ulmeri*, *spinosa*, and *amyda*, the front wing lost vein $M_4$. In all four species curious processes developed on the eighth tergite but the male

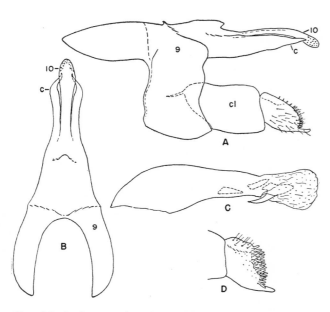

Fig. 96. Male genitalia of *Wormaldia recta*. *A*, lateral aspect; *B*, dorsal aspect; *C*, aedeagus, lateral aspect; *D*, apical segment of clasper, mesal aspect. *c*, cercus; *cl*, clasper.

genitalia in general remained relatively primitive.

In the line leading to Ancestor 2, cross-vein *r* moved anteriorly so that in the front wing it joined $R_{2+3}$ before its fork (Fig. 87). From Ancestor 2 two branches evolved. One changed little and is represented by two species, *sarawakana* and *gressitti*. In the other more specialized branch, the tenth tergite became elongate, narrowed, and upturned at the apex. To this branch belong the Philippine *montana*, the Japanese *kisoensis*, and the American *mohri*. Its broad cerci and simple eighth tergite (Fig. 92) indicate that *gressitti* is the most primitive of these. *Kisoensis* and *mohri* form a pair of more closely related species in which the cerci are narrow and the eighth tergite is highly modified (Figs. 94, 95).

Reviewing the geographic data in Chart 12, it is clear that the *montana* group arose and speciated in Asia, that Ancestors 3 and 5 were middle east-

Asian species which probably spread to the Philippines together, and that Ancestor 4 probably always occurred to the south of these two, enabling it to reach Borneo. The ancestor of the *kisoensis-mohri* branch of Ancestor 5 is best explained as a northeast-Asian form which eventually spread to both Japan and eastern North America. To date collecting has unearthed no species of this complex in the intervening areas.

*Recta Group.* Another odd *Wormaldia*, the species *recta*, occurs in the Philippines. The front wing has lost $M_4$, and in the hind wing fork $R_{2+3}$ is mid-

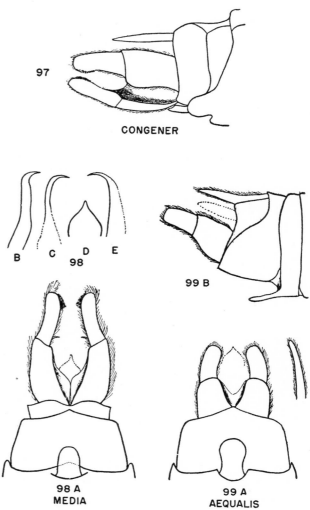

Fig. 97. Male genitalia of *Wormaldia congener*, ventrolateral aspect. (After Ulmer.)
Fig. 98. Male genitalia of *Wormaldia media*. *A*, ventral aspect; *B*, *C*, *E*, cerci of three specimens, ventral aspect; *D*, apex of tenth tergite, ventral aspect. (After Ulmer.)
Fig. 99. Male genitalia of *Wormaldia aequalis*. *A*, ventral aspect; *B*, lateral aspect. (After Ulmer.)

way between *s* and the wing margin. In the male genitalia, the cerci and tenth tergite are fused at the base and elongated to make a three-pronged structure (Fig. 96). No other species is like it, and it stands alone as a distinctive small group.

### Fossil Species

Three of the Baltic amber species placed by Ulmer in the genus *Dolophilus* seem to be true *Wormaldia* (formerly most *Wormaldia* species were

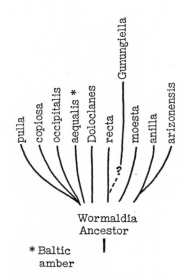

CHART 13. Summary of the phylogeny of *Wormaldia*.

placed in *Dolophilus*). These are *aequalis, media,* and *congener.* On the basis of male genitalia these would appear to form a closely allied group, the *aequalis* group, differing from the *anilla* group chiefly in having a distinctive flap on the seventh sternite (Figs. 97-99). Illustrations of the wings of *aequalis* have 2A represented by a dotted line, suggestive of *Sortosa.* The configuration of the basal anal cells, however, is so unmistakably typical of *Wormaldia* that the dotted line undoubtedly represents a fold which actually does often occur in that area in mounted specimens of existing species.

There is no existing species known from Europe which in any way resembles these amber species. In the fossil specimens the shape of the flap on the seventh sternite (Figs. 97-99) is suggestive of the *montana* group. While only suggestive, this similarity allows consideration of the possibility that this fossil *aequalis* complex may be related to, or

ancestral to, the now primarily Oriental *montana* group. Such a dispersal pattern is reminiscent of that indicated in the genus *Electragapetus* (see p. 149).

### Pupal Characters

Pupae are known for only a few species of *Wormaldia* but these corroborate a number of phylogenetic points suggested by adult structures. In the pupa of *Sortosa,* the progenitor of *Wormaldia,* the right mandible has four distinct teeth, the middle two being the same size as the apical tooth. Within the genus *Wormaldia* several patterns of dentition are found. In the pupa of *occipitalis,* the right mandible exhibits little modification from the primitive pattern found in *Sortosa.* In the pupa of *shawnee,* a member of the *anilla* group, the right mandible has lost the basal tooth. In the pupa of *moesta* all four mandibular teeth are present but the basal two are minute. Thus the *occipitalis* group, representing the end branch of one phyletic line, has retained primitive mandibles whereas the only known representatives of the two other phyletic lines, the *anilla* and *moesta* groups, have specialized mandibles. These structures indicate that neither line arose from the other, but that each must have arisen from a more primitive ancestral form.

This completes an outline of the available evidence on *Wormaldia.* To the comments at the beginning of the discussion, a few more can be added. It seems certain that at least six groups, and possibly more, arose independently from the *Wormaldia* ancestor, or a form essentially as simple. The *kyana* group evidently arose in Africa, the *copiosa-occipitalis-pulla* complex and the *aequalis* group arose in Europe, the *anilla-arizonensis* complex in North America, and the *montana, moesta,* and *recta* groups possibly in Asia. It is therefore reasonable to conclude that the ancestral form of *Wormaldia* became widespread throughout the Holarctic region, and then for some reason its range was broken up into fragments.

The population in each area became a separate phyletic line, and since then little interchange of *Wormaldia* species has occurred between these geographic areas.

### The Genus *Gunungiella*

In the Philopotamidae the genus *Gunungiella* is the most peculiar. Only four species are known, all from Asia, and all freakish in structure of male genitalia.

The venation (Fig. 100) is greatly reduced. In the front wing M is reduced to two branches, but Rs is complete and primitive. In the hind wing greater changes have occurred: $Sc_1$ is atrophied, $R_{2+3}$ is unbranched, M is only 2-branched, and the apical portions of both 2A and 3A are atrophied. In the male genitalia (Figs. 101-103) the cerci are impossible to recognize, and the lateral portion of the ninth segment is much incised.

As far as decisive evidence is concerned, there is none to indicate whether *Gunungiella* arose from *Wormaldia* or from some other derivative of *Sortosa*. There is some circumstantial evidence, however, that *Gunungiella* arose not only from *Wormaldia*, but specifically from the ancestor of *recta*. This is shown by five characters.

1. In *recta* the front wing has lost $M_4$, a reduction process carried a step further in *Gunungiella*.

2. In *recta* the hind wing has $R_{2+3}$ branching close to the wing margin, in sharp contrast to the primitive sessile condition in the front wing; in *Gunungiella* this fork of $R_{2+3}$ has disappeared in the hind wing, in essence, having reached the margin, but in the front wing is unchanged.

3. In *recta* the cerci have fused with the base of the tenth tergite and moved out toward the apex, so that the cerci appear almost as lateral processes of an elongate tenth tergite (Fig. 96). It is possible that the two lateral finger-like processes midway on the tenth tergite of some *Gunungiella* species (Fig. 101, *lp*) are the products of the migrated cerci of *recta*.

4. In *recta* the base of the ninth tergal area is invaginated to form a broad internal base; in *Gunungiella* this same tergal area is also produced internally in somewhat the same fashion.

5. The black dorsal spines of the apical clasper segment are larger than normal and also chiefly peripheral in *recta*; this development of peripheral or dorsal spines occurs also in *Gunungiella*.

These similar trends do not prove the origin of *Gunungiella*, but they are suggestive of it. This is especially true, considering that five different structures show the same indications. The probability is remote that all five are the result of parallel or convergent evolution.

The four known species of *Gunungiella* fall into two groups: *reducta* and *marginalis* have a pair of

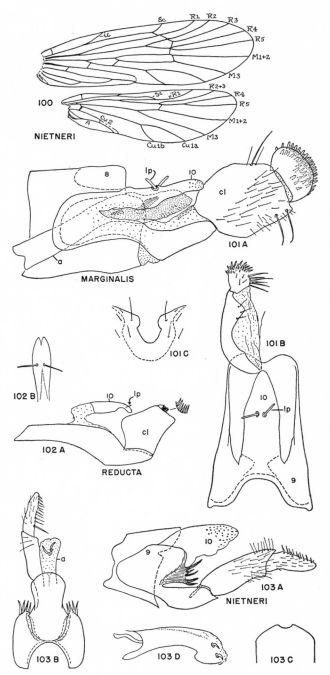

FIGS. 100-103. 100, wings of *Gunungiella nietneri*, 101-103, male genitalia of *Gunungiella*. A, lateral aspect; B, dorsal aspect; C, eighth tergite, dorsal aspect; D, aedeagus, lateral aspect. *a*, aedeagus; *cl*, clasper; *lp*, lateral process of tenth tergite.

prominent large setae near the middle of the tenth tergite, but no armature on the lateral portion of the ninth segment (Fig. 101); *nietneri* and *ulmeri* lack the dorsal spines of the tenth tergite but have a cluster of stout setae on the posterior margin of the ninth segment (Fig. 103). There are abundant and conspicuous differences between the two members of each group.

The geographic distribution of the four species, outlined in Chart 14, indicates that the ancestral form was south Asian. This broke up into two deduced forms, Ancestor 1 which occurred in India and Ceylon, and Ancestor 2 which probably was limited to east Asia. The range of Ancestor 1 subsequently became discontinuous, with a population isolated in Ceylon and another in India. These two populations have evolved into *nietneri* and *ulmeri*, respectively. Ancestor 2 ultimately spread to Java and to the Philippines, where isolation followed, and these outpost colonizations evolved into *reducta* and *marginalis*. This is suggestive of certain dispersal patterns in the Rhyacophilidae.

## The Chimarra Complex

The genus *Chimarra* outnumbers in species all the other groups of Philopotamidae combined. Counting both described and manuscript species on hand, over 150 forms have been collected from almost every part of the globe.

From other members of the Philopotamidae, *Chimarra* adults are set off by the anal loop of the hind wing (Fig. 21), the loss of $M_4$ in the front wing, the separate but single segmented claspers (Fig. 109), and the loss of one preapical spur on the front tibia. The larva and pupa of the most primitive group are remarkably similar to those of *Sortosa* in mandibular characters.

The genus *Protarra* has lost $M_4$ in the front wing and has single segmented claspers, in these points resembling *Chimarra*. In other characters, including the possession of a stub of 2A in the hind wing (Fig. 104), it is seen to be a true offshoot of the *Sortosa* ancestor. On these grounds, we seem justified in regarding *Protarra* as one of the annectent forms illustrating some of the steps in the evolution of *Chimarra* from *Sortosa* (see Chart 4).

If this surmise is correct (and geographic evidence, presented later, favors it) then the line eventually resulting in *Chimarra* first lost its vein $M_4$ in the front wing and the clasper articulation, and as a later step developed the loop in the anal veins. *Protarra* represents such a supposed early stage before the loop evolved in the anal veins.

### The Genus *Protarra*

Apart from its specializations of wing venation and claspers, *Protarra* appears to be very primitive in structure. In the male genitalia the cerci are finger-like and the simple tenth tergite is notched at its apex and has a pair of sclerotized processes either arising at the base (Fig. 105) or produced at the apex (Fig. 107).

The genus contains only four known species, all

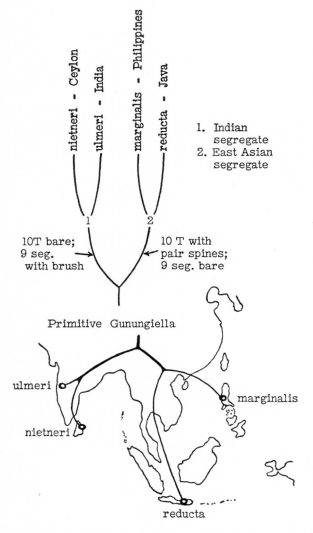

CHART 14. Phylogenetic diagram of *Gunungiella* and (below) the same superimposed on the known distribution.

very similar in general structure and forming a closely knit cluster differing only in details of the tenth tergite. Locality records to date include only Argentina and mountainous areas in Peru. It is possible that intensive collections in higher altitudes in South America might show *Protarra* to be much more abundant and widespread than it now seems. It seems to be a survival and distributional analogue of the North American montane genus *Anagapetus*.

### The Genus *Chimarra*

In addition to having a large number of species, *Chimarra* should also be noted for its diversity. This is one of the few caddisfly genera which has developed showy color patterns. The venation has undergone some changes in certain lines. The larvae and pupae, apparently quite uniform in other philopotamid genera, have developed several specializations. The male genitalia show the greatest diversity, and it at first appears impossible to homologize all the parts in such differing forms as those illustrated in Figs. 108, 112, and 118.

The genus is also widespread, occurring in most of the tropical and warm temperate regions of the world. Further, there is considerable taxonomic diversity in most parts of the world, indicating an amount of dispersal which at first seems entirely strange in contrast to other philopotamids.

The American species, for instance, combine forms such as *laguna* (Fig. 110), having a spatulate, sclerotized, tenth tergite, and forms such as *aterrima* (Fig. 118), in which the middle part of the tenth tergite is formed of a pair of membranous lobes flanked by sclerotized lateral processes appearing to be the chief component of the tenth tergite. In Asia there are forms which appear to have no central part of the tenth tergite, the lateral lobes being the only visible evidence of this segment (Fig. 112). Other types also occur in Asia.

In my original thinking about the phylogeny within *Chimarra*, I was too much influenced by familiarity with the American forms, and thought that the membranous lobes of the tenth tergite in *aterrima* were direct derivatives of the sclerotized single structure in *laguna*. Later I noticed that the two sensillae of the tenth tergal lobes in *aterrima* are probably homologues of the apical sensillae in *laguna*. If this latter were true, then some of the Old World forms with several sensillae on the lateral lobes should have represented the annectent

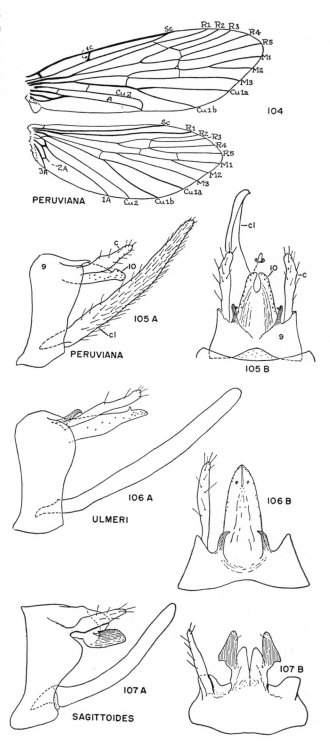

Figs. 104-107. 104, wings of *Protarra peruviana*. 105-107, male genitalia of *Protarra*. A, lateral aspect; B, dorsal aspect. *c*, cercus; *cl*, clasper.

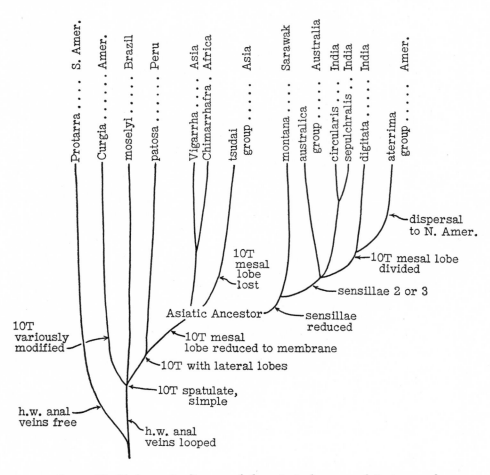

CHART 15. Phylogenetic diagram of the principal groups of *Protarra* and *Chimarra*.

forms between *laguna* and *aterrima*. But these Old World forms have no apparent central tenth tergite at all!

Obviously something was wrong. Evolutionary development of different characters seemed to be going in opposite directions. But with the sudden realization that some form such as *patosa* (Fig. 109) could have lost its mesal strap of the tenth tergite and so given rise to a form like the Asian *tsudai* (Fig. 112), the entire problem seemed to clear. Later, information from the immature stages also tallied with this solution. It is true that there is no known form showing intermediate stages in the loss of the tenth tergal strap, but perhaps none occurred. It could have been an abrupt loss. Since the explanation is the only one which brings into harmony all the known aspects of *Chimarra* evo-

lution, I am proceeding on the assumption that it is correct.

*Chimarra* is not primarily a montane group; hence, it is not my intention to explore all its ramifications here, but simply those which bear on its probable time of origin. In the following account, diagrammed in Chart 15, only the high points have been sketched. There are many other interesting details to be learned, but they will require a detailed study of all available material in the genus. I have already done much of this and hope to continue with the rest of the study.

The most primitive known species of *Chimarra* is *moselyi*. In the front wing the branches of Rs are straight. In the male genitalia (Fig. 108) the tenth tergite is simple and tonguelike, has no lateral lobes, and has numerous sensillae around the apex.

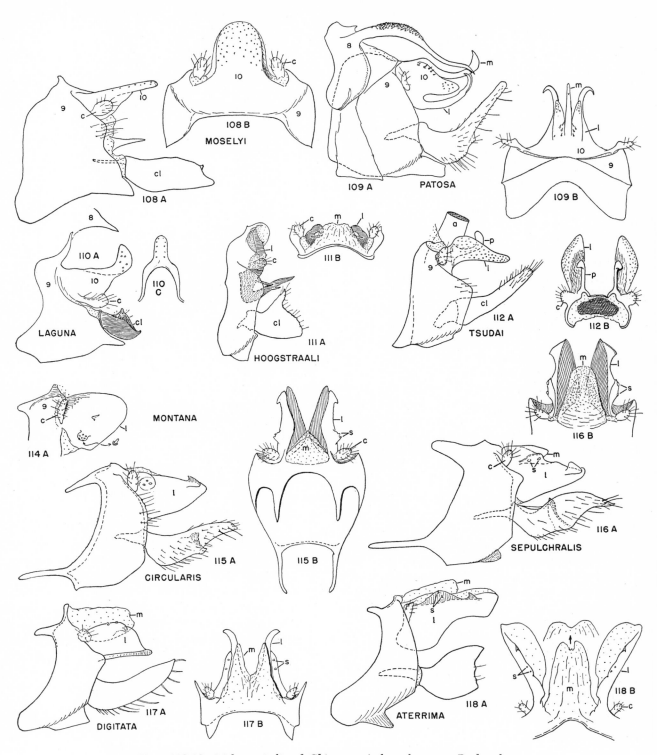

Figs. 108-18. Male genitalia of *Chimarra*. *A*, lateral aspect; *B*, dorsal aspect; *C*, posterior aspect of tenth tergite. 114A is also slightly ventral. 118B inset shows extreme tip of membranous lobe of tenth tergite in an expanded condition. *a*, aedeagus; *c*, cercus; *cl*, clasper; *l*, lateral lobe of tenth tergite; *m*, mesal lobe of tenth tergite; *p*, mesal process of tenth tergite; *s*, sensillae. (Fig. 113 not used.)

Starting from an ancestral form such as this, there arose two lines. One developed into the American group *Curgia,* in which the tenth tergite remained single and sclerotized, frequently knobbed or upturned at apex, as in *laguna* (Fig. 110).

In the other line the tenth tergite developed lateral lobes, and a very curious feature occurred. The mesal lobe of the tenth tergite lost its sensillae (Fig. 109) but they were present in considerable numbers on the lateral lobes. The base of this line is represented in South America by a few species such as *patosa,* which have developed extreme specializations of other parts such as the eighth tergite. At about this point there seems to have occurred a dispersal of this ancestral form to Asia. In the Asian segregate the central lobe of the tenth tergite either atrophied or became reduced to a membranous lobe. No existing species is known which represents the simple type that this Asiatic ancestor must have been. All known species represent one of several offshoots which have evolved from this ancestor. Possibly the living species closest to this ancestor is *hoogstraali* (Fig. 111) which has a reduced, membranous tenth tergite but highly developed lateral lobes. The species now placed in the groups *Vigarrha* and *Chimarrhafra* belong here. Another species close to this ancestor is *tsudai,* in which the tenth tergite is reduced and the lateral lobes are essentially primitive although they have developed an auxiliary dorsal process (Fig. 112). This species represents the base of a compact line present in Japan, Formosa, and China, with even more highly specialized species occurring in Java.

There arose from the Asiatic ancestor another line of great interest. In it the lateral lobes were more platelike and occupied a vertical position, and the sensillae were greatly reduced in number. Very likely they first became grouped into definite clusters, as in *montana* (Fig. 114), followed by further numerical reduction. Most of the known species of this line have only three or two sensillae left. This group seems to have spread throughout Asia and to Australia and Africa, where several offshoot lines or forms occur.

Of especial interest is one line of this group now occurring in India. Typical representatives are *sepulchralis* and *circularis.* The lateral lobes of the former have two sensillae (Fig. 116), and those of the latter have two with an indication of a third (Fig. 115). The mesal area of the tenth tergite is represented by a produced membranous lobe. In *digitata* (Fig. 117) there are two sensillae, and the mesal membranous pad is divided into a pair of fairly large membranous lobes.

This *digitata* type, with two sensillae and a pair of mesal membranous lobes on the tenth tergite, seems to be the form which spread back to the Americas and gave rise to the numerous species comprising the *aterrima* group and its allies. This development has resulted in several distinct subgroups, in all embracing over 30 known species, with a total range from Canada to Argentina.

The little that is known of the immature stages confirms this phylogenetic scheme deduced primarily from characters of the male genitalia. In the species *albomaculata,* belonging to the primitive group *Curgia,* the pupal mandibles have three simple teeth (Palmer 1938, Fig. 8); in *hoogstraali,* a member of the *Chimarrhafra* group, the two basal teeth have merged into a single cusp, as is typical of all species higher on the tree for which this stage is known. In *albomaculata* the larval frons is incised but symmetrical; in *hoogstraali* it is symmetrical and convex, exactly as in *Sortosa;* but in *ambulans* and the *aterrima* group, the frons is emarginate to form a definitely asymmetrical margin. There is thus a progression of larval and pupal characters paralleling the progression of genitalic characters.

## Summary of the Philopotamidae

In reviewing the evolutionary development of the family one very interesting circumstance can be noticed immediately. The primitive *Sortosa* Ancestor spread to all parts of the world, became isolated into different population units, and each of these gave rise to a separate phyletic line. Directly, or nearly so, *Sortosa* gave rise to ten such lines that we know. Of these, seven appear to have remained restricted to a single small region until the present time, and one (*Dolophilodes*) has dispersed only between Asia and North America.

Only two lines have become widespread, the *Wormaldia* line and the *Chimarra* line. Each has acted just as did its parent *Sortosa,* dispersing to many parts of the globe, then fragmenting into isolated populations and the isolates developing into distinctive units. In *Wormaldia* the correspondence with *Sortosa* is almost exact. In *Chimarra* the evolutionary pattern has been a jump-by-jump process with the result that the family tree appears like a pectinate branch rather than a bush.

## SYSTEMATIC ACCOUNT

In the discussion of the Philopotamidae and the following two families many data are cited which concern species new to science, or which introduce phylogenetic concepts necessitating changes in the existing classification. Free use has been made of the many excellent treatments of various groups in the literature, without attempting to repeat the information here.

The aim of this systematic account is not to present a complete taxonomic treatment of the groups involved, but to list and correlate the taxonomic data upon which the foregoing evolutionary conclusions are based.

Unless otherwise specified, keys are to adult males only.

In certain cases, great difficulty has been encountered in setting generic limits. In groups in which all phyletic lines from an ancestral form have developed distinctive characters, and in which intermediate steps are not known, the problem is easy. Each phyletic line can be regarded as a distinctive genus. A case such as the Agapetini in which evolution has resulted in a series of dichotomies appearing as a pectinate branch, also offers little trouble, because it is simply the first example repeating itself. The most acute problem appears in those cases of polychotomy, such as in *Sortosa*, in which evolution has progressed at entirely different speeds in different lines. This situation produces some groups closely related in time but differing greatly from each other, and other groups more distantly related in time but differing little morphologically.

Since genera are basically tools by which to combine the function of identification with the findings of phylogeny, and since these two are clearly not integrated in nature, it is evident that an arbitrary approach must be taken. I have tried, therefore, to segregate as genera those groups which (1) have evidently developed sufficient distinctness to indicate considerable evolutionary change from their near relatives; (2) can be keyed from related forms, preferably in both sexes; and (3) are monophyletic groups. It should be thoroughly understood that this last does not imply that all members arising from a certain ancestor must be one genus, but simply that all members of a genus trace back directly to a common form.

General information of value concerning any of the families discussed is contained in the following references:

Betten (1934)—The Trichoptera of New York.

Martynov (1934)—The Trichoptera Annulipalpia of the U.S.S.R.

McLachlan (1874-80)—A Monographic Revision and Synopsis of the Trichoptera of the European Fauna.

Mosely and Kimmins (1953)—The Trichoptera of Australia and New Zealand.

Ross (1944)—The Caddisflies or Trichoptera of Illinois.

Tsuda (1942)—Japanische Trichopteren.

Ulmer (1907b)—Trichoptera, *in* Genera Insectorum.

Ulmer (1912)—Die Trichopteren der baltischen Bernsteins.

Ulmer (1951)—Kocherfliegen (Trichopteren) von den Sunda-Inseln (Teil I).

### Key to Genera

1. Hind wing with 2A curved up and fusing with 1A to form a large loop (Fig. 21) .....**Chimarra**
   Hind wing with 2A with apex free (Figs. 19, 20) or absent .................... 2
2. Front wing with forks of Rs, M, and Cu₁ arranged in a straight line (Fig. 19); male genitalia with the two claspers fused on the meson, and ninth segment broad on top (Fig. 22) ..**Paulianodes**
   Front wing with fork of M anterior to other two, the three forming a triangle (Fig. 20); male genitalia with the two claspers not fused, ninth segment reduced dorsally by recessed tenth tergite (Fig. 59) ..................... 3
3. Front and hind wings with M 2-branched (Fig. 100)..................... **Gunungiella**
   Front and hind wings with M 3- or 4-branched (Fig. 20) ........................ 4
4. Hind wing with vein 2A atrophied beyond crossvein A2 (Fig. 20)..............**Wormaldia**
   Hind wing with vein 2A extending beyond crossvein A2 (Figs. 23, 27) ................ 5
5. Male clasper with a long, ventral secondary apical segment arising at base of true apical segment (Fig. 50); female eighth segment nearly cylindrical and forming a regular ring.......... ....................... **Philopotamus**
   Male clasper without an extra ventral apical segment (Figs. 57, 64); female eighth segment otherwise .............................. 6

6. Front wing with $M_4$ atrophied, and hind wing with free part of 2A a mere stub (Fig. 104)......
.................................**Protarra**
Either front wing with $M_4$ present, or hind wing with free part of 2A elongate (Fig. 23).....
..............................**Sortosa**

## Paulianodes new genus

Type species: *Paulianodes tsaratananae* new species.

*Diagnosis*: Head with distinct ocelli and with large posterior warts. Maxillary palp with first segment shortest, fourth slightly longer than first, second slightly longer than fourth, third longer than second and fifth only slightly longer than third. Labial palps with first two segments short, third fairly long. Spur count 2-4-4. Front wing with complete venation (Fig. 19), the forks of Rs, M and $Cu_1$ forming nearly a straight line. Hind wing (Fig. 19) with anal vein complete and long, and having the unusual feature of $M_{3+4}$ branched near wing margin. Male genitalia (Fig. 22) with ninth segment forming a comple ring, or set off distinctly from the tenth tergite; the two claspers are highly modified, the basal portions fused together on the meson, and the apical segment either fused with the first or represented by a spiculate dorsal lobe.

This genus is readily distinguished from others of the Philopotamidae by the juxtaposition of forks Rs, M, and $Cu_1$, and by the unique features of the male genitalia.

## Paulianodes tsaratananae new species

*Male*: Length 10 mm. Color various shades of medium brown, the dorsum moderately dark, the venter fairly light, the wings uniformly light brown. General structure as described above for genus. Seventh sternite (Fig. 22E) with a moderately large pointed projection, eighth sternite with a sclerotized crescent but without a projection. Genitalia as in Fig. 22. Ninth segment forming a fairly even round structure. Tenth tergite with the central and apical portions somewhat heart-shaped, the lateral aspect of the apex sharp and curved ventrad; near the apex on the dorsum is a pair of long setae, and around the edge of the tergite is a row of minute sensillae. Cercus leaflike, the lateral aspect deep, the apex oblique, bearing scattered setae. From dorsal view the cercus appears to be a lateral outgrowh of the base of the tenth tergite. The two claspers are fused on the meson to form a

short quadrate and incised structure; the dorsal margin is sinuate and the dorsal area bears three pairs of processes, a slender barrel-shaped pair, a more lateral thick pair curved ventrad at apex, and bearing a few pegs, and a third pair of short spurlike processes. The larger and second pair may be the true apical segments of the claspers. Aedeagus tubular and containing two pairs of internal sclerotized rods, sharp at apex and with the base thick.

*Holotype, male*: Mt. Tsaratanana, Madagascar, 1,700 m. elevation, Oct. 1950 (R. Paulian, ZA 112). In the collection of the Institut Scientifique de Madagascar.

A female collected at 1,500 m. elevation at the type locality certainly belongs to this genus, but lacks the forked $M_{3+4}$ in the hind wing. It has a very simple set of terminal abdominal segments. It is impossible to say whether or not it is this species; for the present, it is identified only as to genus.

## Genus Sortosa Navas

This widespread genus is readily divisible into seven subgenera, defined primarily on the basis of differences in the male genitalia. Each subgenus is apparently restricted to a single zoogeographic area, except *Dolophilodes*, which occurs in two.

### Key to Subgenera

1. Cerci either small and biscuit-like (Fig. 44), or represented only by setose areas (Figs. 40, 42). Australasian region .........**Hydrobiosella**
   Cerci ovate (Fig. 29) or elongate (Figs. 47,48)   2
2. Tenth tergite having a pair of lateral processes which are elongate and sclerotized, in addition to central body of tenth tergite or its divisions (Fig. 35) ...................... 3
   Tenth tergite with no finger-like lateral processes (Figs. 70, 76) .................... 4
3. Lateral processes of tenth tergite arising laterad of cerci (Fig. 35). South Africa....**Thylakion**
   Lateral processes of tenth tergite arising between cerci and tenth tergite (Figs. 47-49). Asia...
   ..............................**Kisaura**
4. Front wing with fork $R_{2+3}$ at or near crossvein *s* ............................. 5
   Front wing with fork $R_{2+3}$ considerably beyond cross-vein *s* (Fig. 26) .........**Dolophilodes**
5. Tenth tergite divided to form a pair of stout, sclerotized, downcurved hooks (Fig. 29). Eastern North America ..................**Fumonta**
   Tenth tergite otherwise .................... 6
6. Tenth tergite divided nearly to base to form a pair of large, foliaceous flaps, with a short mesal projection between them (Fig. 62). North

America. Some specimens of the species *dorca* in . . . . . . . . . . . . . . . . . . . . . . . .**Dolophilodes**
Tenth tergite not divided to base, its lobe never foliaceous . . . . . . . . . . . . . . . . . . . . . . 7

7. Cerci with enlarged base and long, tapering apex; claspers short (Figs. 36-38). South America . . . . . . . . . . . . . . . . . . . . . . . . . . . . . . **Sortosa**
Cerci shorter and finger-like, claspers elongate (Fig. 30). North America . . . . . . . . . . . . . . . . **Sisko**

## Subgenus **Hydrobiosella** Tillyard

*Hydrobiosella* Tillyard (1924:288). Type species: *Hydrobiosella stenocerca* Tillyard (original designation).

*Zelobiosella* Mosely, *in* Mosely and Kimmins (1953: 397). Type species: *Zelobiosella tonela* Mosely (original designation). *New synonymy.*

*Diagnosis*: Wings of simple type with complete venation except for the occasional atrophy of a vein. Genitalia with small or no cerci; claspers simple.

*Distribution*: Australia, Tasmania, New Zealand, and New Caledonia.

### KEY TO SPECIES

1. Cercus present, its base constricted (Fig. 44). Tenth tergite with no processes. New Caledonia . . . . . . . . . . . . . . . . . . . . . . . . . . . . . . . . . . **uncinata**
Cercus either absent or humplike (Figs. 42, 45), or represented by processes with a wide, solid base (Figs. 39-41) . . . . . . . . . . . . . . . . . 2

2. Apical segment of clasper with ventral margin incised to give it a clawlike shape; tenth tergite with a pair of sharply angled processes near middle (Fig. 39) . . . . . . . . . . . . . . . . . . . . 3
Apical segment of clasper with ventral margin straight or nearly so; tenth tergite at most with blunt, small processes . . . . . . . . . . . . . . . . 4

3. Processes of tenth tergite pointed only laterad. Australia . . . . . . . . . . . . . . . . . . . . . . . . . **bispina**
Processes of tenth recurved and pointed anteriad (Fig. 39). Australia . . . . . . . . . . . . . . **arcuata**

4. Apical segment of clasper with tip incised (Fig. 43); front wing with $M_{3+4}$ unbranched. New Zealand . . . . . . . . . . . . . . . . . . . . . . . . . **tonela**
Apical segment of clasper with tip round or pointed; front wing with $M_{3+4}$ branched . . . . . . . . 5

5. A large process with a wide base on each side of base of tenth tergite (Fig. 40) . . . . . . . . . . 6
Tenth tergite with at most low flanges at base . . 7

6. Lateral process of tenth tergite deeply incised and clawlike (Fig. 40). Tasmania . . . . . . **tasmanica**
Lateral process of tenth tergite sinuate (Fig. 41). Tasmania . . . . . . . . . . . . . . . . . . . . . . **cognata**

7. Apical segment of clasper with few spines; basal segment very long (Fig. 42); aedeagus with no large processes. New Zealand . . . . . . **stenocerca**

Apical segment of clasper with a large cushion of black spines; basal segment short (Fig. 45); aedeagus with a pair of long, curved, stout rods (Fig. 119). Australia . . . . . . . . . . . . . . 8

8. Aedeagal rods arising far back on aedeagus . . . . . . . . . . . . . . . . . . . . . . . . . . . . . . . . . . . . **waddama**
Aedeagal rods arising near apex of aedeagus (Fig. 119) . . . . . . . . . . . . . . . . . . . . . . .**michaelseni**

Descriptions and illustrations of these species have been given by Mosely and Kimmins (1953), whose illustrations have been modified for Figs. 39-46 in this paper. Illustrations are added here of the paratype male of *Sortosa michaelseni* kindly loaned by Dr. Ulmer (Fig. 119).

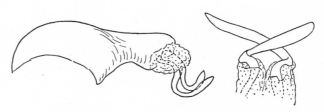

FIG. 119. Aedeagus of *Sortosa michaelseni*. Left, lateral aspect; right, dorsal aspect of apex.

### LIST OF SPECIES

**arcuata** (Kimmins), *Hydrobiosella* (Mosely & Kimmins 1953:397). Australia (Queensland). Fig. 39.
**bispina** (Kimmins), *Hydrobiosella* (Mosely & Kimmins 1953:394). Australia (New South Wales).
**cognata** (Kimmins), *Hydrobiosella* (Mosley & Kimmins 1953:392). Australia (Tasmania). Fig. 41.
**michaelseni** (Ulmer), *Dolophilus* (1908:36). Australia (South West Australia). Figs. 45, 119.
**stenocerca** (Tillyard), *Hydrobiosella* (1924:289). New Zealand. Figs. 23, 42.
**tasmanica** (Mosely), *Hydrobiosella* (Mosely & Kimmins 1953:390). Tasmania. Fig. 40.
**tonela** (Mosely), *Zelobiosella* (Mosely & Kimmins 1953: 397). New Zealand. Fig. 43.
**uncinata** (Kimmins), *Hydrobiosella* (Mosely & Kimmins 1953:250). New Caledonia. Figs. 34, 44.
**waddama** (Mosely), *Hydrobiosella* (Mosely & Kimmins 1953:393). Australia (New South Wales), Tasmania. Fig. 46.

## Subgenus **Sortosa** Navas

*Sortosa* Navas (1918c:16); Schmid (1949:316). Type species: *Sortosa fusca* Navas (original designation).

*Diagnosis*: Front and hind wings with complete venation. $M_{1+2}$ of hind wing occasionally has a short fork. Maxillary palps with first and second segments short, subequal. Male genitalia with large cerci, enlarged at base and tapering to apex; claspers 2-segmented.

Contains three known species from Chile.

### KEY TO SPECIES

1. Two sclerotized dorsal plates between basal and apical segments of claspers (Fig. 38) . . . . . . . . . . . . . . . . . . . . . . . . . . . . . . . . . . . . . . . . . . . . . chilensis
   No sclerites between two segments of claspers (Fig. 36) . . . . . . . . . . . . . . . . . . . . . . . . . . . . . . . 2
2. Tenth tergite elongate, with a small apical knob (Fig. 37) . . . . . . . . . . . . . . . . . . . . . . . edwardi
   Tenth tergite short, with a much larger knob at apex (Fig. 36) . . . . . . . . . . . . . . . . . michelbacheri

### LIST OF SPECIES

chilensis (Navas), Dolophilus (1918c:10); Schmid (1949:316). Chile. *Sortosa fusca* Navas (1918c: 16). Fig. 38.

### Sortosa edwardi new species

*Male*: Length (from tip of head to tip of folded wings) 7.5 mm. Color predominantly gray-brown, the under parts lighter, with darker streaks along the sutures. Wings also uniformly gray-brown. Seventh and eighth abdominal sternites with a median process (Fig. 121C), the one on the seventh sternite slightly the longer. Eighth tergite produced into a broad mesal projection which is incised on the apex and depressed dorsally into a deep, wide trough (Fig. 121A). Genitalia as in Fig. 37. Ninth segment with lateral and ventral areas broad, the segment poorly delineated dorsad from the tenth tergite. Tenth tergite with dorsal aspect generally long, very broad, and the center forming a ridge, the extreme apex forming a small round lobe with sensillae around its margin; in lateral view the tergite looks slender and the apical lobe forms a small dorsal projection at its extreme apex. Cerci broad at base, curved first nearly dorsad, then almost directly posteriad, with minute imbrications at the bend and with only a few scattered setae. Clasper deep, the two segments very nearly the same length; the apical segment is rounded at apex and bears an angulate mesal patch of black spicules at the apex. Aedeagus tubular; inside the folds of the membrane of the apex there are visible two large, slightly curved, sclerotized rods (Fig. 121B).

*Holotype, male*: 50 km. east of San Carlos, Nuble, Chile, Dec. 26, 1950 (Ross & Michelbacher). In the collection of the California Academy of Sciences.

On the basis of the shape and imbricate nature of the base of the cerci and the general proportions of the clasper and ninth segment, this species and the following are undoubtedly close relatives of *chilensis*. From *chilensis* they differ in having the clasper simple, the two segments joined together closely without intervening sclerites. From the following species, *edwardi* is readily distinguished by details of the tenth tergite and aedeagus.

### Sortosa michelbacheri new species

*Male*: Size, general color and structure similar to the preceding. This includes very close similarity in the structures of the seventh and eighth sternites

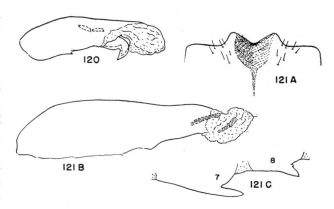

FIG. 120. Aedeagus of *Sortosa michelbacheri*, lateral aspect.
FIG. 121. Parts of *Sortosa edwardi*. A, apex of eighth tergite; B, aedeagus, lateral aspect; C, seventh and eighth sternites, lateral aspect.

and the eighth tergite. Genitalia as in Fig. 36. Ninth segment with lateral and dorsal areas fairly large, mesal portion of dorsum slightly carinate. Tenth tergite short, the apex appearing swollen and beaked from lateral view, somewhat truncate from dorsal view, with minute sensillae along the lateral margins of the swollen portion; the basal part of the tenth tergite forms a wide flanged area. Cerci joined broadly at base to ninth segment, projecting first slightly dorsad, then curved straight posteriad, with slightly imbricate areas at the bend, and bearing short setae, more numerous at the apex. Clasper short and deep, the two segments nearly equal in length, the apical segment nearly triangulate at apex, and bearing a large mesal patch of black spicules on the posterodorsal portion. Aedeagus short and tubular, the apex membranous and bearing a pair of short but very stout hooked sclerotized processes; in addition to these there is a pair of short sclerotized hooks visible inside the aedeagus (Fig. 120).

*Holotype, male*: Los Muermos, Llanquihue, Chile, Jan. 19, 1951, (Ross & Michelbacher). In the collection of the California Academy of Sciences.

This is a close ally of the preceding species, readily distinguished by the shorter and wider tenth tergite and details of the aedeagus.

## Fumonta new subgenus

Type species: *Dolophilus major* Banks

*Diagnosis*: Front and hind wings with complete venation; $R_{2+3}$ forking at or before *s*. Male genitalia with simple claspers, large cerci, and with tenth tergite divided into a pair of downcurved, heavily sclerotized hooklike rods (Fig. 29).

This subgenus occurs only in eastern North America, and contains only the type species: **major** (Banks), *Dolophilus* (1914:254); Ross (1949:155). Great Smoky Mountains and vicinity, North Carolina and Tennessee (Fig. 29).

## Sisko new subgenus

Type species: *Wormaldia sisko* Ross

*Diagnosis*: Front and hind wings with virtually complete venation; $R_{2+3}$ forking at *s*, or slightly beyond it in front wing; hind wing with no cross-vein between 2A and 3A. Claspers elongate and simple; tenth tergite simple and trianguloid; cerci simple— from dorsal view, appearing to arise from tenth tergite (Fig. 30).

Contains only the type species, known from North America: **sisko** (Ross), *Wormaldia* (1949*b*:157). Western Oregon, northwestern North Carolina (Fig. 30).

## Kisaura new subgenus

Type species: *Sortosa obrussa* new species

*Diagnosis*: Front and hind wings with primitive venation except fork $R_{2+3}$ which is variable; it may be near or considerably beyond *s*, or $R_2$ may be atrophied. Genitalia (Figs. 47-49) with a pair of long processes between the tenth tergite and cerci; claspers simple, with a mesoventral plate (*y*) developed between the two segments (Fig. 49D).

*Distribution*: Asia.

In addition to the four species reported here, several new to science were collected in Burma by Dr. René Malaise and await description by Mr. D. E. Kimmins of the British Museum.

### Key to Species

1. Lateral processes of tenth tergite same length as median lobe of tenth (Fig. 48) . . . . . . . . . . 2
   Lateral processes of tenth tergite much longer than median lobe of tenth . . . . . . . . . . . . . . . . . 3
2. Lateral aspect of cercus deep; lateral processes angled at tip (Fig. 48) . . . . . . . . . . . .**pectinata**
   Lateral aspect of cercus shallow; lateral processes almost straight at tip (Fig. 49) . . . . . .**obrussa**
3. Lateral aspect of apical segment of clasper ovoid (Martynov 1934, Fig. 115) . . . . . . . .**aurascens**
   Lateral aspect of apical segment of clasper nearly rectangular (Tsuda 1939, Fig. 2) . . .**kisoensis**

### List of Species

**aurascens** (Martynov), *Dolophilodes* (1934:173). Siberia (South Ussuri region).
**kisoensis** (Tsuda), *Dolophilodes* (1939:296). Japan (Honshu).

### Sortosa obrussa new species

*Male*: Length 7.5 mm. Color various shades of brown, the venter lighter, and the wings with an irrorate pattern of lighter markings caused by light and dark pubescence superimposed on a uniform light brown membrane. Venation complete, with $R_{2+3}$ branched midway between *s* and tip of wing (Fig. 33). Male genitalia as in Fig. 49. Ninth segment fairly elongate, the tenth recessed dorsally to the anterior margin of the ninth. Tenth tergite elongate, the lateral and ventral sclerotized portion apparently divided into two halves which are closely appressed and covered with membranous folds which unite with the sclerotized part at the apex; the entire dorsal portion is membranous and this membrane unites with that of the eighth segment. On each side of the base of the tenth arises a long slender sclerotized process. The cerci are two-thirds as long as the tenth tergite and arise from the base of the tenth. They bear a scattering of setae on the apical portion. Clasper with basal segment short and irregular; apical segment considerably longer, slender, and bearing on the mesal surface a straight comb of black, sclerotized teeth. Arising from the apex of the basal segment is a short, sclerotized ventral mesal process which appears to press against the base of the apical segment and act as an aid in articulation. Aedeagus tubular and simple.

*Holotype, male.* Hassenzan, Formosa, June 21, 1932 (L. Gressitt). In the collection of the Museum of Comparative Zoology.

### Sortosa pectinata new species

*Male*: Length 6 mm. Color similar to preceding, except that the areas of pale hairs on the wings are larger and give them an irregularly spotted appearance. Wings with complete venation, and with vein $R_{2+3}$ branched beyond *s* a distance about equal to length of *s* (Fig. 32). Male genitalia as in Fig. 48. Ninth segment deep but only moderately long. Tenth segment with its dorsal portion entirely membranous at the base, the apex lightly sclerotized and divided into a pair of closely appressed halves. A long, sclerotized process arises on each side where the base of the tenth tergite joins the ninth segment; this process is ribbon-like, sinuate, and suddenly angled mesad and pointed at the apex. Each cercus is fused at the base with the basal lateral portion of the tenth tergite, and bears a scattering of setae on its apical portion. Clasper with short, irregular base; apical segment longer and shallower, with a slightly bowed comb of sclerotized teeth on its mesal face; the articulating process at the apex of the basal segment is small and almost hidden by the membranous folds between the segments. Aedeagus moderately elongate and cylindrical, with an ovate membranous apex which appears to be fused with the membrane beneath the apex of the tenth tergite.

*Holotype, male*: Yim Na Sam, eastern Kwantung, South China, June 16, 1936 (L. Gressitt). In the collection of the Museum of Comparative Zoology.

This species and those preceding are most closely related to *kisoensis* and *aurascens*. All four species may be distinguished by characters given in the key.

I am not certain concerning the fusion of the apex of the aedeagus with the ventral membranous folds arising from the underside of the tenth tergite. Having only one specimen of each species available, I have hesitated to undertake much manipulation and dissection, but such as I have been able to do indicates that the apex of the aedeagus is fastened very securely in about the position indicated. If true, this is a new and rather novel feature of caddisfly morphology.

### Subgenus Thylakion Barnard

*Thylakion* Barnard (1934:384). Type species: *Thylakion urceolus* Barnard (original designation).

*Diagnosis*: Front wings with complete venation; fork $R_{2+3}$ above fork $R_{4+5}$, and both slightly anterior to *s*. Hind wings with complete venation except for 2A which is reduced to a stub (Figs. 27, 28); branches of Rs as in front wing. Male genitalia with lateral processes on base of tenth tergite, situated laterad of cerci (Fig. 35). Claspers simple. Cerci large and trianguloid. Pupal mandible with three large, subequal preapical teeth.

*Distribution*: Known only from South Africa.

#### KEY TO SPECIES

Apical segment of clasper wide, shorter than basal segment (Barnard 1934, Fig. 49 *a-j*); lateral appendages of tenth tergite narrow and pointed; tenth tergite with a pair of spurs at middle (Fig. 35) . . . . . . . . . . . . . . . . . . . . . . . . . . . . . . . . . . . . . **urceola**

Apical segment of clasper narrower and nearly twice length of basal segment (Barnard 1934, Fig. 49 *k-m*); lateral appendages of tenth tergite with an enlarged portion at apex; tenth tergite without spurs or other processes. . . . . . . . . . . . . .**forcipata**

#### LIST OF SPECIES

**forcipata** (Barnard), *Thylakion* (1934:386). River Zonder End Mountains, South Africa. Fig. 27.

**urceola** (Barnard), *Thylakion* (1934:386); Barnard (1940:657). Mountains of South Africa. Figs. 28, 35.

### Subgenus Dolophilodes Ulmer

*Dolophilodes* Ulmer (1909:125). Type species: *Dolophilodes ornata* Ulmer (monobasic).

*Trentonius* Betten & Mosely (1940:11). Type species: *Philopotamus distinctus* Walker (original designation).

*Diagnosis*: Venation complete, except that in the hind wing $R_{2+3}$ is unbranched in some species; $R_{2+3}$ branches close to the wing margin and distant from *s* except in *dorca*, in which $R_{2+3}$ branches at *s* or varying distances from it, the extreme being like other species of the genus. Male genitalia with simple, 2-segmented claspers and with the tenth tergite cleft, deeply in *dorca* (Fig. 62), shallowly in the other species (Fig. 59); aedeagus a large and chiefly membranous sac, with one long, thin, internal sclerotized rod; cerci large.

*Distribution*: Asia and North America.

## KEY TO SPECIES

1. Tenth tergite divided nearly to base to form a pair of large, foliaceous flaps, with a short mesal projection between them at base (Fig. 62). Western North America..............dorca
   Tenth tergite divided at most halfway, the lateral lobes never foliaceous (Fig. 59).........2
2. Lobes of tenth tergite with lateral flanges, with apical points appressed, and with basal portion of segment forming a high, sharp mesal crest ending at the base of the tergal lobes; cercus large, concave laterally and ear-shaped (Fig. 60). Japan................auriculata
   Lobes of tenth tergite simple, tenth with no mesal crest; cercus of only moderate size and not earlike ..................................3
3. Clasper (Fig. 61) with sinuate apical segment and rows of regular long teeth on basal segment. Western North America......novusamericana
   Clasper with margins of apical segment curved or straight, simple (Figs. 58, 59)..........4
4. Apical segment of clasper either hook-shaped or much wider at base than at apex, its ventral margin oblique and concave (Fig. 59)....5
   Apical segment of clasper straight and nearly parallel-sided, sometimes its ventral margin slightly concave, but not oblique (Fig. 58)......8
5. Mesal part of tenth tergite forming a small point situated between the lateral lobes (Martynov 1935:122, Fig. 26). India...........indica
   Mesal part of tenth tergite not pointed (Fig. 59) 6
6. Apical segment of clasper with dorsal margin concave at extreme end, the tip therefore appearing suddenly narrowed (Martynov 1933:141, Figs. 3, 4). Japan................japonica
   Apical segment with dorsal margin evenly convex .................................. 7
7. Lateral lobes of tenth tergite curved dorsad at tip (Martynov 1934:170, Fig. 114). Siberia..... ............................orientalis
   Lateral lobes of tenth tergite with tip straight or curved ventrad (Fig. 59). Eastern North America ......................distincta
8. Cercus narrow at base and enlarged at apex; apical segment of clasper about 4 to 4½ times as long as deep (Fig. 57). Asia..............ornata
   Cercus of nearly equal width throughout; apical segment of clasper wider, less than 4 times as long as deep (Fig. 58). Western North America .................................. 9
9. Lateral lobes of tenth tergite very short, not projecting beyond tip of cercus (Denning 1949a:114, Fig. 4); pale in color, femora straw color or pale yellow ...................pallidipes
   Lateral lobes of tenth tergite projecting beyond tip of cercus (Fig. 58); color of body and legs dark brown to black..............aequalis

## LIST OF SPECIES

aequalis (Banks), *Philopotamus* (1924:450); Denning (1949a: Fig. 5). Western North America. Fig. 58.
auriculata (Martynov), *Dolophilodes* (1933:142). Japan. Fig. 60.
cercata (Navas), *Dolophilodes* (1936a:126). China. Not seen.
distincta (Walker), *Philopotamus* (1852:104); Betten (1934:167); Betten & Mosely (1940:11); Ross (1944:47). Eastern North America. Fig. 59.
dorca (Ross), *Philopotamus* (1938a:132). Western North America. Figs. 24-26, 62.
   *Philopotamus oregonensis* Ling (1938:63).
indica (Martynov), *Dolophilodes* (1935:122). India (Punjab).
japonica (Banks), *Philopotamus* (1906:111). Japan. *Dolophilodes exscisus* Martynov (1933:140). *New synonymy.*
novusamericana (Ling), *Philopotamus* (1938:63); Denning (1949a:113); Ross (1949:159). Western North America. Fig. 61.
orientalis (Martynov), *Dolophilodes* (1934:170). South Ussuri, Siberia.
ornata (Ulmer), *Dolophilodes* (1909:126). Central Asia. Fig. 57.
   *Philopotamus sinensis* Banks (1940:209). *New synonymy.*
pallidipes (Banks), *Philopotamus* (1936:267); Denning (1949a:114). Western North America.

### Genus **Philopotamus** Leach

*Philopotamus* Leach (1815:136). Type species: *Philopotamus scopulorum* Leach (monobasic).

*Diagnosis*: Wings with complete venation; branching of $R_{2+3}$ variable, occurring at *s* or nearer the wing margin, in extremes resembling typical *Dolophilodes*. Male genitalia (Figs. 50-56) with tenth tergite having a simple mesal lobe, and a pair of lateral processes arising laterad of the cerci; clasper 2-segmented, with an apparent extra segment arising from the tip of the basal segment and extending below the apical segment; cerci large.

*Distribution*: Europe to Caucasia.

### KEY TO AVAILABLE SPECIES

1. Apical segment of clasper much shorter than its ventral appendage (Fig. 54); tenth tergite extending far posteriad of its lateral processes ...........................ludificatus
   Apical segment of clasper about same length as its ventral appendage (Fig. 50); tenth tergite extending at most a little beyond its lateral processes ..........................2
2. Dorsal aspect of tenth tergite with apical two-thirds finger-like and narrow, slightly thickened at apex (Martynov 1934, Fig. 112)......tenuis

Dorsal aspect of tenth tergite triangular or wide and oval (Figs. 50, 51) .................. 3

3. Aedeagus with ventral sclerite nearly straight at tip (Fig. 51) ........................ 4
   Aedeagus with ventral sclerite hooked or angled ventrad at tip (Fig. 50) .............. 6

4. Apex of tenth tergite divided into a pair of upright processes (Fig. 53) ...........**amphilectus**
   Apex of tenth tergite upturned but simple (Fig. 51) ............................... 5

5. Color of front wings yellow or light tawny with darker spots ...................**flavidus**
   Color of front wings dark with lighter spots ...... .......................... **variegatus**

6. Apical segment of clasper with ventral margin sinuate and bearing a dense brush of spines (Fig. 50) ........................**corsicanus**
   Apical segment of clasper with ventral margin curved and bearing only scattered spines (Fig. 55) ................................. 7

7. Tenth tergite cleft at tip (Fig. 56) ...... **perversus**
   Tenth tergite not cleft at tip (Fig. 55) .... **insularis montanus**

## LIST OF SPECIES

The synonymy in the following list is compiled chiefly from McLachlan (1878). Certain species are unplaced in the key because of lack of information regarding diagnostic criteria. I have made no attempt to evaluate the status of named varieties, simply listing them under the specific name to which they apply. To go further will require more intensive collecting and study over the entire ranges of the various forms.

**amphilectus** McLachlan (1884:48). Portugal. Fig. 53.
**caucasicus** Navas (1933*a*:111). Caucasus. Not seen.
**corsicanus** Mosely (1938*a*:204) (also Mosely 1930*a*: 168, as *siculus*). Corsica. Fig. 50.
**flavidus** Hagen (1864:44); McLachlan (1878:386). Corsica. Fig. 51.
**hamatus** Ulmer (1912:45). Baltic amber.
**insularis** McLachlan (1878:384). Isle of Guernsey. Fig. 55.
**ludificatus** McLachlan (1878:381); Ulmer (1907*b*:pl. 41). Europe. Fig. 54.
**montanus** Donovan (1813:pl. 548); McLachlan (1878: 382). Europe.
  *Philopotamus scopulorum* Leach (1815:136).
  *Phryganea charpentieri* Zetterstedt (1840:1068).
  *Philopotamus tigrinus* Brauer (1857:39).
  var. *scoticus* McLachlan (1862*a*:34). Scotland.
  var. *pyrenaicus* McLachlan (1878:384). Pyrenees.
  var. *cesareus* McLachlan (1884:74). Isle of Jersey.
  var. *chrysopterus* Morton (1884:273). Scotland.
**perversus** McLachlan (1884:46). Portugal. Fig. 56.
**siculus** Hagen (1860:278); McLachlan (1878:385). Sicily.
**tenuis** Martynov (1913*a*:32 and 1934:169). Caucasus.
**variegatus** Scopoli (1763:266); McLachlan (1878: 385). Europe. Fig. 52.

*Philopotamus pedemontanus* Navas (1934:158).
  var. *hispanicus* McLachlan (1878:386). Spain.

## **Ulmerodina** new genus

Type species: *Dolophilus impar* Ulmer.

*Diagnosis*: Head with ocelli. Maxillary palp with second segment short, fourth a little longer, and third twice length of fourth; fifth subequal to third, minutely subdivided. Wings typical for *Sortosa* (Fig. 23) but with R$_2$ lost. Male genitalia with claspers separate, elongate, and appearing to be 1-segmented (Fig. 63).

This descriptive material is taken from Ulmer's description of the genotype (1912:53), the only described species in the genus, which is known only from Baltic amber.

There is considerable doubt as to the correct phylogenetic position of this form. The wing venation, especially the completeness of the anal veins in the hind wing and M$_{3+4}$ branching beyond *m* in the front wing, and the possession of ocelli, indicate fairly definitely that *impar* is near the *Sortosa* complex. On the other hand, the apparently single-segmented claspers combined with the loss of R$_2$ set off this form as a distinctive unit which it seems better to segregate as a separate genus.

## Genus **Wormaldia** McLachlan

*Diagnosis*: Primitive forms with full complement of veins except in hind wing, in which 2A has atrophied beyond the basal cross-veins and the basal anal cells are realigned as in Fig. 20, with the basal cross-veins forming a linear bar, and 1A and 3A divergent. Spur count 2-4-4. Cerci elongate or large and rhombic, sometimes fused to ninth pleural region. In all characters except genitalia the various lines of the genus are sufficiently homogenous to be treated as simple species groups, with one exception. This exception is *Doloclanes*, which is a line set off by the fusion of R$_1$ and R$_2$ in the hind wings. This line displays other wing changes in its more specialized members, including partial or full fusion of Sc$_2$ and R$_1$ at the base of the stigmal area, decrease in size of the discal cell, and in the hind wing a crowding together of the branches of Rs (Fig. 87). These changes seem to indicate a definite change in the selection pressures acting on the wings, a phenomenon not expressed in other species groups in the genus. *Doloclanes* is therefore recognized as a subgenus.

KEY TO SUBGENERA

Hind wing with $R_1$ and $R_2$ ending some distance apart at wing margin (Fig. 20) . . . . . . . **Wormaldia s. st.**
Hind wing with $R_1$ and $R_2$ fused just before wing margin (Fig. 87) . . . . . . . . . . . . . . . . . . . **Doloclanes**

## Subgenus **Wormaldia** McLachlan

*Wormaldia* McLachlan (1865:140). Type species: *Hydropsyche occipitalis* Pictet (designation of Ross 1949).

*Dolophilus* McLachlan (1868:303). Type species: *Dolophilus copiosus* McLachlan (monobasic).

*Paragapetus* Banks (1914:202). Type species: *Paragapetus moestus* Banks (monobasic).

*Dolophiliella* Banks (1930b:230). Type species: *Dolophiliella gabriella* Banks (original designation).

*Distribution*: The Americas, Eurasia, and Africa.

### KEY TO SPECIES

1. Seventh sternite with a long, tongue-shaped mesal process (Fig. 83) . . . . . . . . . . 2
Seventh sternite at most with a large, triangular process (Fig. 65) . . . . . . . . . . . . . 3
2(1). Apical segment of clasper curved dorsad (Fig. 84) . . . . . . . . . . . . . . . . . . . . **gabriella**
Apical segment of clasper straight (Fig. 83) . . . . . . . . . . . . . . . . . . . . . . . . . **moesta**
**chinensis**
**relicta**
3(1). Cerci fused with upper edge of ninth pleural region (Fig. 78) . . . . . . . . . . . . . . . . 4
Cerci attached only at base (Fig. 77) or partially fused with tenth tergite . . . . . . 5
4(3). Claspers elongate (Fig. 78) . . . . . . . . . **pulla**
Claspers shorter and stubby (McLachlan 1884, pl. 5) . . . . . . . . . . . . . . . . **corvina**
5(3). Tenth tergite with a short, spatulate, mesal flap near middle (Fig. 77) . . . . . **copiosa**
Tenth tergite without a dorsal flap, but sometimes with a dorsal point (Fig. 81) 6
6(5). Eighth tergite, seen from lateral view, produced hoodlike over base of genitalia (Figs. 68, 69) . . . . . . . . . . . . . . . . 7
Eighth tergite not hoodlike . . . . . . . . . . . 8
7(6). Tenth tergite much longer than cercus; hood of eighth tergite elongate and incised at apex (Fig. 69) . . . . . . . . . . . . . . **hamata**
Tenth tergite slightly shorter than cercus; hood of eighth tergite shorter and nearly truncate at apex (Fig. 68) . . . . . . **thyria**
8(6). Apex of tenth tergite recurved to form a hook as in Fig. 72 . . . . . . . . . . . . . . . **dampfi**
Apex of tenth tergite sometimes with a dorsal point near apex, but never with the entire tip curved back upon itself . . . . . 9

9(8). Tenth tergite elongate, the basal portion with lateral flanges, which may be narrow, as in Fig. 73, or wide and sharp as in Fig. 76 . . . . . . . . . . . . . . . . . . . . . . . . . 10
Tenth tergite either without lateral flanges (Fig. 79), often short (Fig. 68), or flanges near apex (Fig. 85) . . . . . . . 13
10(9). Cercus wide, short, and earlike (Fig. 74) . . . . . . . . . . . . . . . . . . . . . . . . . **arizonensis**
Cercus narrow, slender, and finger-like (Fig. 73) . . . . . . . . . . . . . . . . . . . . . . . . 11
11(10). Lateral flanges of tenth tergite with dorsal aspect rounded (Fig. 73) . . . . . . . **ostina**
Lateral flanges of tenth tergite with dorsal aspect pointed (Fig. 75) . . . . . . . . . . . 12
12(11). Tenth tergite narrowed near apex to a thin neck (Fig. 75) . . . . . . . . . . . . . . **planae**
Tenth tergite tapering evenly to apex (Fig. 76) . . . . . . . . . . . . . . . . . . . . **esperonis**
13(9). Tenth tergite with a small dorsal point just before apex (Figs. 79-82); front wing with $M_4$ atrophied . . . . . **occipitalis group**
Tenth tergite with no dorsal point (Fig. 66); front wing with $M_4$ present . . . . . . . 14
14(13). Cerci arising from dorsum of base of tenth tergite (Fig. 85), the two fairly close together; apex of tenth tergite bifid . . . . . . . . . . . . . . . . . . . . . . . . . . . . **pauliani**
Cerci arising from a more ventral position (Fig. 66); apex of tenth tergite simple and entire . . . . . . . . . . . . . . . . . . . . 15
15(14). Apical segment of clasper deeply constricted in middle, the apex enlarged and bearing rows of black spicules (Mosely 1939, Figs. 91-94) . . . . . . . . . . . . . . . . . **kyana**
Apical segment of clasper simple and nearly parallel-sided, never constricted more than in Fig. 64 . . . . . . . . . . . . . . . . 16
16(15). Cerci and tenth tergite elongate, appressed, and fused for a short distance at base (Fig. 96) . . . . . . . . . . . . . . . . . . . **recta**
Cerci free to base . . . . . . . . . . . . . . . . . . 17
17(16). Apical segment of clasper much longer than basal segment (Fig. 67) . . . . . . **shawnee**
Apical segment of clasper subequal to or shorter than basal segment . . . . . . . . 18
18(17). Tenth tergite truncate and hooked ventrad at extreme tip (Fig. 66) . . . . . . . . . . **strota**
Tenth tergite with tip pointed or rounded and not hooked (Fig. 65) . . . . . . . . . . . . . 19
19(18). Seventh sternite with a triangular apical process as long as Fig. 65 or longer . . 20
Seventh sternite with only a low apical projection as in Fig. 64, or none . . . . . . . . 21
20(19). Clasper with apical segment slender and upcurved (Fig. 71) . . . . . . . . . . **endonima**
Clasper with apical segment shorter, stout, and straight (Fig. 65) . . . . . . . . . **occidea**

21(19). Dorsal bridge of ninth segment bearing a small, thin, transverse, semicircular, dorsally projecting plate (Fig. 70) . . **dorsata**
Dorsal bridge of ninth segment without a projecting plate . . . . . . . . . . . . . . . . . 22
22(21). Apical segment of clasper definitely constricted near middle (Fig. 64) . . . . **anilla**
Apical segment of clasper parallel-sided, rounded at tip . . . . . . . . . . . . . . **cruzensis**

### LIST OF SPECIES

Dr. Edwin W. King has kindly agreed to the inclusion here of the descriptions of several species new to science discovered during our joint study of the Dampf collection of Mexican Trichoptera. The species in question should be credited as jointly described and are so marked.

#### Anilla Group

**anilla** (Ross), *Dolophilus* (1941:50). Western North America. Fig. 64.
**cruzensis** (Ling), *Dolophilus* (1938:64). California.
**hamata** Denning (1951:158). California. Fig. 69.
**occidea** (Ross), *Dolophilus* (1938a:134). Western North America. Fig. 65.
**shawnee** (Ross), *Dolophilus* (1938a:133). Eastern North America. Fig. 67.
**strota** (Ross), *Dolophilus* (1938b:118). Eastern North America. Fig. 66.
**thyria** Denning (1950a:98). North Carolina. Fig. 68.

#### Wormaldia dorsata Ross & King, new species

*Male*: Length, 7 mm. Color various shades of medium brown. General structure typical for the genus. Eighth tergite (Fig. 131) with shallow median notch on apical edge; remainder of apical margin crenulate. Seventh and eighth sternites each with the apical margin slightly produced, closely resembling those of *dampfi*. Genitalia as in Fig. 70. Tenth tergite elongate and tapering to a bluntly rounded tip. Cerci cylindrical, bluntly pointed. Basal segment of clasper short, barrel-shaped; apical segment slightly constricted at center, with apical spinose area obliquely truncate (Fig. 70A). Aedeagus with basal dorsal sclerotized portion reduced to a narrow rod; apical portion with two sclerotized rods as in *dampfi* (Fig. 122), and a short, curved rod ventrally at the midpoint.

*Holotype, male*: Finca Vergel, Chiapas, Mexico, May 19, 1935, at light (A. Dampf). In the collection of the Illinois Natural History Survey.

This species is a close relative of *anilla*, differing chiefly in the longer tenth tergite and the dorsal sclerotized projection (*r*) arising from the narrow dorsal band of the ninth tergite.

#### Wormaldia endonima Ross & King, new species

*Male*: Length 4.5 mm. Color and general structure similar to the preceding. Eighth tergite rectangular, with an apical median notch flanked by two small projections (Fig. 127). Seventh sternite strongly produced apically to form a triangular apex. Eighth sternite with only a slight, broad, angular projection. Genitalia as in Fig. 71. Tenth tergite tapering smoothly to a rather sharp point. In this feature the species closely resembles *dampfi*, but lacks the dorsal recurved hook on the tergite that distinguishes *dampfi*. Basal clasper short, inflated, the apical distinctly longer, curving slightly dorsad. Apical spinose area of second clasper segment obliquely truncate (Fig. 71A). Basal sclerotization of aedeagus broad and straplike, two sclerotized arms in apex as in *dampfi* (Fig. 122).

*Holotype, male*: Finca Germania, Chiapas, Mexico, June 20, 1935, at light (A. Dampf). *Paratypes*. Finca Maravillas, Chiapas, Mexico, Dec. 16, 1931, at light (A. Dampf), 1♂; Finca Esperanza, Chiapas, Mexico, June 20, 1938, at light (A. Dampf), 1♂. Types in the collection of the Illinois Natural History Survey.

This is also a close relative of *anilla*, differing from it chiefly in its small size, slightly thicker basal segment of the clasper, and slightly longer tenth tergite.

#### Arizonensis Group

**arizonensis** (Ling), *Dolophilus* (1938:63). Southwest North America. Figs. 20, 74.
**insignis** (Martynov), *Dolophilus* (1912:29). Peru.

#### Wormaldia dampfi Ross & King, new species

*Male*: Length, 5.5 mm. Color various shades of brown. General structure typical for the genus. Genitalia as in Fig. 72. Eighth tergite with apical margin slightly indented (Fig. 128). Seventh sternite produced apically into a short, wide, blunt projection, eighth only very slightly produced. Tenth tergite elongate, tapering to a point without lateral processes, the apex with a large hook, recurved dorsally. Cerci clavate, four-fifths as long as tergite. Clasper with basal segment barrel-shaped, slightly setiferous, and slightly prolonged ventroapically. Apical clasper segment elongate for the genus, subcylindrical, obliquely truncate apically;

the apical patch of spines on this truncate face nearly circular. Aedeagus elongate, inner sclerotization consisting of two lateral rods, fused basally at about the midpoint of the aedeagus (Fig. 122).

*Holotype, male*: San Cristobal, Chiapas, Mexico, March 9, 1938, at light (A. Dampf). *Paratype*: Finca Germania, Chiapas, Mexico, June 20, 1935, at light (A. Dampf), 1♂. Types in the collection of the Illinois Natural History Survey.

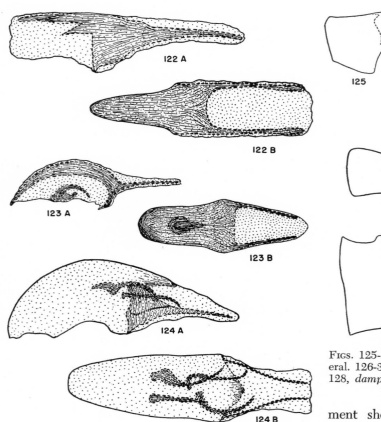

FIGS. 122-24. Aedeagi of *Wormaldia*. A, lateral aspect; B, dorsal aspect. 122, *dampfi*. 123, *planae*. 124, *esperonis*.

The recurved apex of the tenth tergite will serve to distinguish this species from all others in the genus.

**Wormaldia esperonis Ross & King, new species**

*Male*: Length 6 mm. Color and general structure similar to the preceding. Seventh and eighth sternites not produced, their posterior margins practically transverse. Eighth tergite with apical margin

indented at the center, otherwise convexly rounded; its central indented area bears on its inner surface three short tubercles, one median and two lateral (Fig. 129). Genitalia as in Fig. 76. Tenth tergite with a pair of strong dorsolateral teeth at the basal third, the apex curving ventrad, depressed and with the edges slightly up-rolled. Tergite deeply incised at the base of the cerci, which are elongate, compressed, and tapering at tips. Basal clasper seg-

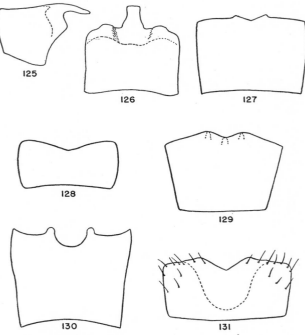

FIGS. 125-31. Eighth tergite of *Wormaldia* males. 125, lateral. 126-31, dorsal aspect. 125, 126, *ostina*. 127, *endonima*. 128, *dampfi*. 129, *esperonis*. 130, *planae*. 131, *dorsata*.

ment short, obliquely truncate. Apical segment longer than basal, tapering to a bluntly rounded tip. Apical spinose area a parallelogram, not sharply truncate, with the spines on the ventral edge extending along the apical two-thirds of the segment (Fig. 76A). Aedeagus with the internal sclerotization consisting of a pair of lateral rods in the apex and four irregularly curved, sickle-shaped rods in the central region (Fig. 124).

*Holotype, male*: Finca Esperanza, Chiapas, Mexico, Feb. 6-12, 1939, at light (A. Dampf). *Paratype*: "Mexico, A. Dampf," 1♂. Types in the collection of the Illinois Natural History Survey.

This species is a close relative of the following

on the basis of the shape of the tenth tergite. The very wide, sharp, lateral projection of the tenth tergite will distinguish this species.

## Wormaldia planae Ross & King, new species

*Male:* Length 4 mm. Color and general structure typical for genus. Eighth tergite (Fig. 130) with a semicircular central indentation on its apical margin, this indentation flanked by a pair of small knob-like protuberances, and lateral to them the remainder of the apical margin concave. Seventh and eighth sternites with posterior margins transverse. Genitalia as in Fig. 75. Tenth tergite expanded at basal third into a pair of blunt lateral lobes; thence tapering to a narrow neck and expanding slightly but sharply into a quadrate tip (Fig. 75B). In profile (Fig. 75A) the neck just described is seen to be dorsally notched, as well as laterally compressed. Cerci clavate. Tenth sternite shallowly concave apically. Basal clasper segment thick, cylindrical, truncate; apical segment elliptical in cross-section, the long (dorsoventral) axis nearly as long as diameter of basal segment, the short axis only about half this diameter. Truncate spinose apical area nearly circular. Aedeagus with inner sclerotization reaching the entire length, the basal portion broad and convex, apical arms straight and converging posteriorly. A second, separate, comma-shaped sclerotized structure occurs ventrally in the center of the basal region (Fig. 123).

*Holotype, male:* Finca Vergel, Chiapas, Mexico, May 19, 1935, at light (A. Dampf). *Paratypes:* Same data as for holotype, 2♂; Finca Vergel, Chiapas, June 12, 1935, 1♂; May 11, 1935, 1♂; May 25, 1935, 1♂; May 21, 1935, 1♂; Finca Maravillas, Chiapas, Dec. 16, 1931, 2♂; all at light (A. Dampf). No data (presumably Mexico, A. Dampf), 1♂. In the collection of the Illinois Natural History Survey.

This species is a close relative of the preceding but may be identified by the fact that the lateral flanges of the tenth tergite follow imperceptibly with the contour of the segment. In addition the emargination of the eighth tergite is distinctive of this species.

## Wormaldia ostina new species

*Male:* Length 5.5 mm. Color medium shades of brown, the pubescence on the wings darker, appearing almost black. General structure typical for genus. Eighth tergite (Figs. 125, 126) with a narrow, truncate projection from posterior margin. Posterior margin of seventh sternite almost transverse; of eighth sternite, gently bowed. Genitalia as in Fig. 73. Ninth segment moderately long and deep. Tenth tergite elongate, constricted just before middle, the apex rhomboidal, the base with a pair of narrow flanges; in lateral view the apex has a small dorsal point. Cercus elongate, narrow, and parallel-sided. Clasper with basal segment tapering slightly; apical segment slightly shorter, constricted in middle sufficiently to make the dorsal and ventral margins gently concave, and with mesal face of apical third covered with a mat of black spicules. Aedeagus simple.

*Female:* Size, color, and general structure similar to male. Abdomen with apical segments simple and more or less tubular.

*Holotype, male:* Santa Isabel, Valley of Cosnipata, Department of Cusco, Peru, Jan. 9, 1952 (F. Woytkowski). *Allotype, female:* Same data except for the date, Dec. 23. *Paratype:* Same data except for the date, Dec. 26. Types in the collection of the Illinois Natural History Survey.

This species is undoubtedly a near relative of *insignis,* also described from Peru. Martynov's illustrations of *insignis* are of a dry, uncleared abdomen, hence only a general idea of the species can be gleaned from them. It will be necessary to study the types before a definite comparison can be made of *insignis* with *ostina.*

### Copiosa Group

**copiosa** (McLachlan), *Dolophilus* (1868:303). Europe. Fig. 77.

### Occipitalis Group

Kimmins (1953c) has studied the aedeagi of this group and proposed that certain forms be accorded subspecific status. Keys are given for the species and subspecies of the entire group, which occurs only in Europe.

**mediana** McLachlan (1878:391). Europe. Fig. 82.
**occipitalis** (Pictet), *Hydropsyche* (1834:211); McLachlan (1878:389). Europe. Fig. 79.
   ?*Hydropsyche brevicornis* Pictet (1834:211).
   *Aphelocheira subaurata* Stephens (1836:180).
   *Wormaldia* lambda Navas (1934:159).
   subsp. **subterranea** Radovanovic (1932a:101). Czechoslovakia.
**subnigra** McLachlan (1865:142). Europe. Fig. 81.
**triangulifera** McLachlan (1878:390). Europe. Fig. 80.
   subsp. **moselyi** Kimmins (1953c:806). France.
**variegata** Mosely (1930a:169). Corsica.
   subsp. **maclachlani** Kimmins (1953c:807). Italy.

### Pulla Group

**pulla** (McLachlan), *Dolophilus* (1878:389). Europe. Fig. 78.

**corvina** (McLachlan), *Dolophilus* (1884:49). Portugal.

### Aequalis Group

**aequalis** (Hagen & Pictet), *Agapetus* (1856:125). Baltic amber. Fig. 99.

**congener** (Ulmer), *Dolophilus* (1912:52). Baltic amber. Fig. 97.

**media** (Ulmer), *Dolophilus* (1912:51). Baltic amber. Fig. 98.

### Kyana Group

**kyana** (Mosely), *Dolophilus* (1939:30). Ruwenzori, Africa.

## Wormaldia pauliani new species

*Male*: Length 7.5 mm. Color various shades of brown, wings unicolorous. General structure typical for genus. Eighth tergite simple and without processes. Seventh sternite transverse, eighth produced into a short, wide, arcuate area. Genitalia as in Fig. 85. Ninth segment with dorsal portion narrowed steeply, apicoventral portion produced into an arcuate lip beneath bases of claspers. Tenth tergite elongate, with central part raised into a rounded lobe, lateral portion forming a flange around it, the apices of the two flanges extending beyond the central part, nearly meeting at tip, and giving the dorsal aspect a bifid appearance. Cercus elongate and slender, situated high at base of tenth tergite, the two cerci close together. Clasper elongate, the basal segment irregular, the apical one parallel-sided, with the apex rounded and beset with black spicules. These latter form a curved patch on the mesal surface of the apex of the segment. Aedeagus irregular in shape, with a long, sclerotized internal rod fully half the length of the aedeagus.

*Holotype, male*: Mt. Tsaratanana, 1,500 m. elevation, Madagascar (R. Paulian). In the collection of the Institut Scientifique de Madagascar.

There is some doubt as to the inclusion of this species in the same group as *kyana* because of striking differences in the shape of the claspers and tenth tergite. The elongate general condition, the similar shape of the ninth segment, and the elongate cerci, however, seem to indicate a community of origin for the two species. Each has changed much since its isolation.

### Moesta Group

**chinensis** (Ulmer), *Dolophiliella* (1932:43). China.

**gabriella** (Banks), *Dolophiliella* (1930b:230). Western North America. Fig. 84.

**moesta** (Banks), *Paragapetus* (1914:202). Eastern North America. Fig. 83. *Dolophilus breviatus* Banks (1914:254).

**relicta** (Martynov), *Dolophiliella* (1935:121). India, Burma.

### Recta Group

**recta** (Ulmer), *Chimarrha* (1930:375). Philippine Islands. Fig. 96.

### Subgenus **Doloclanes** Banks

*Doloclanes* Banks (1937:168). Type species: *Doloclanes montana* Banks (original designation).

*Nanagapetus* Tsuda (1942:253). Type species: *Nanagapetus kisoensis* Tsuda (original designation). *New synonymy.*

*Gatlinia* Ross (1948:22). Type species: *Gatlinia mohri* Ross (original designation). *New synonymy.*

*Distribution*: Asia and Eastern North America.

#### KEY TO SPECIES

1. Tenth tergite with tip curved sharply dorsad (Figs. 93-95); front wing, usually with cross-vein *r* considerably basad of fork of $R_{2+3}$ (Fig. 87) . . . . . . . . . . . . . . . . . . . . . . . . . . . . . . . . . 2
   Tenth tergite with tip straight or slightly depressed (Fig. 88); front wing usually with cross-vein *r* nearly interstitial with fork of $R_{2+3}$ (Fig. 86) . . . . . . . . . . . . . . . . . . . . . . . . . . . . . . 4
2. Apex of tenth tergite produced and divided into a pair of long, whiplike processes (Fig. 93) . . . . . . . . . . . . . . . . . . . . . . . . . . . . . . . **montana**
   Apex of tenth tergite neither whiplike nor deeply divided . . . . . . . . . . . . . . . . . . . . . . . 3
3. Tenth tergite very narrow, and with a single, short, sharp, laterodorsal spine projecting from each side near middle (Fig. 94) . . . . . . . . **kisoensis**
   Tenth tergite wider, each side with a serrate flange extending from near base nearly to upturned hook (Fig. 95) . . . . . . . . . . . . **mohri**
4. Pleural region of ninth segment with dorsal corner produced into a posterior, finger-like process (Fig. 90) . . . . . . . . . . . . . . . . . . . . . **amyda**
   Pleural region of ninth segment without projections . . . . . . . . . . . . . . . . . . . . . . . . . . . . . . . 5
5. Tenth tergite with a row of spiny setae down each side (Fig. 88) . . . . . . . . . . . . . . . . . . . . 6
   Tenth tergite without lateral spinose setae . . . . . 7
6. Apex of eighth tergite forming a spatulate sclerotized area (Fig. 88) . . . . . . . . . . . . . . . **ulmeri**
   Apex of eighth tergite deeply incised and with a pair of long, curved, filamentous processes (Fig. 89) . . . . . . . . . . . . . . . . . . . . . . **spinosa**

7. Apical segment of clasper hooked; eighth tergite with a pair of slender apical processes (Fig. 91) . . . . . . . . . . . . . . . . . . . . . . . . . .alticola
   Apical segment of clasper nearly ovate; eighth tergite without paired apical processes (Fig. 92) . . . . . . . . . . . . . . . . . . . . . . . . . . . . . . . . 8
8. Cercus straight (Fig. 92) . . . . . . . . . . . . .gressitti
   Cercus curved dorsad (Kimmins 1955, Figs. 9-12) . . . . . . . . . . . . . . . . . . . . . . . . sarawakana

### LIST OF SPECIES

alticola (Banks), *Doloclanes* (1937:169). Philippine Islands. Figs. 86, 91, 135, 136.

kisoensis (Tsuda), *Nanagapetus* (1942:253). Japan. Fig. 94.

mohri (Ross), *Gatlinia* (1948:23). Eastern North America. Fig. 95.

montana (Banks), *Doloclanes* (1937:169). Philippine Islands. Fig. 93.

sarawakana (Kimmins), *Doloclanes* (1955:376). Sarawak.

### Wormaldia amyda new species

*Male:* Length 4.5 mm. Color various shades of medium to dark brown. Wings with dark brown hairs. General structure typical for genus. Seventh and eighth sternites with apical processes as illustrated for *alticola* (Fig. 91). Posterior margin of eighth tergite (Figs. 137, 138) produced on the meson into a long, sharp process, in lateral view deep and angulate ventrad; on each side of this process is a small finger-like projection almost completely concealed beneath the tergite. Genitalia as in Fig. 90. Ninth segment with the lateral margin produced anteriorly into a wide flange within the eighth segment, and with the posterodorsal corner produced into a long, finger-like process which is downcurved and parallel-sided, fairly deep from lateral view, slender from dorsal view. Tenth tergite short, the basal two-thirds fairly wide and somewhat quadrate; from the center of this arises the narrow apical portion which is finger-like and slightly beaklike from lateral view. Cerci attached closely to base of the tenth tergite, finger-like and regular. Aedeagus tubular and simple.

*Female:* Similar in size, color, and general structure to male, the apical segments tubular.

*Holotype, male:* Hong San, Southeast Kiangsi, China, June 26, 1936 (L. Gressitt). *Allotype, female:* Same data as for holotype, and collected in population with it. *Paratype:* Same date, 1♂. Holotype and allotype in the collection of the Museum of Comparative Zoology, paratype in the collection of the Illinois Natural History Survey.

This is one of the more primitive members of the genus, with cross-vein $r$ near or at the fork of $R_{2+3}$, but lacking $M_4$ in the front wing, and having a very simple tenth tergite. The quadrate base and narrow, well-differentiated apex of the tenth tergite will distinguish the species from others in the genus.

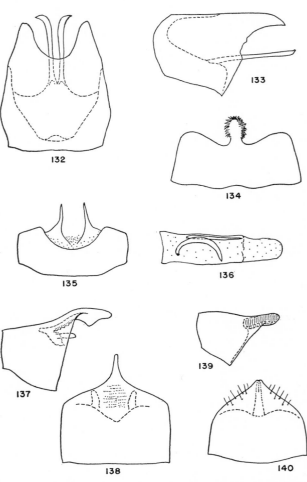

FIGS. 132-40. Male structures of *Wormaldia* subgenus *Doloclanes*. 132, 133, *spinosa*, eighth tergite, dorsal and lateral aspects. 134, *ulmeri*, eighth tergite, dorsal aspect. 135, 136, *alticola*, eighth tergite and aedeagus, dorsal aspect. 137, 138, *amyda*, eighth tergite, lateral and dorsal aspects, 139, 140, *gressitti*, eighth tergite, lateral and dorsal aspects.

### Wormaldia gressitti new species

*Male:* Length 5.5 mm. Color various shades of brown, the dorsum and wings darker. General structure typical for genus. Seventh and eighth sternites with mesal projection on the posterior margin as in *alticola*. Eighth tergite (Figs. 139, 140) with a posterior margin produced and triangular, with a mesal ridge on the underside of the apical one-third. Genitalia as in Fig. 92. Ninth segment with a deep anterior projection but without any posterior projections. Tenth tergite very simple, composed of a tonguelike structure with slightly thinned sides. Cerci broad and nearly as long as the tenth tergite, rounded at apex. Clasper with fairly deep basal segment, apical segment much broader, slightly enlarged at apex, and with the typical areas of black spines on the mesal face of the apical one-third or one-fourth of the segment. Aedeagus with a large, wide base, tapering to a narrow cylindrical apical portion; associated with it is a sinuate and slender sclerotized rod which is almost threadlike and whose exact connection could not be determined.

*Holotype, male*: Yim Na Sam, East Kwantung, China, June 16, 1936 (L. Gressitt). In the collection of the Museum of Comparative Zoology.

This species belongs to the portion of the subgenus in which the front wing has cross-vein *r* basad of the fork of $R_{2+3}$ and near the fork of Rs, and also has $M_4$ present. The simple, flaplike tenth tergite will separate this species from others in the group.

### Wormaldia spinosa new species

*Male*: Length 4 mm. Color various shades of brown, darker dorsally. General structure typical for genus. Seventh and eighth segments with projections on the posterior margins as in *alticola*. Eighth tergite (Figs. 132, 133) with the posterior margin produced into a long overhanging area which is itself deeply incised to form a wide arcuate notch; from beneath this area a pair of approximate slender, sclerotized processes project straight posteriad until near the apex, at which point they curve laterad. Genitalia as in Fig. 89. Ninth segment fairly shallow and small, its anterior margin produced into a sharp upcurved point. Tenth tergite elongate, slightly swollen just beyond middle and from there tapering to a point, bearing a pair of sharp dorsolateral projections, and along each side a series of about six long peglike setae. Cercus long and slender. Clasper with two segments of about equal length but the apical one much shallower, with a linear area of black spicules extending almost its entire length. Aedeagus simple.

*Holotype, male*: Hong San, Southeast Kiangsi, China, June 26, 1936 (L. Gressitt). In the collection of the Museum of Comparative Zoology.

This belongs to the same group of the subgenus *Doloclanes*, as does *amyda*. In the front wing cross-vein *r* is near or at the fork of $R_{2+3}$ and $M_4$ is absent. From other members of the group it is readily distinguished by the peculiar shape of the eighth and tenth tergites.

### Wormaldia ulmeri new species

*Male*: Length 5 mm. Color various shades of brown, the dorsum darker. General structure typical for genus. Seventh and eighth sternites as in *alticola*. Eighth tergite (Fig. 134) has posterior margin produced into a simple clavate process shaped like a blunt spearhead. Genitalia as in Fig. 88. Ninth segment with anterior margin forming a broad, produced lobe but without posterior projections. Tenth tergite elongate, the basal two-thirds nearly parallel-sided, the apex narrowed to a point; along each side is a row of three or four long peglike setae. Cerci with a broad base and a sharply delineated apical finger-like portion which angles laterad from the base. Clasper with basal segment fairly long and barrel-shaped; the apical segment is missing on both claspers. Aedeagus simple and tubular.

*Holotype, male*: Kosempo, Formosa, Feb., 1908 (Sauter) # 18552. In the collection of Dr. Georg Ulmer, Hamburg.

This species is apparently closely related to *spinosa*, as evidenced by the similarity of the tenth tergite and the lack of $M_4$ in the front wing. It has, however, cross-vein *r* basad of the fork of $R_{2+3}$. For purposes of identification the curious process of the eighth tergite is distinctive.

### Unplaced Species

**Cabreraia tagananana** Enderlein (1929:229). Canary Islands.

I have not seen this genus and species. Dr. Ulmer has expressed the opinion that it is a species of *Wormaldia* because of the many points of similarity in the venation, and with this opinion I agree. The species is described as having only one preapical spur, as in *Chimarra*, but this condition may represent either a broken specimen or simply a case of parallel evolution.

**Wormaldia algirica** Lestage (1925:14). Algeria. Not seen.

**Wormaldia ambigua** Navas (1916a:600). Spain. Not seen.

## Genus **Gunungiella** Ulmer

*Gunungiella* Ulmer (1913:82). Type species: *Gunungiella reducta* Ulmer (monobasic).

*Diagnosis*: Front and hind wing with both $M_{1+2}$ and $M_{3+4}$ undivided; hind wing with $R_{2+3}$ also undivided (Fig. 100). Male genitalia lacking cerci, and with anterior margin of ninth segment invaginated deeply into cavity of eighth and sometimes seventh segments.

### Key to Species

1. Ninth segment with lateral brush of spines (Fig. 103); tenth tergite without spines . . . . . . .    2
   Ninth segment without lateral brush; tenth tergite with a pair of large, stout spines (Fig. 101)   3
2. Lateral brush of about 5 spines (Fig. 103); tenth tergite short and wide . . . . . . . . . . . . .**nietneri**
   Lateral brush of 2 spines; tenth tergite elongate and spatulate, narrowed in middle (Schmid 1949, Figs. 20-23) . . . . . . . . . . . . . . . . . . . . .**ulmeri**
3. Apical segment of clasper large and ovoid, with spicules all around its margin (Fig. 101) . . . .
   . . . . . . . . . . . . . . . . . . . . . . . . . . . **marginalis**
   Apical segment of clasper minute, associated with a small comb of spicules below it (Fig. 102) . . .
   . . . . . . . . . . . . . . . . . . . . . . . . . . . **reducta**

### List of Species

**marginalis** Banks (1939:142). Philippine Islands. Fig. 101.
**nietneri** Banks (1920:362). Ceylon. Figs. 100, 103.
**reducta** Ulmer (1913:84, and 1951:93). Java. Fig. 102.
**ulmeri** Schmid (1949:323). India (Bombay).

## **Protarra** new genus

Type species: *Protarra peruviana* new species

*Diagnosis*: Head with ocelli, and with posterior portion swollen so that it extends as far behind the eyes as the length of an eye. Maxillary palps with first, second and fourth segments short, third twice length of fourth, and fifth longer than third. Tibial spur count 2-4-4. Front wing (Fig. 104) with complete venation except for the loss of $M_4$. Hind wing with no *r*, but with all branches of Rs present; 2A is bowed downward and atrophied just beyond the cross-vein beneath it, which is situated considerably beyond the cross-vein above it. Seventh and eighth sternites and eighth tergite without processes. Male genitalia with ninth segment indistinct dorsally and with clasper composed of only one segment.

*Distribution*: South America.

The presence of vein 2A in the hind wing allies this genus with *Sortosa* and its allies, from which it is readily distinguished by the single-segmented clasper in the male. From *Ulmerodina*, which may have a single segmented clasper, *Protarra* may be distinguished by the presence of $R_2$ and the absence of $M_4$ in the front wing. The large head, single-segmented clasper, and general contour of the ninth segment are suggestive of a relationship with *Chimarra*.

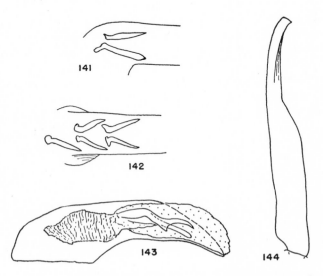

Fig. 141. Base of aedeagus of *Protarra sagittoides*, lateral aspect, showing internal spines.
Fig. 142. Base of aedeagus of *Protarra ulmeri*, dorsal aspect, showing internal spines.
Fig. 143. Aedeagus of *Protarra peruviana*, lateral aspect, showing internal spines.
Fig. 144. Clasper of *Protarra ulmeri*, dorsal aspect.

### Key to Species

1. Tenth tergite with a pair of short lateral processes arising at its base (Fig. 105) . . . . . . . . . . .    2
   Tenth tergite with a pair of lateral processes appearing to arise from its sides, and extending beyond the apex of the tergite (Fig. 107)   3
2. Tenth tergite with cleft of apex fairly wide and with only sensillae (Fig. 105) . . . . . . . . . .**peruviana**
   Tenth tergite with cleft of apex narrow, and with a pair of sclerotized teeth near tip (Fig. 106) . .
   . . . . . . . . . . . . . . . . . . . . . . . . . . . . . . . . **ulmeri**
3. Apicolateral processes of tenth tergite with base and apex swollen and rounded (Fig. 107) . . . .
   . . . . . . . . . . . . . . . . . . . . . . . . . . . **sagittoides**
   Apicolateral processes of tenth tergite with apex sharp, the whole narrower (Martynov 1912, Figs. 48-52) . . . . . . . . . . . . . . . . . . . . . .**galeata**

List of Species

galeata (Martynov), *Chimarrha* (1912:30). Peru.

## Protarra peruviana new species

*Male*: Length 7 mm. Color light reddish brown, the venter lighter, the legs and wings covered with dark brown hair which has a slightly bluish cast. General structure typical for genus. Genitalia as in Fig. 105. Ninth segment deep but short, on the meson merging imperceptibly with the tenth tergite. On each side of the tenth tergite there arises, apparently from the ninth segment, a pair of short, heavily sclerotized processes bearing a mesal tooth near apex; from lateral view these are hidden behind the cerci. Tenth tergite moderately long, tapering, with a fairly wide apical incision; the lateral lobes so formed nearly meet on the meson at apex and each has a slight dorsal projection; the lateral margin of the tergite bears a row of minute sensillae. Cercus longer than tenth tergite, in lateral view slightly thickened just before middle, clothed with a scattering of setae. Clasper elongate, single segmented, nearly straight but with the apical portion curved slightly dorsad and mesad. Aedeagus (Fig. 143) simple and chiefly tubular, with a pair of heavily sclerotized internal rods, one of them simple and the other somewhat claw-shaped.

*Holotype, male*: Paucartambo, Cosnipata Valley, Cusco, Peru, Nov. 12, 1951 (F. Woytkowski). In the collection of the Illinois Natural History Survey.

## Protarra ulmeri new species

*Male*: Length, 7 mm. Color and general structure similar to the preceding. Genitalia as in Fig. 106. General outline of ninth segment and claspers as in *peruviana*. Lateral process at base of tenth tergite short and with the extreme apex curved mesad. Tenth tergite as long as the cerci, with only a narrow mesal cleft, but with a short but sharp sclerotized point on each lobe a short distance before apex; lateral margins with sensillae. Cercus slender and slightly clavate, irregular in outline. Aedeagus moderately long and tubular; it contains a lightly sclerotized set of structures within the apex, and below that a set of five evenly sclerotized pointed rods which have sharp apices and a widened base (Fig. 142).

*Holotype, male*: Alna, 1,400 m. elevation, South Peru, July 5, 1936 (Hamburg South Peruvian Expedition 1936, # 652). In the collection of the Hamburg Museum.

This species and *peruviana* form a closely related pair of species differing in characters mentioned in the key.

## Protarra sagittoides new species

*Male*: Length 7.5 mm. Color and general structure similar to *peruviana*. Genitalia as in Fig. 107. Ninth segment with posterolateral margin considerably sinuate. The structures which in the preceding two species appear to be lateral processes of the ninth segment are, in this species, associated more closely with the ventrolateral region of the tenth tergite, and project beyond the tenth tergite itself; they are large, well sclerotized, the apical portion roughly shaped like a spearhead but with a rounded apex and a rounded basal heel. Tenth tergite moderately short and incised to form a pair of semimembranous diverging apical lobes. Cercus elongate and slender, the base slightly constricted. Clasper elongate and curved dorsad, in ventral view tapering very gradually from base to apex. Aedeagus with a pair of heavily sclerotized internal rods, each with the apex pointed and the base slightly expanded (Fig. 141).

*Holotype, male*: Mapiri, Bolivia. In the collection of Dr. Georg Ulmer, Hamburg.

This species is closely related to *galeata* but differs from Martynov's illustrations of that species in the more extensive, rounded, apical portion of the lateral lobes of the tenth tergite.

## Genus **Chimarra** Stephens

This genus is set off from all others in the family by the fusion of 2A with 1A in the hind wing to form a large closed cell (Fig. 21). The claspers are composed of a single segment, and in the front wing $M_4$ is absent.

The genus is large and practically cosmopolitan. The primitive species and many specialized groups are restricted to the tropical or subtropical regions. Many types of genitalic structure and a few differences in wing venation are found in the genus. On these bases the genera *Curgia* Walker, *Vigarrha* Navas and *Chimarrhafra* Lestage have been erected for various components within the broad definition of *Chimarra*. A more detailed analysis of the genus may indicate that these will serve a useful purpose as names for subgenera. The brief outline given earlier in this paper is not sufficient for determining this so the matter must be left for future consideration.

The attempt here is not to list the species of the genus, but simply to describe the species which have been used for illustrations in the phylogenetic analysis on page 49.

### Chimarra hoogstraali new species

*Male*: Length of body exclusive of wings, 5 mm. Color various shades of medium brown, the wings and legs apparently with no conspicuous markings. General structure typical for genus. Wing venation not discernible but presumably typical for *Chimarrhafra*, with no knot on Rs. Genitalia as in Fig. 111. Ninth segment deep but short, the anterior sclerotized thickening completely across the dorsum, but the dorsal part of the segment exclusive of this entirely membranous and, together with the anterior part of the tenth tergite, forming a pair of low, membranous lobes. Lateral lobes of ninth segment sinuate with a deep, short base, the apex produced into a long, outcurved process, the ventral corner curved sharply dorsad and a little mesad to form a long curved sclerotized process. Cercus small, round, somewhat biscuit-shaped. Clasper in lateral aspect short and bearing a short dorsal lobe. The apicomesal corner bears internally a sharp spine. Aedeagus (Figs. 152, 153) with a short sclerotized central portion from which protrudes a large central membranous head, and a pair of ventral, heavily sclerotized and bifid prongs; the aedeagus seems to contain no internal rods. The eighth sternite has no ventral processes and the ninth only a small one.

*Female*: Length longer than male. Color and general structure similar to it. Abdomen with apical segment cylindrical and without conspicuous processes.

*Holotype, male; Allotype, female; pupae and larvae*: Torit District, Equatoria, Anglo-Egyptian Sudan, in rivulet in Lotti Forest, 4,000 ft. elevation, April 8, 1950 (H. Hoogstraal). *Paratypes* and additional larvae and pupae from the Ogun River near Katire, also in Equatoria, 3,000 ft. elevation, Dec. 4, 1952 (H. Hoogstraal). Types and paratypes in the collection of the Chicago Natural History Museum, paratypes in the collection of the Illinois Natural History Survey.

This species is most closely related to *georgensis* Barnard from South Africa, but differs in having only two processes on the lateral lobe of the tenth tergite, in lacking linear rods in the aedeagus, and in having the cerci small rather than finger-like.

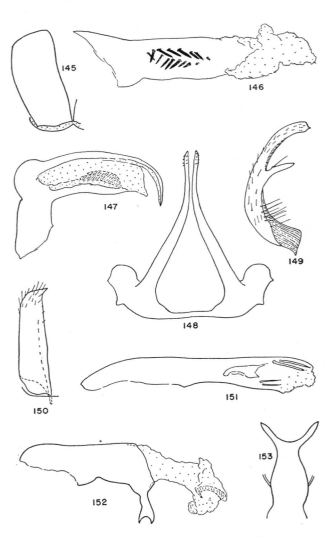

FIGS. 145-53. Male structures of *Chimarra*. 145, 146, *moselyi*, clasper, ventral aspect, and aedeagus, lateral aspect. 147, 148, 149, *patosa*, aedeagus, lateral aspect, eighth tergite, dorsal aspect, and clasper, posterior aspect. 150, 151, *tsudai*, clasper, ventral aspect, and aedeagus, lateral aspect. 152, 153, *hoogstraali*, aedeagus, lateral aspect, and ventral aspect of sclerotized portion.

It gives me great pleasure to name this in honor of Captain Harry Hoogstraal who has collected so many interesting caddisflies in many parts of the **world**.

## Chimarra moselyi new species

*Male*: Length 9 mm. Color black, the hair black-ish brown, the wings smoky with a slightly bluish iridescence. Structure typical for genus. Front wing with no knot on Rs, both wings with branches of Rs crowded together. Genitalia as in Fig. 108. Ninth segment fairly large, complete across the dorsum and merging imperceptibly with the sclerotized tenth tergite, which forms a broad tapered lobe having sensillae around its edge. Cerci short, about as long as wide. Clasper small and platelike (Fig. 145), the ventral aspect with the basal portion rectangular and the outer apical corner rounded. In lateral view this corner is seen to have a sharp, sclerotized point. Ninth sternite forming a sharp process of moderate size beneath the base of the claspers. Aedeagus tubular, the eversible sac containing about thirty small sharp black rods (Fig. 146).

*Holotype, male*: Petropolis, Rio de Janeiro, Argentina. Originally from the McLachlan collection, now in the British Museum.

This species was originally labeled "Chimarra ?morio Burmeister," and may indeed be that species. The only recorded Burmeister types of this species are females. On the other hand several species having black males occur in Argentina. Until these can be associated with the correct females and these accurately diagnosed, the only unambiguous course seems to be to describe these species as new.

The large, flat, simple tenth tergite will differentiate this species from all others described in the genus.

## Chimarra patosa new species

*Male*: Length 5 mm. Color dark brown, almost black, the hair also very dark and the membrane of the wings dark smoky. General structure typical for genus. Front wings with no knot on Rs. Eighth tergite highly modified (Fig. 148); from each side there arises a long, slender, sinuate process with the basal portion thickened and imbricate, and the apexes of the two processes nearly meeting and running parallel on the meson; actually these tips form a sort of fork into which fits the apex of the tenth tergite in repose. Genitalia as in Fig. 109. Ninth segment unusually long and massive, forming a deep, long keel beneath the claspers, and hav-

ing the dorsal portion complete. The unusual width of this dorsal portion is due to an invaginated ridge which nearly encircles the segment. Tenth tergite divided into the following parts: 1) a slender up-curved and sharp mesal process having no sensillae; 2) a pair of wide and fairly deep lateral processes, these being fairly short and having sensillae at the base and what appear to be minute sensillae present at the apex; and 3) a pair of slender upcurved processes arising from the base of the lateral lobe and having their extreme apexes narrowed. Cercus short and irregular. Clasper with a broad and angled base, and a long, tapering apex; near the base of the apical portion there arises a long sharp process seen to best advantage from the posterior view (Fig. 149). Aedeagus angled, the dorsal portion of the apex curved ventrad, the eversible pocket containing a pair of black stout rods (Fig. 147).

*Holotype, male*: Paucartambo, Cosnipata Valley, Cusco, Peru, Nov. 12, 1951 (F. Woytkowski). *Paratype*: Callanga, Peru, 1♂. Holotype in the collection of the Illinois Natural History Survey. Paratype in the collection of Dr. Georg Ulmer, Hamburg.

This species forms a distinctive group of its own characterized by the division of the tenth tergite into a mesal lobe with no sensillae and lateral lobes with sensillae.

## Chimarra tsudai new species

*Male*: Length 7 mm. Color medium shades of brown, the venter lighter. General structure typical for genus. Front wing with a small knotlike sinuation at the branching of Rs. Genitalia as in Fig. 112. Ninth segment with lateral and ventral portions moderately long, the venter with a long but shallow keel, the dorsal portion entirely membranous. Tenth tergite with central membranous portion apparently atrophied; there are two pairs of lateral lobes, an outer lobe which is wide-set, constricted at the base, then thickened, then tapering to apex, the whole covered with sensillae; arising from the inner side of the base of each of these lobes is a short, curved, capitate process. This process appears to be connected jointly to the bottom of the tenth tergite lobe and to the membrane which forms the lower edge of the aedeagal foramen. Claspers fairly long (Fig. 150), the lateral aspect thin, with two blunt teeth at apex, the ventral aspect parallel-sided, having a mesal projection at the extreme apex. Aedeagus cylindrical and having two pairs of sclerotized rods which are slender and of moderate length (Fig. 151).

*Female*: Length 8 mm. Color and general structure typical for male, apex of abdomen without conspicuous processes.

*Holotype, male*; *Allotype, female*; 3 *Paratypes*: Chigonozawa, Kiso-fukushima, Nagano, Japan, July 12, 1936 (M. Tsuda). In the collection of the Illinois Natural History Survey.

This species belongs to the *concolor* group but differs from *concolor* and other described species in the shape of the lobes of the tenth tergite.

I take great pleasure in dedicating this species to Dr. Tsuda, who has contributed so abundantly to our knowledge of Japanese caddisflies.

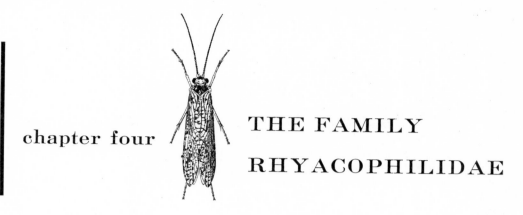

chapter four THE FAMILY

RHYACOPHILIDAE

## EVOLUTION AND DISPERSAL

The Rhyacophilidae is the most primitive known family at the base of the caddisfly line which eventually led to the case makers. The great bulk of the Rhyacophilidae are confined to mountain streams. In general the species of the family have small geographic ranges, and a great many species appear to be individually restricted to only one or two high mountains. The larvae are predaceous, living on other aquatic insects.

Only two major branches of the family are known, the Rhyacophilinae and the Hydrobiosinae. Each has preserved certain primitive characters which have become specialized in the other. It is possible, by careful consideration of these primitive characters, to reconstruct an ancestral form which could have given rise to the two major branches. This reconstructed ancestral form is indicated as Ancestor 1 in Chart 26. It possessed a simple, complete wing venation, having in the front wing cross-vein *s*, short anal veins and curved $Cu_2$ (Fig. 154). The genitalia possessed 2-segmented claspers and probably small, round cerci like those in Fig. 159. It is highly likely that the tenth tergite was simple. The larva had simple thoracic legs and a primitive dorsal strap on the anal claw.

The line leading to Ancestor 2, and becoming the subfamily Rhyacophilinae, at first changed very little. The wings lost cross-vein *s*. The larva remained primitive except for a widening of the dorsal strap of the anal claw (Fig. 9B). The Rhyacophilinae was the more cool-adapted of the two lines, apparently never crossing to the south of the equator except locally in the East Indies.

The line leading to Ancestor 3 changed in several ways. In the front wings the anal veins became elongate and $Cu_2$ became sinuate (Fig. 156). In the male genitalia a pair of elongate, cercus-like processes (*fc*) developed beside the button-like cercus (Fig. 159). The most profound change occurred in the larva. Its front legs developed into chelate grasping claws (Fig. 158), and a sclerotized ventral plate developed as a supporting bar between them. This line early became more warm-adapted than the Rhyacophilinae, in fact undoubtedly evolved as a warm-adapted line, because it is distributed across the equator in the Oriental and Australian region, and in the Neotropical Region.

### The Subfamily Rhyacophilinae

This subfamily has evolved into several hundred species with little change in body or wing structure, but has developed a most amazing set of complicated structures in the male genitalia. Certain large groups of species can be correlated into a well-integrated phylogenetic scheme, but dozens of others are difficult to place in relation to each other or to the larger groups. As a consequence the best arrangement I have been able to make leaves much to be desired. Knowledge of the females and larvae should be of great value. Unfortunately, reared specimens and associated males and females are rarely available. For this reason I have had to rely primarily on male characters as a basis for this account.

The small genus *Himalopsyche* seems to be a well-differentiated unit. In this genus the metascutellum has a pair of warts; the branches of R and M curve backward, so that in the front wings $R_4$

73

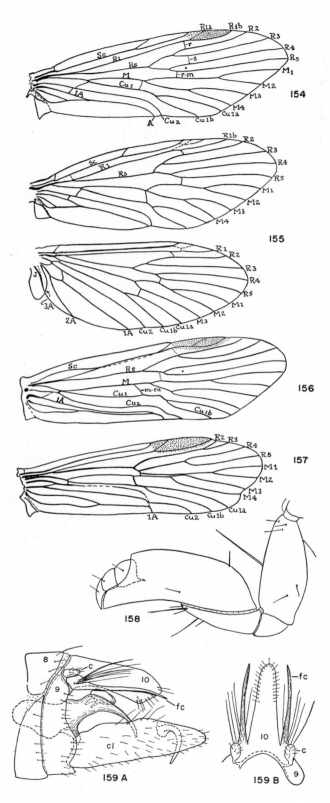

and $R_5$ are on each side of the apical wing point (Fig. 155); and the lateral portions of the tenth tergite form large processes (Figs. 276-87). In *Rhyacophila* the metascutellum has no warts, the branches of R are anterior to the wing tip and those of M are posterior to it, and the tenth tergite is otherwise. There are certain exceptions to the wing character, and these will be better understood after we have discussed the large genus *Rhyacophila*.

The ancestor of the Rhyacophilinae apparently developed certain peculiarities of the male genitalia which have undergone further evolution. The most unusual feature was a projecting process situated above the anal opening and associated with the hinge area between the tenth tergite and the membrane connected to the base of the aedeagus. This *anal sclerite* (*as*) developed an internal sclerotized piece shaped like a tap root, extending into the tenth segment. The evolution of this sclerite is very puzzling. It is present throughout many phyletic lines, absent in occasional species of a few lines, and absent in all members of others. This situation poses two alternatives, (1) that the anal sclerite evolved independently several times, or (2) that the anal sclerite developed in the early Rhyacophilinae ancestor and has subsequently atrophied several times hit-and-miss in the family tree. The remarkable similarity of the anal sclerites of many different branches of *Rhyacophila* indicates that the structure arose only once in that genus. In certain branches of *Rhyacophila* having the anal sclerite present in some species and absent in others, such as the *sibirica* branch, evidence from other structures indicates that the anal sclerite occurs in the primitive species of the branch.

Some branches of *Rhyacophila* in which all members lack the anal sclerite may have arisen before this structure had evolved. This is particularly true of the *acropedes* and the *fletcheri* branches. In both of these the genital structure is simple. If this is true, then *Himalopsyche* could have arisen after

---

Fig. 154. Front wing of *Rhyacophila fuscula*.
Fig. 155. Front and hind wings of *Himalopsyche phryganea*.
Fig. 156. Front wing of *Iguazu ulmeri*.
Fig. 157. Front wing of *Apsilochorema malayana*.
Fig. 158. Front leg of larva of *Atopsyche* sp. (Redrawn from Hinton.)
Fig. 159. Male genitalia of *Apsilochorema banksi*. A, lateral aspect; B, dorsal aspect; c, cercus; cl, claspers; fc, filicercus.

these groups had branched from the main line of development.

One bit of evidence argues against this possibility. In *Himalopsyche* only loose membrane connects the area of the anal sclerite with the dorsal portion of the base of the aedeagus (Fig. 283, *ts*). In *Rhyacophila* species such as *acropedes* (Fig. 185) and *vaefes* (Fig. 169), the area beneath the tenth tergite or the anal sclerite has developed a sclerotized crescent, the lateral edges of which function as general areas of articulation. From this sclerotized crescent there runs a more or less sclerotized strip connecting the anterior margin of the crescent with the dorsum of the base of the aedeagus. In the examples cited, crescent and strip merge imperceptibly with each other, and with the membrane closing the posterior end of the body cavity. They are simply thickenings of this membrane, not new structures. This advance in hinge mechanism would seem to indicate that *Himalopsyche*, lacking it, was an older branch of the Rhyacophilinae than any branches of *Rhyacophila*.

### The Genus Rhyacophila

The male genitalia have undergone such complex changes in various species of this genus that it has seemed feasible to introduce a distinctive terminology for the parts most frequently encountered. Familiarization with this scheme at the outset will, I believe, make the following section much easier to follow. The parts are illustrated and labeled in Fig. 160, and explained below:

*Aedeagus.* This is composed of a cuplike or tubular base (*b*), into which fits the membranous base of the apical portion or phalicata (*ph*), and often a pair of lateral processes (*lp*). The base frequently bears one or two dorsal processes (*dp*) which are joined solidly with the base. From each side of the base arises a sclerotized process or flap, the clasper hangers (*ch*), which join and articulate with a basal process of the claspers (*cl*), the clasper tendon (*ct*). The point of juncture or attachment is designated as *j*.

*Tenth tergite.* This may be a simple structure, often divided into a pair of lateral lobes (Fig. 184). In some groups the tergite proper does not extend posteriorad but ventrad, and may have a dorsal projection (10) pointing posteriorly (Fig. 273). Below its apex typically it has an anal sclerite (*as*) bearing an internal root (*r*). In all but a few primi-

tive groups, a tergal strap (*ts*) connects the apex of the tenth tergite and the dorsum of the aedeagal base, the apex of the strap usually differentiated into a well-defined crescentic, U-shaped, or wishbone-shaped piece (*U*). The tergal strap usually joins the aedeagal base without visible suture.

### Primitive Groups (Branch 1)

There are several small groups which lack any indication of the tergal strap. These appear to be primitive groups which arose before the strap evolved. For the most part each group shows some peculiarity which sets it off distinctly, yet fails to give a clear indication of phylogenetic affinities with related groups. It is therefore possible to indicate on Chart 16 only that these primitive groups represent a cluster of early offshoots from the *Rhyacophila* line.

*Lobifera Group.* This group contains a single species, *lobifera*, occurring in the eastern part of North America. The male genitalia are extremely simple (Fig. 161). The tenth tergite is large, the anal sclerite is undivided but has a deep root, the tergal strap is only membranous, and the aedeagus

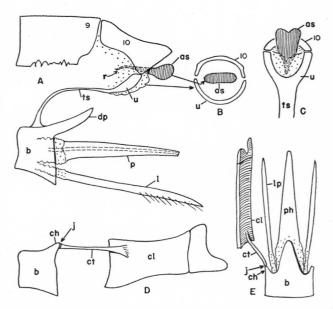

Fig. 160. Diagram of a simplified male genital capsule of *Rhyacophila*, to show use of abbreviations used in the section dealing with this genus. A, lateral aspect of the tenth tergite and aedeagus; B, posterior aspect of tenth tergite; C, ventral aspect of tenth tergite; D, lateral diagram of base of aedeagus and clasper; E, dorsal aspect of aedeagus and clasper. Abbreviations explained in adjoining text.

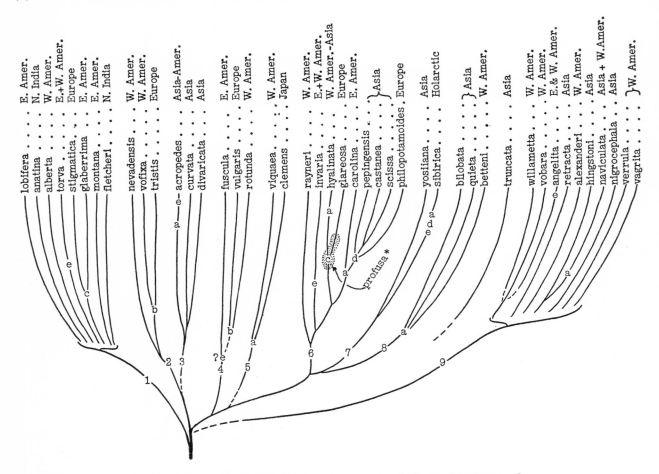

CHART 16. Phylogenetic diagram of the groups of *Rhyacophila*. Dispersals deduced between or within phyletic lines are indicated as follows: *a*, Asia–western North America; *b*, Europe–western North America; *c*, Europe–eastern North America; *d*, Europe–Asia; *e*, eastern–western North America.

bears a relatively simple phalicata and a pair of simple lateral processes. In many ways *lobifera* is one of the most primitive known members of the genus, being specialized chiefly in the undivided anal sclerite, which is primitively bilobed.

*Anatina Group.* This group also contains only a single species, *anatina*, known from India. The anal sclerite is almost completely divided into a pair of crescentic bodies. There is no tergal strap. The aedeagus is simple, having a slender phalicata and a pair of lateral processes, but is specialized in having a large dorsal process on the base. This unusual species (illustrated by Kimmins, 1953*b*) is of doubtful affinity and may well be a primitive form which arose early in the history of the genus.

*Alberta Group.* The male genitalia (Fig. 162) are

primitive in many respects, having a fairly typical aedeagus with a pair of long lateral processes, large anal sclerites, and simple tenth tergites. Specialized characters include the long clasper hangers and elongate clasper tendons. There is only a membranous fold between the top of the clasper hangers and the apex of the tenth tergite.

The group includes only three species, all confined to the western montane region of North America. Of these *alberta* is known only from the eastern portion of the range; *tucula* is known from the northern portion of this area and also in the western part of the mountains; and *kincaidi* is known from the Cascade Mountain region in the state of Washington.

*Torva Group.* In the only typical species of the

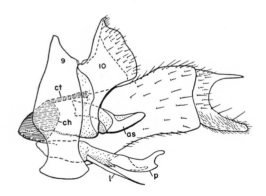

FIG. 161. Male genitalia of *Rhyacophila lobifera*, lateral aspect.

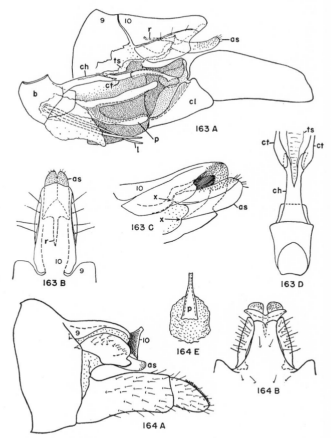

FIGS. 163-64. Male genitalia of *Rhyacophila torva* (163) and *ecosa* (164). A, lateral aspect; B, dorsal aspect; C, lateroventral aspect of apex of tenth tergite; D, base of aedeagus, dorsal aspect; E, aedeagus, ventral aspect, x, points of articulation.

group, *torva*, the various primitive parts are represented (Fig. 163) and the clasper hangers and tendons are elongate as in the preceding species. The claspers are unusual in that the apical segment is very long and the basal one short and with a complex series of mesal ridges. The sides of the tenth tergite are separated from the dorsum by a suture. This is an unusual feature.

Tentatively another species, *ecosa*, is placed in this group. The genitalia (Fig. 164) resemble those of *torva* chiefly in having a lateral plate detached from the tenth tergite, and a large anal sclerite. They differ from those of *torva* in that the anal sclerite is deeply divided and the short, flared dor-

sal part of the tenth tergite is at the end of a long hood formed by the ninth tergite.

The species *torva* is widespread in the Allegheny Mountains of eastern North America, and *ecosa* is known only from California and Oregon.

*Montana Group.* The small species *montana*, known only from the Great Smoky Mountains of southeastern North America, is most peculiar. In the genitalia (Fig. 165) the aedeagus is reduced, there is neither tergal strap nor anal sclerite, and the tenth tergite is formed of two widely separated, thin processes connected with each other by a narrow, sclerotized ribbon. No species are known even remotely related to it, and *montana* therefore appears to be both a geographic and phylogenetic relic of an old phyletic line.

*Fletcheri Group.* This group is set up for the

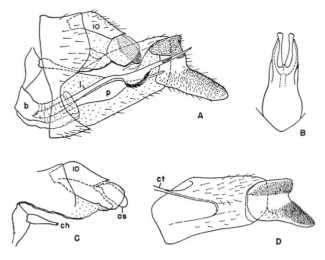

FIG. 162. Male genitalia *of Rhyacophila alberta* (A-C) and *tucula* (D). A, lateral aspect; B, tenth tergite, dorsal aspect; C, tenth tergite and associated structures, lateral aspect; D, clasper, mesal aspect.

FIG. 165. Male genitalia of *Rhyacophila montana*, lateral aspect.

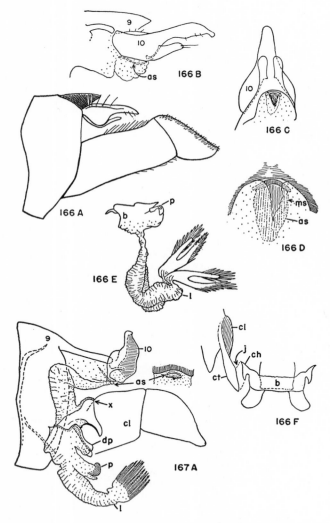

FIGS. 166-67. Male genitalia of *Rhyacophila glaberrima* (166) and *stigmatica* (167). *A*, lateral aspect; *B, C*, details of tenth tergite, lateral and ventral aspects; *D*, detail of *as; E*, aedeagus; *F*, relation of aedeagus and clasper base. *x*, point of articulation.

single species, *fletcheri*, from Sikkim, India. The tenth tergite is extremely simple, the anal sclerite is lacking, the phalicata is long and simple, and the lateral processes are fused with the base of the aedeagus to form a curious ventral structure below the phalicata. The fifth sternite has a finger-like lateral filament instead of the customary small wart. The relationships of this species are difficult to determine. It could be related to a more complex form and have become simplified by atrophy of parts. On the other hand, the membranous tergal strap may indicate that it is actually a very primitive simple type forming another relict group.

*Glaberrima Group.* As with the *torva* and *montana* groups, this one also contains a single species, *glaberrima*. The tenth tergite has a distinctive shape (Fig. 166). The aedeagus is small, with only a minute phalicata. The lateral arms of the aedeagus are elongate and extensile, formed of pleated membrane, and each is terminated with a U-shaped piece. The anal sclerite is small, consisting chiefly of the root, its apex being visible only through the triangular anal slit in the membrane beneath the apex of the tenth tergite. The clasper hangers and tendons are short, as is typical of most species of *Rhyacophila*. The range of *glaberrima* includes the eastern portion of North America, with records westward to Illinois.

The reduced phalicata and anal sclerites, as well as general configuration of the ninth and tenth tergites, suggest an affinity between the *glaberrima* group and the European *stigmatica* group, treated next.

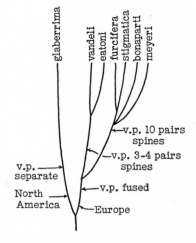

CHART 17. Phylogenetic diagram of the *Rhyacophila stigmatica* and *glaberrima* groups.

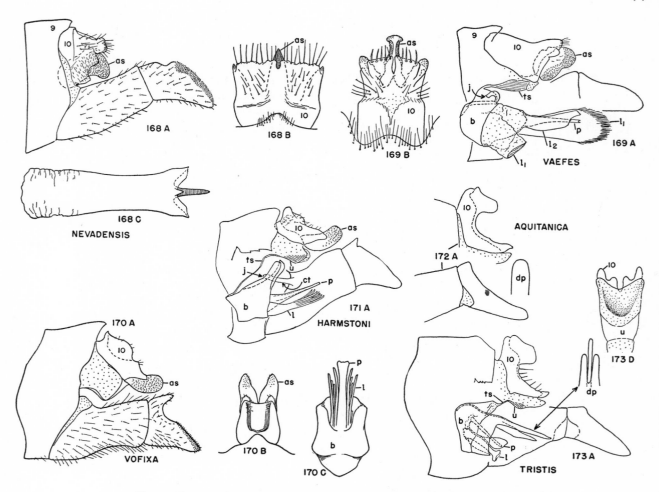

FIGS. 168-73. Male genitalia of *Rhyacophila nevadensis, vofixa,* and *tristis* groups. *A,* lateral aspect; *B,* dorsal aspect; *C,* ventral aspect of aedeagus; *D,* ventral aspect of posteroventral area of tenth tergite.

*Stigmatica Group.* In this group also (Fig. 167) the anal sclerite is reduced to a flat root. The aedeagus has only a small phalicata, but the lateral arms have fused to form an extensile tube ending in a crown of serrate spines. The tenth tergite is simple, articulating at the end of a shelflike dorsal projection of the ninth sternite.

Six species are known in the group (Chart 17), all restricted to the mountains of southern and western Europe. In two species, *eatoni* and *vandeli,* the ninth tergite is produced into a broad extension over the tenth tergite and the lateral arms of the aedeagus have only three or four pairs of spines at the apex. In the other four species (*bonaparti, meyeri, furcifera,* and *stigmatica*) the lateral arms of the aedeagus have 10 or more pairs of processes

at the apex (Fig. 167) and the ninth tergite has either finger-like projections or none.

The *eatoni* complex is known only from the Pyrenees, the *stigmatica* complex from various ranges of the Alps. This distribution suggests that the ancestor for the entire group first became widespread through the mountains of southern Europe, then became isolated into two segments. The segment in the Pyrenees developed into the *eatoni* complex, and the one in the Alps into the *stigmatica* complex.

If the *glaberrima* and *stigmatica* groups are indeed old branches of the same line, they are widely separated geographic relics of a Holarctic ancestral form.

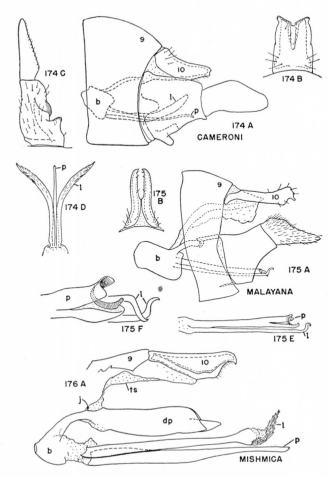

FIGS. 174-76. Male genitalia of *Rhyacophila curvata* group. A, lateral aspect; B, dorsal aspect of tenth tergite; C, ventral aspect of clasper; D, E, F, ventral lateral and sagittal aspects, respectively, of aedeagus.

### Branch 2

The second assemblage of species groups for which there is some reason for its being considered a monophyletic branch contains three groups with the tergal strap membranous, but with its apex being at least a fairly well-defined, sclerotized crescent (Figs. 169-73).

*Nevadensis Group.* This is one of the two more primitive groups of the branch, having genitalia of simple general structure (Fig. 169). The large anal sclerite is a single structure in which the posterodorsal portion forms a keel and the base is flared out laterally. The tenth tergite is divided into simple apical lobes. Only three species are known in the group, all from western North America: *nevaden-*

*sis* (with very reduced and fused aedeagus) from the Sierra Nevada Mountains, *jewetti* (with one pair of lateral processes on the aedeagus) from Oregon, and *vaefes* (with two sets of lateral processes on the aedeagus) from the Cascade Mountain region.

As it seems to have no known close relatives, the *nevadensis* group appears to be another relict group confined to a single series of mountain ranges.

*Vofixa Group.* In this group also the genitalia (Figs. 170, 171) are simple, similar in general to the preceding, but the anal sclerite is divided and has large ovate lobes (Fig. 170). The aedeagus has a large base bearing short dorsal processes; the phalicata is short, and has a pair of short lateral processes which are divided at the apex into long, comblike teeth. The phalicata itself has a dorsal finger-like process projecting above the slender ventral piece bearing the gonopore.

The group contains only two known species, *vofixa* and *harmstoni*, both restricted to western North America. In *vofixa* the dorsal arm of the phalicata is wide, but in *harmstoni* it is very slender and pointed at the apex. The species *harmstoni* is known only from the more eastern ranges, in Utah and Colorado, and *vofixa* is apparently widespread throughout the montane area to the north. These species form another relict group which has apparently persisted for a long time.

*Tristis Group.* In general plan, the genitalia (Fig. 173) are much like the preceding, especially in the short but complex phalicata and the presence of distinct dorsal processes on the aedeagal base. The anal sclerite, however, is completely lacking. It is possible that this group is an offshoot of the ancestral stem of the *vofixa* group in which the atrophy of the anal sclerite has been the principal change.

The group contains only two species, *tristis* and *aquitanica*, separated chiefly by minute details of the dorsal processes of the aedeagus (Figs. 172, 173). Both species are confined to alpine and subalpine regions of central and southern Europe. This relict group is probably the European counterpart of the North American *vofixa* group.

### Branch 3

Three distinct groups of species comprise this branch. In these groups there are no tergal straps, and the anal sclerites are completely absent. In

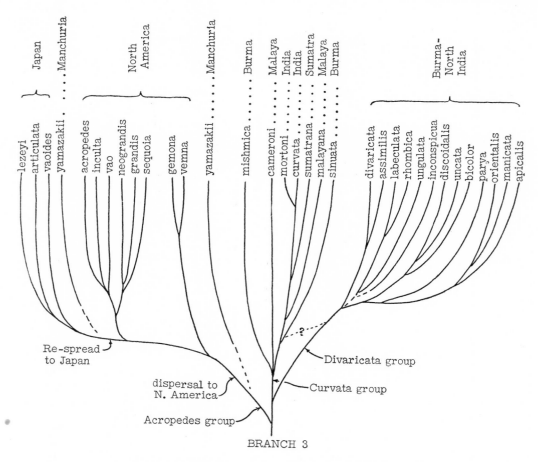

CHART 18. Phylogenetic diagram of Branch 3 of *Rhyacophila*.

the primitive form of each group the tenth tergite is either a simple lobe or a pair of lobes and the aedeagus has a simple phalicata and a pair of elongate lateral processes. This branch (Branch 3 in Chart 16) contains the *divaricata* group, the *curvata* group (Figs. 174-76) and the *acropedes* group (Figs. 177-85).

In many respects primitive forms of this branch show much similarity with the *tristis* group. If this is indicative of relationship, the *tristis* group may actually belong to Branch 3, or Branch 3 may be only an offshoot of Branch 2. Elucidation of this point must await further data.

Of the three groups, the *curvata* group is the most primitive in all characters and appears to represent a form similar in many respects to the ancestor of the entire branch. The simple tenth tergite and sclerotized lateral arms of the aedeagus (Fig. 174) provide the best evidence for this view.

The *divaricata* group is an offshoot in which the lobes of the tenth tergite became contorted and excavated on the mesal face. The *acropedes* group, an offshoot which developed various specializations of the tenth tergite, has evolved extensile, membranous, lateral processes of the aedeagus (Figs. 184, 185). These groups are diagrammed in Chart 18.

*Curvata Group.* The simplest known species is *cameroni* (Fig. 174). In the male genitalia of this species the tenth tergite is a simple flat piece and the aedeagus is composed of a simple base and phalicata, and a pair of unmodified sclerotized, lateral processes. Two branches arose from an ancestral form much like this. In one, of which *mishmica* is the only known species, a large dorsal process developed on the aedeagal base (Fig. 176). In the other the tenth tergite became cleft down the meson. This second line gave rise to the *curvata*

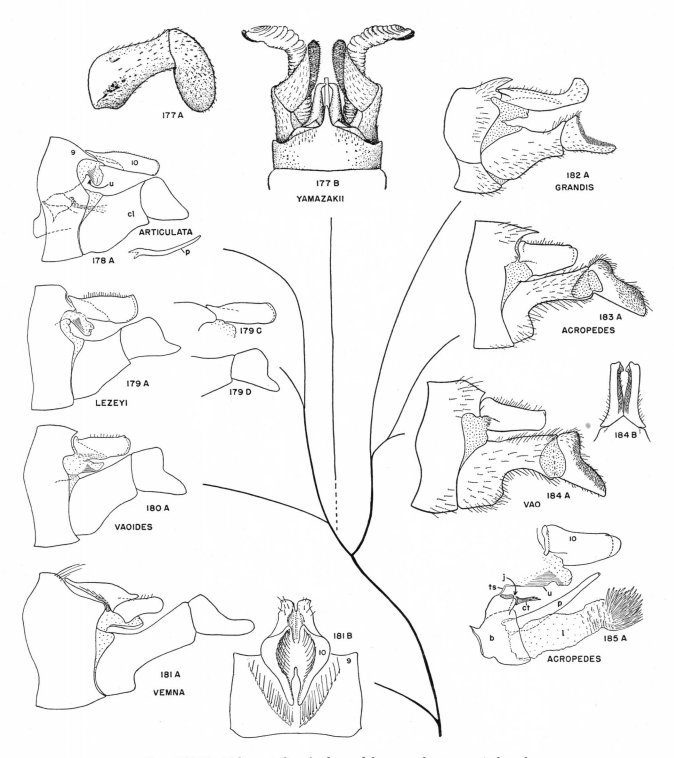

Figs. 177-85. Male genitalia of *Rhyacophila acropedes* group. *A*, lateral aspect; *B*, dorsal aspect of tergites; *C*, *D*, lateral aspect of tenth tergite and tip of clasper of a second specimen. Fig. 177 after Tsuda.

complex, in which the lobes of the tenth tergite are narrow (Fig. 175), and to the *sinuata* complex, in which the lobes of the tenth tergite are deep and excavated or concave on the mesal side at the apex. The *curvata* complex is represented by four species, *curvata* and *mortoni* from northern India, *sumatrana* from Sumatra, and *malayana* from Malaya. All are remarkably similar and the first two can be separated by only minute morphological details.

It is obvious that this group arose in Asia and has evolved into its present species pattern entirely in the Himalayan–southeast Asian montane region.

*Divaricata Group.* In the species comprising this group the lobes of the tenth tergite have evolved a curious twisted shape and the aedeagus possesses numerous specializations. It is at first difficult to believe that the most complicated species in the group arose from such a simple ancestor as a species similar to *cameroni*.

The various species in the group do fall into a well-defined pattern of development, starting with the two species *assimilis* and *divaricata*. These two differ from *cameroni* chiefly in having the ventral margin of the lobes of the tenth tergite twisted slightly mesad at the end, and in having additional processes on the aedeagus. From an ancestral type such as this several lines have radiated. Illustrations for these are given in detail by Kimmins (1953*b*). In each line the lobes of the tenth tergite became more twisted or modified. One line preserved a simple aedeagal base, giving rise to (1) *labeculata* and *rhombica*, each with an extremely short phalicata; (2) *inconspicua*, with subdivided phalicata; and (3) *ungulata*, with long clasper hangers and a single, large, angled process on the aedeagus. A second line developed a pair of erect, clavate dorsal processes on the aedeagus. In *discoidalis, uncata,* and *bicolor* these processes are of moderate length and spiny; in *parva* they are twisted and quadrate in outline; in *orientalis, manicata,* and *apicalis* they are regular in shape but large and long.

The entire group is known only from the montane region of the north Burma and adjoining mountain ranges. Since its origin the group has probably been restricted to this area, in which it has evolved into a well-defined species flock.

*Acropedes Group.* While the *divaricata* group was evolving in southern Asia, another offshoot of

Branch 3 was developing possibly in North America. What I believe to be the most primitive known species is *vemna* (Fig. 181), which has the apical part of the tenth tergite flat and feebly incised, as in *cameroni,* but the base or anterior part is produced into a pair of long points projecting over the ninth tergite. The aedeagus has a simple base and phalicata, but the lateral arms are modified into membranous, pleated, extensile tubes capped with a brush of setae (as in Fig. 185A). The other species have a simpler tenth tergite, so it seems logical to assume that the progenitor of the group differed from *cameroni* chiefly in the extensile lateral arms of the aedeagus.

Two main lines evolved. One developed the curious basal processes on the tenth tergite as already described for *vemna*. Only two species are known for this line, *vemna* and *gemona,* a pair of closely related forms.

In the second line, containing *acropedes,* the tenth tergite seems to have become simultaneously sunk and split down the middle, so that the two former dorsal surfaces face each other across the meson (Fig. 184). This is the only way in which I can account for the fact that these two opposing surfaces bear setae typical of an exterior surface. I have been able to study two groups of species in this line, one group of three in Japan, and a group of six in North America. One of the Japanese species (*vaoides,* Fig. 180) is similar in many ways to a North American species (*vao,* Fig. 184), and suggests that a form similar to these was the progenitor of both groups. In the other Japanese species, *lezeyi* and *articulata,* the base of the tenth tergite forms an angular projection above the ninth tergite (Figs. 178, 179). The six North American species are confined to the western montane region with the exception of *acropedes,* which occurs also in the Northeast. Two species (*inculta* and *acropedes*) closely related to the primitive *vao,* differ from it in having a spinelike mesal projection of the ninth tergite over the tenth (Fig. 183). In three other species (*grandis, neograndis,* and *sequoia*) the lobes of the tenth tergite are enlarged and upturned at the apex (Fig. 182).

Illustrations of the Manchurian species *yamazakii* (Fig. 177) suggest a possible relationship with a *vao*-like form, but with independent specialization in the shape of the claspers. The dorsal aspect of the tenth tergite, however, is remarkably like that of *malayana* (Fig. 175B), and may indicate that *yamazakii* is actually more representative of the ancestor of the entire *acropedes* group.

In attempting to deduce the dispersal pattern of the entire *acropedes* group, it is evident that there has been one or perhaps two spreads of ancestral forms between northeast Asia and western North America. If *yamazakii* is indeed the most primitive member, then the group probably became differentiated in Asia and then spread to North America. After the formation of the *vao*-like ancestor, there occurred a dispersal of this form back to northeastern Asia, with the subsequent isolation of an Asiatic segregate and a North American one. These have since evolved into the end branches at present restricted to these areas.

The distribution of the *acropedes* group in North America suggests some intriguing possibilities of isolation and dispersal within the continent. It will be noted on Chart 18 that, so far as is known, the *vemna* line is restricted to two neighboring high mountains in the Cascades; that the *grandis* line is restricted to the Cascade Range and contiguous ranges in California, with the exception of a more eastern record in British Columbia; and that in the *vao* line the two more primitive species (*vao* and *inculta*) are confined to the Cascades, while the most specialized member (*acropedes*) is widespread through the eastern Rockies and extends eastward across the continent to New Hampshire and westward into the Cascades. Thus, of the nine Nearctic species in the group, eight occur primarily in the western ranges of the western montane region, and only one has an extensive range eastward.

It seems probable, therefore, that (1) the three Nearctic lines of the group differentiated in a western range of mountains; (2) that moderately recently a population of the *vao* line spread into a more eastern mountain system, became isolated there, and developed into *acropedes*; (3) that during even more recent times (possibly during the last glacial advance and retreat) *acropedes* became widespread; and (4) that during these two periods the other species of the *acropedes* group continued to be ecologically restricted in such a manner that they were unable to spread out of the extreme western ranges.

Future discoveries of range extension may show that these conclusions need modification, but at least this presentation will give some organization to the data and, perhaps, stimulate further thought and investigation.

### Specialized Groups (Branches 4 to 9)

The ancestral form which gave rise to Branches 4 to 9 (in Chart 16) had evolved a definite band-like apex at the end of the tergal strap in the male genitalia. Branches 2 and 3 of Chart 16 represent a primitive stage of this condition. Beyond the point of origin of Branch 4 the apical band is either more definite or highly modified. Branches 4 to 9 contain the great bulk of the species in the genus.

It is a relatively simple matter to arrange these species into closely knit groups, but it is difficult to arrange the groups into a cohesive evolutionary pattern. Certain characteristics common to some groups appear to be indicative of genetic relationships, because it seems highly improbable that the individual characteristic would develop twice independently. On the basis of such evidence, plus other criteria of a less definite nature, I have deduced what seem to be the main evolutionary lines for the more specialized species of the genus. Where affinities of certain species are doubtful, the various possibilities are mentioned in detail in the discussion of the groups.

General characteristics of the major evolutionary lines comprising Branches 4 to 9 of Chart 16 are as follows:

Branch 4: Larvae with a sword-shaped lateral spur on the basal sclerite of each anal leg. Adults of primitive species with very simple genitalia.

Branch 5: Male genitalia with the anal sclerite appearing double, the external parts forming two pairs of processes (Fig. 192).

Branch 6: The apical band of the tergal strap extending beyond the tenth tergite and the aedeagus typically with a lower, scooplike process.

Branch 7: The apical band of the tergal strap connected directly to the base of the aedeagus.

Branch 8: The apical band elongated or the base of the aedeagus elongated, and the aedeagus without a ventral lobe on the phalicata.

Branch 9: The apical band articulating with the anal sclerite rather than with the ventral corners of the tenth tergite, as it does in the other branches.

### Branch 4

The spur on the anal leg of the larva is identical in the *fuscula* and *vulgaris* groups, and on this basis the two are considered members of the same branch. The larva of the *rotunda* group is unknown, but in the adults individual parts of the male genitalia bear a striking similarity to corresponding parts in the *vulgaris* group. For this reason the *rotunda* group is tentatively considered to be a division of Branch 4.

*Fuscula Group.* The male genitalia are generalized. The anal sclerite has a deep root (Fig. 186); the tergal strap is sclerotized; and the apical band is crescent-shaped, forming a hinge with the tergal strap. The aedeagus has a tubular base with small phalicata and lateral arms, both especially short in *vuphipes* (Fig. 187).

band projects beyond the extremity of the tergite. The anal sclerite, which has no root, is divided nearly completely, the two pieces joined at the extreme base. The anal sclerite can be moved without causing movement of other parts of the genitalia. The dorsolateral corners of the tenth tergite form earlike projections which usually protrude from beneath the sides of the posterior process of the ninth tergite.

This is by far the largest group in the genus. The most primitive members are *lusitanica* and *munda*,

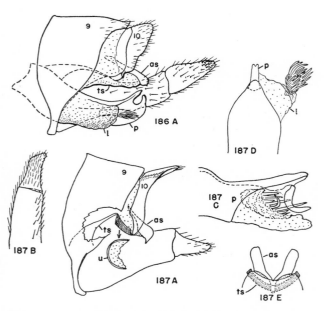

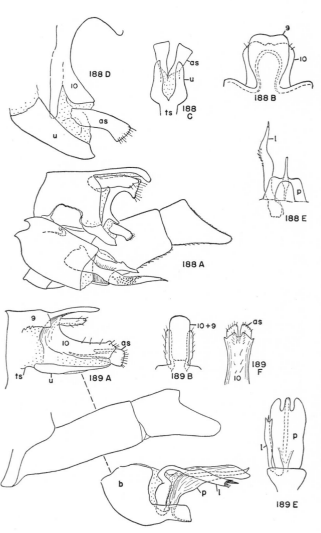

Figs. 186-87. Male genitalia of *Rhyacophila fuscula* (186) and *vuphipes* (187). *A*, lateral aspect; *B*, tip of right clasper, ventral aspect; *C*, *D*, lateral and dorsal aspect, respectively, of aedeagus; *E*, dorsal aspect of anal sclerites.

Only two species are known, *fuscula* and *vuphipes*, both restricted to eastern North America. They are both confined to cold streams in hilly country or mountains. The range of *vuphipes* occurs within that of *fuscula*, but is much more restricted and local in nature.

*Vulgaris Group.* In this group (Fig. 188) the tergal strap is membranous. The apical band is a sclerotized prong, articulating at its *base* with the ventral edges of the tenth tergite. The apex of the

Figs. 188-89. Male genitalia of *Rhyacophila fasciata* (188) and *hageni* (189). *A*, lateral aspect; *B*, tenth tergite, dorsal aspect; *C*, tergal strap, ventral aspect; *D*, anal sclerite and associated parts, lateral aspect; *E*, aedeagus, dorsal aspect in 188, ventral in 189; *F*, anal sclerites, dorsal aspect.

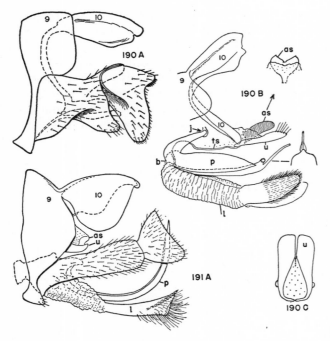

Figs. 190-91. Male genitalia of *Rhyacophila norcuta* (190) and *oreta* (191). *A*, lateral aspect; *B*, the same, cut away to show details of aedeagus and other parts; *C*, apex of tergal strap, ventral aspect.

in which the sides of the apical band are in a vertical position. Some of the more specialized members of the group have the lateral arms of the apical band curved underneath, so that the arms of the prong are as wide ventrally as laterally. I have not attempted to outline a detailed phylogenetic tree to the 40 or more species in the group. This task could be done with great scientific profit by a student situated in Europe, with more complete study material and collections. I have, however, investigated over 30 species in sufficient detail to feel sure that this *vulgaris* group is a much-branched, monophyletic unit. In all advanced members of the group the ninth tergite bears an apical process projecting over and partially covering the top of the tenth tergite (Figs. 188, 189). The tenth tergite itself is chiefly vertical in position, and its top is expanded laterally into large earlike lobes. The ventral portion is divided into narrow lateral straps articulating with the apical band of the tergal strap, and a central portion, curved posteriorly, which extends over the base of the anal sclerite. The various species are marked by a profusion of distinctive traits and curious combinations of characters. One of the most interesting developments is found in *hageni* (Fig. 189), in which the dorsum of the tenth tergite has fused solidly with the apex of the ninth.

Confined as it is to the European mountain systems, from Portugal to the Caucasus, there is no doubt that the *vulgaris* group constitutes the most remarkable species flock in the family. Unravelling the details of phylogeny, dispersal and evolution of its component units will be a fascinating venture.

*Rotunda Group.* In this small distinctive group the tenth tergite is chiefly vertical in position. Its dorsal portion is fused with a dorsal projection of the ninth tergite, and its ventral arm articulates with the bilobed apical band (Fig. 190). The anal sclerite is distinct. The apical band is the only sclerotized portion of the tergal strap, the portion between the band and the aedeagus being entirely membranous. In repose, the vertical portion of the tenth tergite and its associated ventral structures are swung back into the cavity of the ninth segment. The aedeagus has a simple or only slightly modified phalicata and a pair of membranous and extensile lateral arms.

The group is confined to the western montane region of North America. It contains two complexes, fundamentally similar but superficially quite distinct. One complex has a wide, shallow dorsal projection and deep claspers (Fig. 190), whereas the other has a narrow, deep dorsal projection and claspers with a shallow basal segment (Fig. 191). The first complex contains four species, *rotunda*, *ebria*, *norcuta*, and *latitergum*. *Rotunda* and *ebria* occur primarily in the eastern Rockies with isolated records of *rotunda* from California and Nevada. *Norcuta* is found chiefly in the western ranges with isolated records from the eastern ranges, and *latitergum* is known only from the Cascade region in northwestern Washington. The second complex contains *basalis* and *oreta*, the former known only from southwestern California, the latter from both eastern and western mountain ranges to the north.

It would appear from this distribution that species in the *rotunda* group either have spread into different montane areas with greater facility than many related groups, or their isolated populations have developed into distinctive species less frequently. Similar alternatives are encountered in explaining data from the western montane elements of the genus *Sortosa* in the Philopotamidae.

## Branch 5

The curious, seemingly double nature of the anal sclerite (Fig. 192D) is not only distinctive for this branch, but also a condition difficult to explain. Only two species are known which appear to belong to the branch, and these are sufficiently different that they may be not at all closely related.

The simpler species is *viquaea*, known only from the western montane region of North America. It has the ventral pair of anal sclerites definitely joined with the ends of the apical band (Fig. 192), and this may indicate that these ventral pieces are actually a modification arising from the apical band.

The other species is *clemens*, known only from Japan. Here the parts are more complex (Fig. 193), but offer no evidence that the sclerites beneath the anal sclerite could not have arisen from the apical band.

The affinities of these two species are doubtful. There is a possibility that they arose as an offshoot of Branch 9 (Chart 16), but since Branch 9 is such a heterogeneous assemblage, demonstrable affinity with it would tell us little.

The members of this Branch 5 are therefore of interest chiefly in emphasizing again the unusual survival of isolated forms which has occurred in the montane caddisflies.

## Branch 6

This branch (Chart 19) is one of several in which the tergal strap is definite and sclerotized, in contrast to the condition found in Branch 4. This strengthening of the tergal strap was probably an advance in genitalic structure which opened up new channels for evolutionary change.

In Lower California, there occurs a species *rayneri* (Fig. 194) which might represent the extreme base of Branch 6. In this species the essential structure of the male genitalia is simple. The apical band is simple and the moderately sclerotized tergal strap is long. The aedeagus has the apex of the phalicata divided into a dorsal sclerotized process and a ventral process bearing the gonopore. This cleft phalicata would place *rayneri* on Branch 6 rather than on Branch 7 or 8; with the addition of only a ventral process to the phalicata, it could be a direct forerunner of the *invaria* group. Certainly *rayneri* is a most interesting phylogenetic and geographic relict form.

In addition to *rayneri*, seven other species groups comprise Branch 6. The *invaria* group is the most primitive. In it the apical band of the tergal strap is a well-sclerotized, curved structure (Fig. 197) differing from that of most previous groups chiefly in its better delimited margins and the definite relation of its lateral edges to those of the tenth tergite. In this respect it also resembles Branch 4, but the known larvae lack the lateral tooth on the anal leg which characterizes that branch. The aedeagus of the *invaria* group is specialized by the addition of a ventral membranous lobe beneath the aedeagus. This structure links this primitive group with more specialized members of Branch 6.

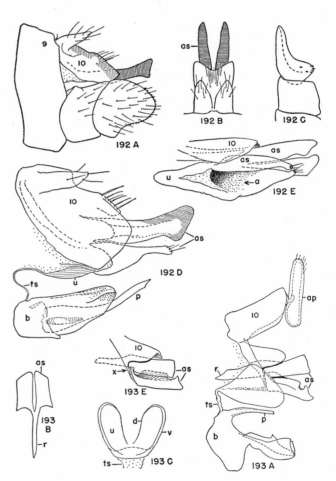

FIGS. 192-93. Male genitalia of *Rhyacophila viquaea* (192) and *clemens* (193). *A*, lateral aspect; *B*, tenth tergite, dorsal aspect (anal sclerites only in 193); *C*, clasper (192) and apex of tergal strap (193), ventral aspect; *D*, details of lateral aspect; *E*, details of anal sclerite. *a*, anus; *ap*, apical hinged process of tenth tergite; *d*, dorsal edge; *v*, ventral edge; *x*, point of articulation.

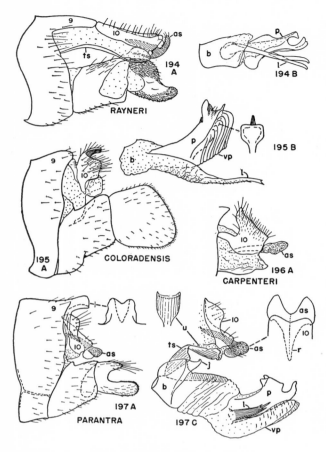

FIGS. 194-97. Male genitalia of *Rhyacophila rayneri* and
*invaria* groups. *A,* lateral aspect; *B,* aedeagus, lateral aspect;
*C,* details of lateral aspect.

*Invaria Group.* The male genitalia of primitive
species (Fig. 197) are simple in general structure.
The anal sclerite is large and has a deep root. The
aedeagus has an ornate phalicata, a pair of lateral
processes, and a membranous ventral lobe which
is a specialized feature. The heavily sclerotized
tergal strap arises from the aedeagal base and is
expanded into a well-sclerotized apical band.

The group is confined to North America. It consists of two branches, an eastern one in which the
female eighth segment is tubular and long, and a
western branch in which the female eighth segment
is short and deeply emarginate. The eastern branch
has developed into two complexes. In the one containing *invaria, vibox, banksi,* and *parantra* the
tenth tergite of the male has no crest (Fig. 197).
In the complex containing *nigrita, mycta,* and *carpenteri,* the tenth tergite of the male has a high

crest (Fig. 196). These are two complexes restricted to either the Appalachian mountain system
or to cold brooks in outlying territory. The western
branch is composed of three species, *bifila* and *coloradensis* which are widespread throughout most of
the western montane region, and *kernada* which is
known only from southern California.

It is evident that the group originated from an
ancestral form which was widespread across North
America, then became segregated into an eastern
and western element. Since that time each segregate has evolved into a distinctive group but neither
has dispersed across the central part of the continent.

*Specializations of Branch 6.* From the ancestor
of the *invaria* group (Ancestor 1, Chart 19) another
line arose to form Ancestor 2 in which the apical
band of the tergal strap projected beyond the ventral corner of the tenth tergite. In its simplest form
it probably looked like the condition now found in
either the *carolina* group (Fig. 200) or the *hyalinata* group (Fig. 198). Ancestor 2 gave rise to two
lines. In one line the ventral process of the phalicata
became sclerotized and the apical band formed a
solid structure (Ancestor 3). This line evolved into
the *carolina* group in which the apical band is
chiefly membranous (Fig. 200), and the *pepingensis, castanea* and *philopotamoides* groups in which
the apical band is hard and sclerotized and has a
pair of lateral straps joining the tenth tergite (Fig.
205). The specialized *scissa* group seems to have
developed from the base of the *castanea* group.

In the other line arising from Ancestor 2 the ventral process of the phalicata remained membranous,
but the apical band became bowed forward to form
a loop. The first step, representing Ancestor 4, was
probably similar to that now found in *hyalinata*
(Fig. 198). A more advanced step is found in *glareosa,* in which the U-shaped apical band is dorsal
and faces opposite to its normal direction (Fig.
199).

*Carolina Group.* The male genitalia (Fig. 200)
have a simple tenth tergite, a large anal sclerite
with a large root, a semimembranous apical band,
and a large, scoop-shaped process ventral to the
phalicata. The lateral processes of the aedeagus
have a slender base and a clavate apex bearing
rows or patches of spines.

The group contains five closely related species
occurring only in eastern North America. There are

some interesting differences in range between them: *teddyi* and *carolina* occur only in the Appalachian uplift area and northward; *kiamichi* is known only from the Kiamichi Mountains in Oklahoma; and *ledra* and *fenestra* occur in small cool streams (sometimes only semipermanent) in the intervening area.

*Philopotamoides Group.* The male genitalia (Fig. 205) have a beaked tenth tergite, have retained a primitive type of anal sclerite with a definite root, and have a solid apical band with lateral dorsal arms arising from its base and joining the tenth tergite. The aedeagus is in general a smaller edition of that found in the *carolina* group.

Typical of this description are the two species, *philopotamoides* and *hirticornis*, both restricted to Europe. Without much doubt another European

species, *pubescens* (Fig. 202), is a specialized offshoot of this line. In it the anal sclerite has coalesced extensively with the tenth tergite (only a pair of knobs represent the anal sclerite) and the phalicata is reduced to a simple, short tube.

On the basis of these three species, the *philopotamoides* group would appear to be a dispersal product of Ancestor 3 which has persisted in Europe for some time with little species multiplication. Another species, *orghidani*, from Roumania may also belong to this group.

*Pepingensis Group.* Two species known from China are remnants of a primitive Asiatic isolate of Ancestor 3. One of these species is *pepingensis*. In it the aedeagus and apical band are typical for the group (Fig. 203), but the anal sclerite is not in evidence and the tenth tergite has evolved a dorsal

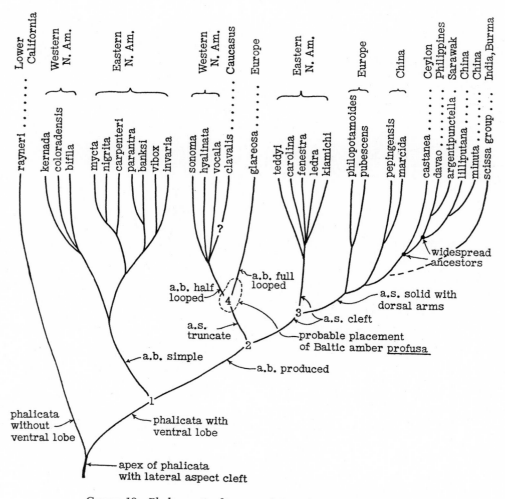

CHART 19. Phylogenetic diagram of Branch 6 of *Rhyacophila.*

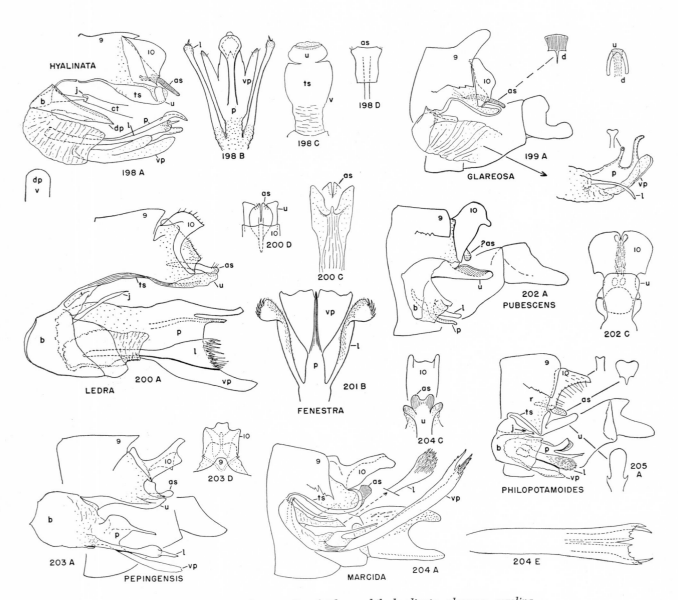

Figs. 198-205. Male genitalia of *Rhyacophila hyalinata, glareosa, carolina, philopotamoides*, and *pepingensis* groups. *A*, lateral aspect; *B*, aedeagus, dorsal aspect; *C*, apex of tergal strap, ventral aspect; *D*, anal sclerite, dorsal aspect; *E*, ventral process of aedeagus, ventral aspect. *d, v*, dorsal and ventral aspects, respectively, for insects.

projection unlike any other species in the group. The other species is *marcida* (Fig. 204), which appears more bizarre in genitalic structure than *pepingensis* but shares with it many of the same modifications. These include the dorsal projection of the tenth tergite, the low dorsal crest on the phalicata, and the elongate ventral process of the phalicata. The most interesting difference between the two concerns the anal sclerite. In *marcida* it is readily identifiable, root and all, from the lateral view, but from other views it appears to be completely fused with the apical band. It is possible to deduce from the two species an ancestral form differing little from the postulated condition of Ancestor 3.

The *pepingensis, carolina,* and *philopotamoides* groups indicate that Ancestor 3 of Chart 19 was a Holarctic form which first divided into Nearctic and Palearctic segregates. The Nearctic segregate evolved into the *carolina* group. The Palearctic segregate in turn was broken up into a European segregate, ultimately evolving into the *philopotamoides* group, and an Asiatic segregate. The latter evolved into the *pepingensis* and *castanea* groups.

*Castanea Group.* In the few Asiatic species comprising this group the male genitalia (Fig. 206) resemble those of the *carolina* group in general appearance. The aedeagus follows the same general pattern, with the addition of a pair of lateral arms to the ventral process of the phalicata. The anal sclerite is small and has lost its root. The apical band forms a small, tonguelike projection, which has a pair of arms arising at the base and joining the ventral corner of the tenth tergite. The tergal strap is unusually long and slender.

Five species are known in the group, all from Asia: *castanea* from Ceylon, *davao* from the Philippine Islands, *argentipunctella* from Sarawak (Borneo), and *lilliputana* and *minuta* from southwestern China. Using characters of the tenth tergite it is possible to segregate these species into three subgroups. In *castanea* (Fig. 206) the profile of the tenth tergite is ovate with a projecting posterior tooth. In *davao* (Fig. 207) and *argentipunctella* the tenth tergite has the dorsal corner angulate and it also has the posterior tooth. In *lilliputana* (Fig. 209) and *minuta* (Fig. 208) the base of the tenth tergite is also angulate but the posterior tooth is not visible in side view. The phylogenetic arrangement deduced from these data is shown in Chart 19.

The distribution pattern of these five species suggests that the ancestral form of the group occurred in the mountains of southern Asia and spread first to Ceylon. After the Ceylon population was isolated, the mainland population evolved the posterodorsal corner on the tenth tergite and at this point spread to some of the Pacific Islands, at least Borneo and the Philippines. These latter populations became isolated when their respective areas next

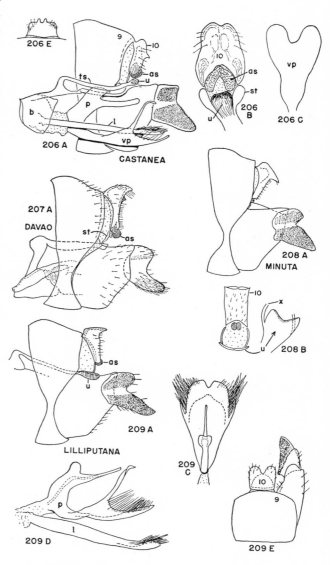

FIGS. 206-209. Male genitalia of *Rhyacophila castanea* group. *A,* lateral aspect; *B,* anal sclerite and associated structures, posterior aspect; *C, D,* aedeagus or its parts, dorsal and lateral aspects, respectively; *E,* tenth tergite, dorsal aspect. *st,* sclerotized lateral arm of tergal strap; *x,* point of articulation with tenth tergite.

became islands. The mainland population again continued to change more than the island populations.

*Scissa Group.* There occur in Burma and northern India a group of four species which seem to be an offshoot of the *castanea* stem in which the anal sclerite is either atrophied or fused with the tenth tergite. The aedeagus appears to be highly modified by consolidation and reduction of parts. The tergal strap and the profile of the tenth tergite are much the same as in *castanea.* More annectent forms are needed to be sure of the exact relationships of this group. The four species are *scissa, scissoides, obscura,* and *bidens,* all illustrated by Kimmins (1953*b*). Another Burman species, *burmana,* also treated by Kimmins, may also belong here. It differs from the four members of the *scissa* group in having several parts of the genitalia reduced or simplified.

*Hyalinata Group.* In this group the male genitalia (Fig. 198) have a simple tenth tergite, a truncate anal sclerite with a definite root, and a wide tergal strap with the apical band projecting beyond the tenth tergite. The aedeagus is much like that of the *invaria* group.

Only four species are known, differing from one another in details of the ninth and tenth tergites and aedeagus. Three species occur in the western montane region of North America: *hyalinata,* chiefly from the Rocky Mountain system, *sonoma* from California, and *vocala,* chiefly in the Cascade Range from Oregon to British Columbia. The fourth species is *clavalis* from the Caucasus, and judging from Martynov's illustrations it is a close relative of *vocala.* I have seen no specimens of *clavalis;* further study may show this placement of it to be entirely erroneous.

*Glareosa Group.* The European species *glareosa* forms a sister group of the *hyalinata* group. In the male genitalia (Fig. 199) the apical band forms a complete posterior loop and is therefore dorsal instead of ventral in position.

It is evident that the *hyalinata* and *glareosa* groups arose from a widespread common ancestor, of which two primary segregates exist. After the initial isolation of the groups, the *glareosa* line has apparently been restricted to Europe, but a population of the *hyalinata* line has apparently dispersed to Asia at a relatively recent date.

### Branch 7

The two groups comprising this branch have the apical band almost U-shaped. The upper ends of the U are attached to the sides of the tenth tergite, and the bottom of the U is attached directly to the aedeagus (Fig. 210C). In a few species the basal part of the tergal strap may appear to be represented by a dorsal hump, seemingly a part of the aedeagal base (as in Figs. 210, 216), but this hump is a secondary development of the aedeagus itself. The anal sclerite occurs as a small piece in a few primitive forms but is absent in most. The similarities found in other structures indicate that the anal sclerite was reduced in the ancestral form and dropped out independently in several lines.

*Yosiiana Group.* In the *yosiiana* group (Figs. 210-13) the tenth tergite forms an undivided dorsal structure wide at the base and narrow or bell-shaped at the apex. The aedeagus has a small base, a phalicata divided at the apex, and a pair of separate lateral processes bearing a series of large spines. These primitive, separate processes are the primary distinction which sets off the *yosiiana* group from the *sibirica* group, and demonstrate that both arose from an earlier ancestor more primitive than existing members of either group.

The five known species of the *yosiiana* group (Chart 20) have been collected only in Japan and

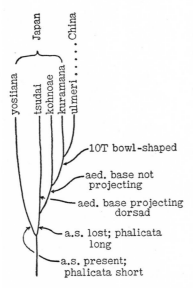

CHART 20. Phylogenetic diagram of the *Rhyacophila yosiiana* group.

China. Three separate lines are represented. The *yosiiana* line, known only from the Japanese *yosiiana,* has preserved a small vestige of the anal sclerite (Fig. 212), but the phalicata is very short. The *tsudai* line, known only from the Japanese *tsudai,* has no anal sclerite, but has a long phalicata and has a dorsal projection arising from the aedeagal base and extending under the tenth tergite. The *ulmeri* line is relatively simple in these characters but has no anal sclerite (Fig. 213). Three species of the *ulmeri* line are known, *ulmeri* from China and *kuramana* and *kohnoae* from Japan. Of these, *kohnoae* is the most primitive, having the tenth tergite solid and relatively simple (Fig. 211). In *kuramana* and *ulmeri* the tenth tergite is excavated and bowed to form a curious hollow oval (Fig. 213).

This group represents another offshoot of a primitive line which has survived in a montane area in eastern Asia.

*Sibirica Group.* Compared with *yosiiana* and its allies, the typical distinctive feature of this group is the fusion of the lateral processes of the aedeagus to form a ventral, extensile membranous base which is capped with an ovate or elongate scoop bearing a dorsal brush of hair. A few species of the group represent the condition of these structures before fusion occurred, and in some of the more highly specialized species the product of the fusion is either highly modified or lost. With few exceptions the aedeagal base has a dorsal process. This is highly modified in certain species. A phylogenetic outline of the group is given in Chart 21.

The species *ophrys* (Fig. 215) and *velora* appear to represent a very early stage in the development of the group. The tenth tergite is simple, the anal sclerite is small but of a primitive shape, and the lateral processes of the aedeagus are separate, foliaceous, membranous, and tipped with a brush of setae.

It is likely that *visor* (Fig. 217) is an offshoot from an early point which has undergone much independent change since its separation from the main line. In the species *oreia,* known from western North America, the U-shaped apical band is attached to the aedeagus, which is simple in struc-

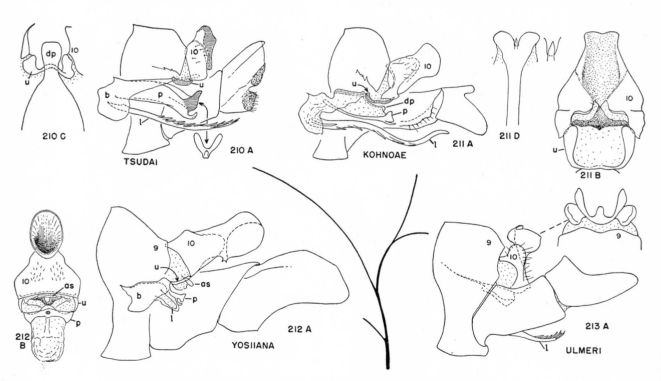

FIGS. 210-13. Male genitalia of *Rhyacophila yosiiana* group. *A,* lateral aspect; *B,* posterior aspect; *C,* ventral aspect; tip of phalicata, ventral aspect.

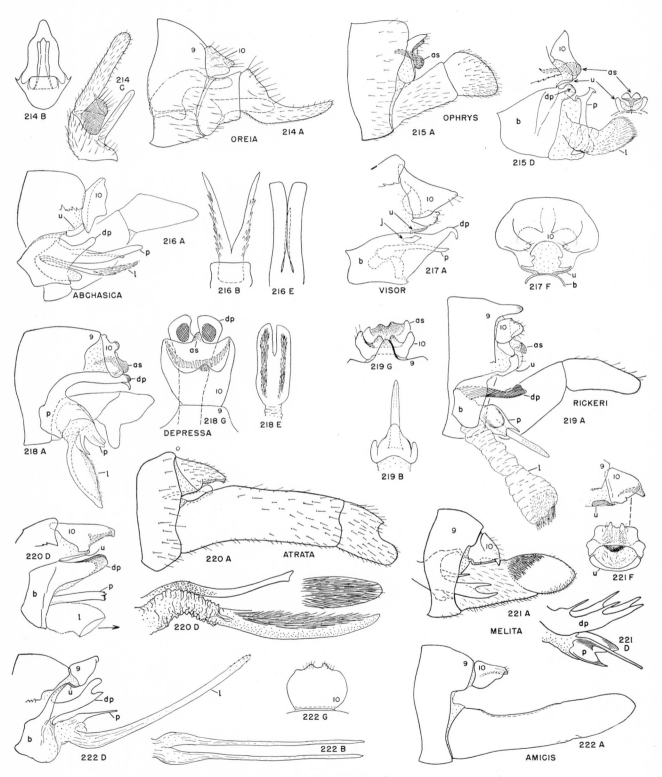

FIGS. 214-22. Male genitalia of *Rhyacophila sibirica* group. A, lateral aspect; B, aedeagus or its ventral process, ventral aspect; C, clasper, ventral aspect; D, details of lateral aspect; E, aedeagus or its ventral process, dorsal aspect; F, G, anal sclerite and tenth tergite, posterior and dorsal aspects, respectively.

ture and has no lateral processes (Fig. 214). It has been impossible to determine the exact phylogenetic position of this species within the group.

What appears to be the next major evolutionary development is illustrated by *abchasica* (Fig. 216), in which the lateral processes of the aedeagus are fused at their base. A more advanced but still incomplete stage of this fusion is found in *depressa* (Fig. 218), in which the lateral processes have become fused nearly to the apex to form a single ventral process bearing a double row of hairs. Since it left the main line, *depressa* has developed certain striking characteristics. The dorsum of the aedeagal base has become elongated and forms a long, bowed structure. The anal sclerite and the tenth tergite have fused so that the anal sclerite is not delimited externally, although its internal root persists and can be seen in cleared specimens from either a lateral or posterior view.

The complete fusion of the aedeagal arms is illustrated by the species *rickeri* (Fig. 219). Concurrently with this development, a long dorsal process (*dp*) was formed on the aedeagal base. In *rickeri* the tenth tergite is short and the anal sclerite large and distinct, indicating that the species is more primitive than those placed higher on the tree.

The ancestral form which gave rise to *rickeri* was also the parent of a more specialized line which evolved into Ancestor 1 of Chart 21. In Ancestor 1 the tenth tergite developed a dorsal overhang or ledge, probably much as in *pellisa* (Fig. 224). From Ancestor 1 two lines arose. In one, leading to the Nearctic *atrata* complex, little change occurred except for a lengthening of the claspers (Fig. 223). In the other line, leading to Ancestor 2, the tenth tergite became more elongate and developed lateral flanges. The *atrata* complex contains two species in the western part and three in the eastern

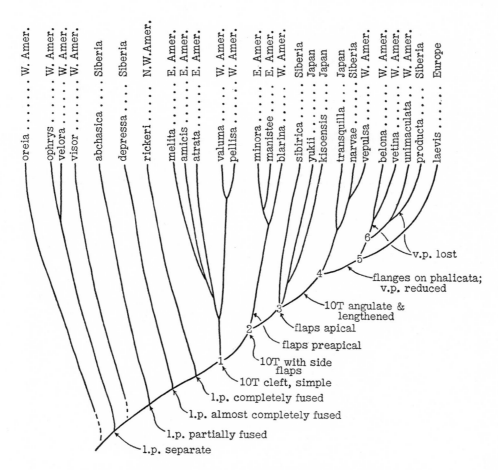

CHART 21. Phylogenetic diagram of the *Rhyacophila sibirica* group.

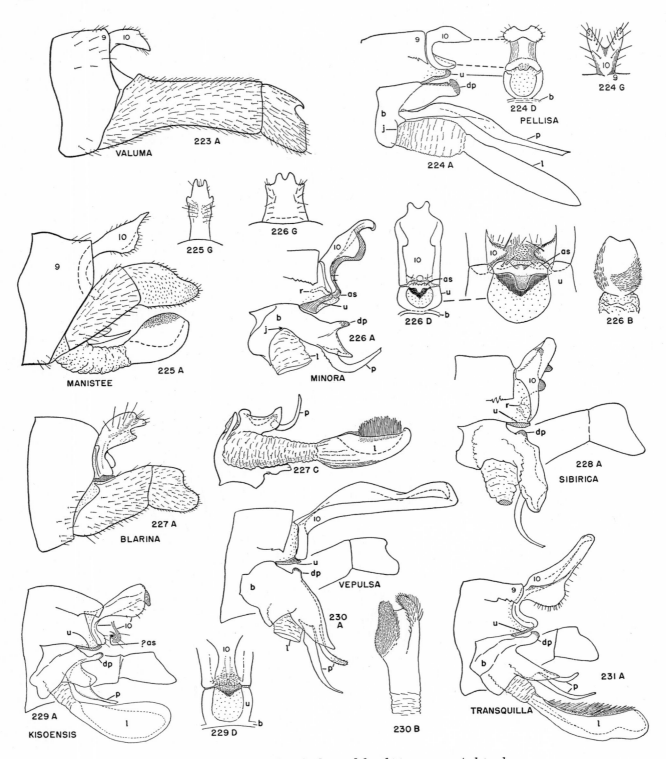

FIGS. 223-31. Male genitalia of *Rhyacophila sibirica* group. *A*, lateral aspect; *B*, ventral process of aedeagus, dorsal aspect; *C*, aedeagus, lateral aspect; *D*, *G*, tenth tergite and associated structures, posterior and dorsal aspects, respectively.

part of North America. The two species in the western montane region (*valuma* and *pellisa*) are closely related forms in which the apex of the ventral aedeagal process is elongate (Fig. 224) and the tenth tergite has definite dorsal and ventral projecting parts.

The three species occurring in the eastern part of the continent show unusual modifications. The simplest one is *atrata* (Fig. 220), in which the ventral projecting piece of the tenth tergite is greatly reduced. The more complex species are *amicis* (Fig. 222) and *melita* (Fig. 221). Each has a somewhat similar tenth tergite, but in both the phalicata is apparently fused with the ventral aedeagal process, and the two segments of the clasper are partially fused. In *amicis* (Fig. 222) the ventral process forms a scoop contiguous with and beneath the phalicata. The scoop has a pair of long, slender processes reaching the tip of the claspers. Its curious texture, semisclerotized but wrinkled, suggests that an original scooplike ventral process such as shown in Fig. 218A became shortened and fused solidly beneath the phalicata. Such a structure does occur in *melita* (Fig. 221D). From this evidence, the long arms of the ventral process of *amicis* would appear to be a specialization. In other respects *amicis* is relatively primitive, as evidenced by the fact that the dorsal process of the aedeagus has only two projections and the claspers are elongate as in *atrata*. In *melita* (Fig. 221) the claspers are shortened and the dorsal process is divided into five long teeth.

Ancestor 2 also gave rise to two lines. One of these is now represented by a group of three Nearctic species which differ little from what Ancestor 2 must have been like. They have preserved a very small, platelike anal sclerite (Fig. 226) and have a short, curved phalicata. The most primitive species is *blarina* (Fig. 227), known from the Cascade Range in the West. The other two species, *minora* (Fig. 226) and *manistee* (Fig. 225), occur in the eastern part of the continent and are characterized by the better developed lateral flanges of the tenth tergite.

In the other line arising from Ancestor 2, the side flanges of the tenth tergite extended along the tergite nearly to its apex. This stage, called Ancestor 3, is well exemplified by *kisoensis* (Fig. 229). An internal vestige of the root of the anal sclerite still persists in this species. It is probable that *sibirica*

(Fig. 228) is also an offshoot of Ancestor 3 in which the tenth tergite became straight. In Ancestors 1 and 2 and their immediate derivatives the mesal part of the tenth tergite was cleft at the apex (Fig. 226). In Ancestor 3 the mesal part of the tenth tergite became single.

In addition to the *sibirica* and *kisoensis* lines, Ancestor 3 gave rise to a third line in which the lateral flanges grew past the mesal part of the tenth tergite. This line evolved into Ancestor 4. It is represented in our modern fauna by the Japanese species *transquilla* (Fig. 231) and a pair of closely related species, *narvae* from Siberia and *vepulsa* from western North America. The latter two have an even longer tenth tergite than does *transquilla*. The branch represented by these three species developed an extra finger-like aedeagal process arising just above the phalicata.

Also from Ancestor 4 a line evolved in which lateral flanges were developed on the phalicata (Fig. 233) and the ventral aedeagal process underwent some reduction. These developments characterize Ancestor 5. Ancestor 5 gave rise to a European line, represented in the present fauna by *laevis* (Fig. 236), which is little changed from the postulated characters of Ancestor 5; and to Ancestor 6, in which the ventral aedeagal lobe became even more reduced, probably to a thin flap as shown in Fig. 234. Ancestor 6 gave rise to a line in which the ventral aedeagal process was completely lost but other parts changed little. This line is represented by the Nearctic species *vetina* (Fig. 233) and *belona* (Fig. 232), both found only in high mountain areas in the western montane region. In another line which evolved from Ancestor 6, the tenth tergite developed a curious acute angulation (Fig. 234). This line is represented by another western Nearctic high mountain species *unimaculata*. The Siberian species *producta* seems to have diverged from the *unimaculata* line. In *producta* the ventral aedeagal process is lost, and long lateral processes have developed at the apex of the phalicata (Fig. 235).

From an analysis of the distribution data in Chart 21, three observations are apparent: (1) the northern nature of the existing fauna, (2) its apparent absence from the India–Southern China areas, and (3) the obviously high number of dispersals that seem to have occurred across the Bering Bridge. In attempting to synthesize a hypothetical dispersal

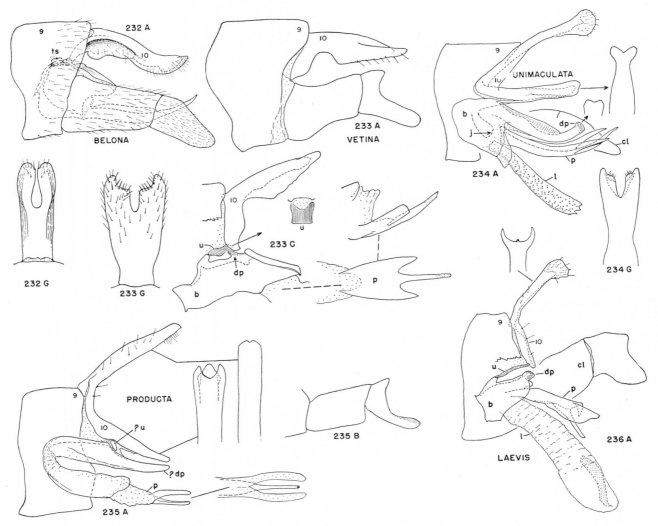

Figs. 232-36. Male genitalia of *Rhyacophila sibirica* group. *A*, lateral aspect; *B*, clasper, lateral aspect; *C*, details of lateral aspect; *G*, tenth tergite, dorsal aspect.

pattern that will explain these data, the first conclusion seems to be that the group has always occupied a range embracing the northeast Asia–northwest North America area. The remnants of the first stages of evolution in the group (*ophrys* to *rickeri*) support this view. Ancestors 1 and 2 were undoubtedly in western North America. From each of these lines a population reached and colonized the eastern part of the continent, one colonization resulting in the *atrata-melita* complex, the other in the *minora-manistee* complex.

It is logical to suppose that a population from Ancestor 2 reached Asia and developed into the series Ancestors 3, 4 and 5, of which 3 and 4 gave rise to primarily Asiatic groups. Ancestor 5 presumably became Holarctic, one population reaching Europe to produce the *laevis* line, and another reaching western North America to produce the *vetina* line. Subsequently a population of the Asiatic *transquilla* line reached North America and gave rise to the western American species *vepulsa*, and a population of the western American line *vetina* spread to Asia and gave rise to the Asiatic species *producta*.

### Branch 8

The species grouped together in this branch (Chart 22) are a heterogeneous assemblage, but all have in common an unusual retraction of the aedeagus within the body. This has come about (1) by the elongation of the base of the aedeagus and (2) by an elongation of the apical band of the tergal strap. The tergal strap is either short, or not recognizable as a part distinct from the apical band. On this basis, Branch 8 appears to be a fairly close relative of Branch 7, in which the tergal strap is extremely short. The anal sclerite has been preserved in the entire branch, but in most groups has either a short root or none.

Three distinct species groups have evolved and survived to the present, two of them Asiatic and one North American.

*Bilobata Group.* The male genitalia (Fig. 237) have a moderately simple tergal strap and apical band, but have developed certain specializations. These include the loss of the root of the anal sclerite and the development of a long, large dorsal process on the aedeagal base. In *bilobata* (Fig. 238C) the aedeagal base is elongate, but in *pacata* (Fig. 237) it is not.

These two Japanese species are the only two that I can definitely assign to the group, although a third Japanese species, *diffidens*, may belong here.

*Quieta Group.* The male genitalia (Fig. 239) are characterized primarily by the elongate apical band and aedeagal base. In addition the ninth tergite is produced as a long hood extending over the small tenth tergite. The anal sclerite has no root.

This curious group is known only from a pair of extremely closely related species, *quieta* from Japan and *angulata* from Altai (Siberia).

*Betteni Group.* The male genitalia (Fig. 240) are characterized by the unusually long lateral aedeagal processes which are also ventral in position and in some species become fused. The species *chilsia* (Fig. 241) and *fenderi* (Fig. 240) are among the primitive species in which the lateral processes are separate and a long dorsal process arises from the aedeagal base. In these species the apical band is U-shaped and attached to a broad sheath connecting it with the aedeagus. From an ancestral form similar to these a branch arose in which the lateral aedeagal processes became fused into a long, rod-like structure (Fig. 242A, *1*) bearing a double row

of stout spines at the apex (Fig. 244C, *1*). The first step in this evolutionary line is illustrated by *betteni* (Fig. 242), which has preserved the U-shaped apical band. From this condition the apical band apparently fused at the tip to form a solid, ribbon-like strap joining the tenth tergite and the aedeagus (Fig. 245). This advanced type is found in *vedra* (Fig. 245), *vaccua* and *malkini* (Fig. 244). The

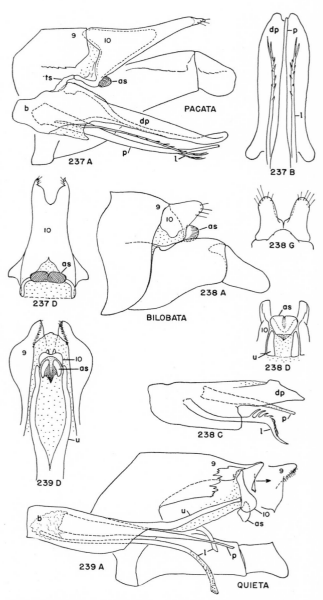

Figs. 237-39. Male genitalia of *Rhyacophila bilobata* and *quieta* groups. A, lateral aspect; B, C, aedeagus, ventral and lateral aspects, respectively; D, C, tenth tergite and associated structures, ventral and dorsal aspects, respectively.

Figs. 240-45. Male genitalia of *Rhyacophila betteni* group. *A*, lateral aspect; *C*, tergal strap, lateral aspect; *D, G*, tenth tergite and associated structures, ventral and dorsal aspects, respectively.

phylogenetic tree of this group is shown in Chart 22.

The entire group has been found to date only in the western montane region of North America. A study of the known distribution, although woefully incomplete, offers the basis for some interesting speculation regarding the origin and dispersal of the group (Chart 22). The two primary branches of the *betteni* group contain four species each.

Three species of each branch are confined to the extreme western mountain ranges. The species so confined include the most primitive member of each branch. Only one species in each branch (*vaccua* and *chilsia*, respectively) occurs outside this region. It seems highly likely, therefore, that the group originated from an ancestral form which became isolated in a western mountain area and that its principal evolution has taken place in the same

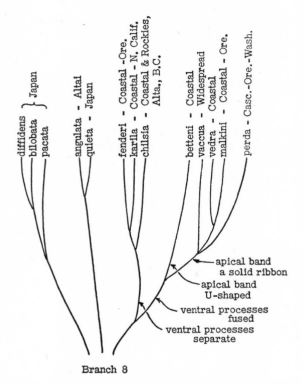

CHART 22. Phylogenetic diagram of Branch 8 of *Rhyacophila*.

general area. None of the group appears to have reached any of the southern ranges of the eastern mountains.

· · · ·

The available information for Branch 8 indicates strongly that it originated from an ancestral form which occurred in both northeastern Asia and northwestern North America. This ancestral population was broken up into at least three segregates, not necessarily simultaneously, and these three segregates have dispersed little since then. Otherwise, species bearing at least some kinship with the known forms should be found in other areas.

· · · ·

*Truncata Group.* Two southern Asiatic species, *annulicornis* (Fig. 246) and *truncata,* have become so specialized that it has been impossible to assign them to a definite branch. The genitalia are fully illustrated by Kimmins (1953b); mention will be made here of only a few salient points. The tergal strap is long, much as in the *castanea* group, but the apical band is invaginated curiously within the end of the segment (Fig. 246). The anal sclerite

is small and projects under an apical hood formed by the ventromesal part of the tenth tergite. These two species represent the end of a highly specialized line of which no less specialized forms are known to aid in placing it in a phylogenetic scheme.

### Branch 9

In the male genitalia of this most diverse branch of *Rhyacophila*, as mentioned on page 84, the apical band articulates with the anal sclerite rather than with the ventral corners of the tenth tergite. Ten distinctive species groups or phyletic lines can be recognized. Forms such as *iranda* (Fig. 247) are almost as primitive and simple as primitive groups of Branch 2, indicating that Branch 9 began as a distinctive and separate line very early in the history of the genus (see Chart 16).

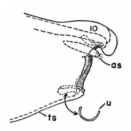

FIG. 246. Anal sclerites and associated structures of *Rhyacophila annulicornis,* lateral aspect.

The simplest of the ten groups of Branch 9 undoubtedly arose directly from a primitive form which must have been quite similar to the ancestor of Branch 9. The most specialized groups of the branch are so bizarre that one could not have evolved directly from another. The logical deduction, therefore, is that even the specialized groups arose independently from relatively primitive ancestral types. The following discussion of the various species groups explains this situation.

*Vobara Group.* The two species of this group (Fig. 247) are simple forms in which the U-shaped apical band is attached directly to the ends of the anal sclerite. The shape of the tenth tergite, claspers, and aedeagus are strikingly similar to the condition found in *vofixa,* of Branch 2, so much so that the *vobara* and *vofixa* groups can probably be considered archaic remnants representing the bases of their respective branches.

Both of the closely related species known in the

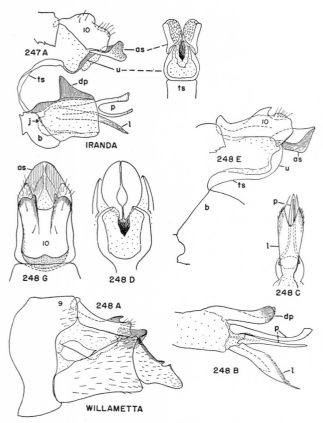

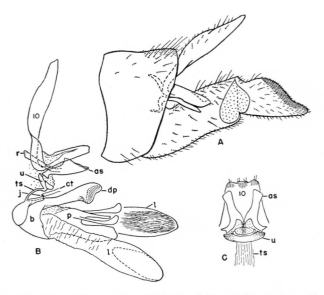

FIGS. 247-48. Male genitalia of *Rhyacophila iranda* and *willametta*. A, lateral aspect; B, C, aedeagus, lateral and ventral aspects, respectively; D, E, G, tenth tergite and associated structures, ventral, lateral, and dorsal aspects, respectively.

FIG. 249. Male genitalia of *Rhyacophila angelita*. A, lateral aspect; B, details of lateral aspect; C, anal sclerite and associated structures, ventral aspect.

group, *vobara* and *iranda*, are restricted to the western montane region of North America. *R. vobara* is known from the Rockies of eastern British Columbia and Alberta, and from the Yukon, whereas *iranda* is known only from the Cascade Range and westward.

*Willametta Group.* This group contains only one Nearctic species, *willametta*. The male genitalia (Fig. 248) are simple in regard to the tenth tergite, anal sclerite, and apical band, but the aedeagus has evolved a number of oddly shaped parts. The most conspicuous of these developments are: (1) the dorsal and ventral rodlike portions of the phalicata which have become separated to form a pair of independently articulating processes, and (2) the lateral processes of the aedeagus which have moved ventrad and fused to form a bifid ventral scoop.

*R. willametta* is probably an early offshoot from the base of the *vobara* line. At the present time it is known only from the mountains of southwestern Oregon.

*Angelita Group.* Another distinctive group which might have arisen from the base of the *vobara* line is the *angelita* group, known from western North America. Fundamentally *angelita* is of a simple pattern, but with each part individually modified (Fig. 249). The tenth tergite has developed a high dorsal flap, the anal sclerite has enlarged rather than reduced its root, the dorsal process of the aedeagal base is enlarged, and an extra pair of lateral processes has developed on the phalicata.

This group contains three closely related species, *angelita*, *perplana*, and *vuzana*. The latter two are known only from the Cascade Range; the former is widespread over the entire western montane region and occurs also in the northern Appalachian system.

*Retracta Group.* The one known species in this group, *retracta*, is simple in structure of male genitalia (Fig. 250), differing from the *vobara* and *willametta* groups in the shapes of various parts. In particular the anal sclerite is undivided and has a deep root.

The only collection records for *retracta* are from

eastern Siberia. The species would therefore appear to be a remnant of another, perhaps Asiatic, phyletic line.

*Alexanderi Group.* In this group also only a single species is known, *alexanderi* (Fig. 251). In the male genitalia, the tenth tergite and aedeagus are generalized but the anal sclerite is solid, elongate and beaklike, and the tergal strap and clasper tendons are fused into a long, compound strap. The males have an unusual feature on tergites 3 to 6: the long, hairlike setae are grouped into round, wartlike patches (Fig. 251C).

tenth tergite. Perhaps in these characters the common ancestor looked much like Fig. 258, but the apical band was less well defined and the anal sclerite had a root as in Fig. 253.

The more primitive of these two groups is the *hingstoni* group, composed of three species, *hingstoni* and *hobsoni* from Tibet and *sinensis* from southwestern China. The latter two are extremely similar, differing only in minute details of parts. The anal sclerite is simple in *hingstoni* (Fig. 252) but convoluted in *sinensis* (Fig. 253). In both, the

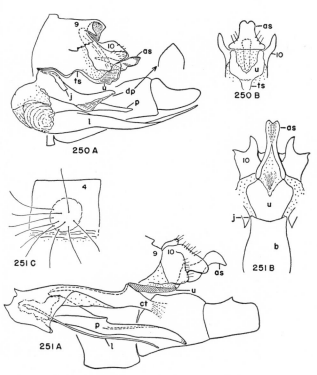

FIGS. 250-51. Male genitalia of *Rhyacophila retracta* (250) and *alexanderi* (251). A, lateral aspect; B, anal sclerite and associated structures, ventral aspect; C, fourth tergite, lateral aspect.

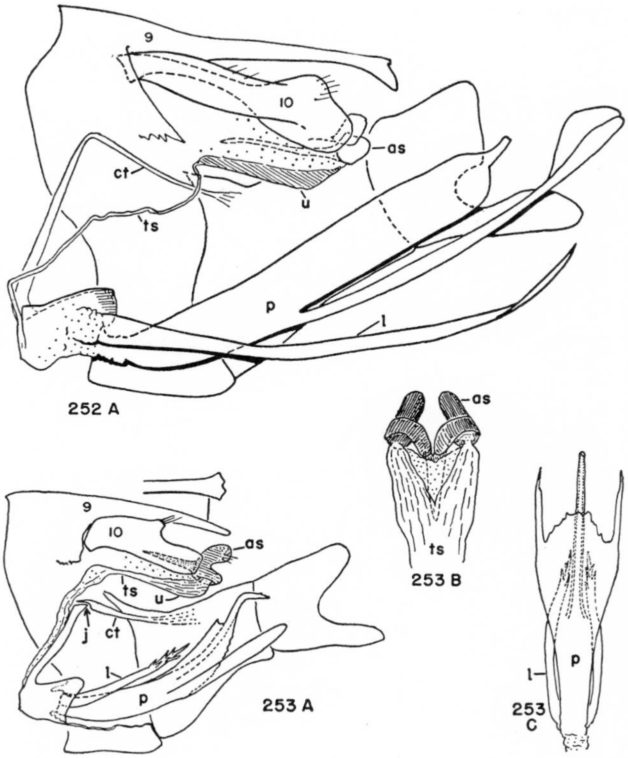

FIGS. 252-53. Male genitalia of *Rhyacophila hingstoni* (252) and *sinensis* (253). A, lateral aspect; B, anal sclerite, ventral aspect; C, aedeagus, ventral aspect.

This species is known only from the Rocky Mountain region of North America, and represents the survival of a line that may be of considerable age.

*Hingstoni Group.* This is one of two most interesting groups (*hingstoni* and *naviculata*). Both of these groups may have evolved from a common ancestral type in which the ninth tergite possessed a long apical process overhanging the long, horizontal

apical band is fairly simple, and the tergal strap is membranous. An unusual feature is the high, slender pair of clasper hangers. In the aedeagus the pair of lateral processes are simple and the phalicata has a pair of processes or a ventral lobe.

*Naviculata Group.* The 13 species placed in the *naviculata* group (Chart 23) represent stages in a line evolving from a form like *arnaudi*, the most

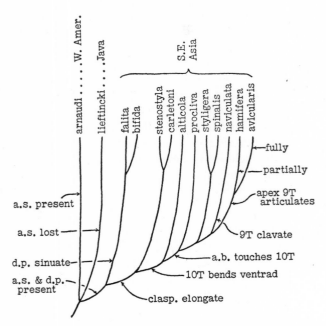

CHART 23. Phylogenetic diagram of the *Rhyacophila naviculata* group.

primitive, to a specialized form like *avicularis*. In the primitive species in this group, *arnaudi*, the tergal strap is sclerotized and bandlike (Fig. 254), the clasper hangers are short, and the phalicata lacks lateral processes. These latter two characters distinguish *arnaudi* from the *hingstoni* group. Otherwise *arnaudi* is typical of the deduced ancestral form of both the *hingstoni* and *naviculata* groups.

In the Nearctic species *arnaudi* (Fig. 254) the anal sclerite is large but the aedeagal base has no dorsal process. The Javanese species *lieftincki* is remarkably similar (Fig. 255), differing chiefly in that the anal sclerite has disappeared completely and the apical band simply fades into membrane where it formerly connected with the anal sclerite. This loss of the anal sclerite is an individual development in the *lieftincki* line. The sclerite is well developed in more specialized members of the group.

In the next evolutionary step (Chart 23) a curved dorsal process evolved on the aedeagal base, as in *stenostyla* (Fig. 258). The species *carletoni* is a close relative (Fig. 259); in this illustration the dorsal process was omitted. Two specialized lines developed from a form similar to these. In one line the claspers remained short, the dorsal process be-

came sharply sinuate and the anal sclerite became more ventral in position in relation to the tenth tergite. The species *falita* (Fig. 256) and its close relative *bifida* (Fig. 257) represent this stage. In the other line the claspers became elongate but the

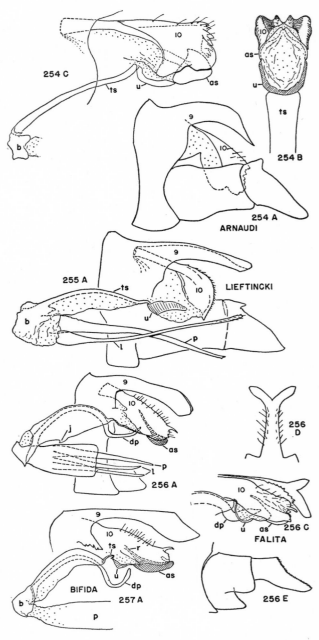

FIGS. 254-57. Male genitalia of *Rhyacophila naviculata* group. *A*, lateral aspect; *B, C*, tenth tergite, ventral and lateral aspects, respectively; *D*, apex of ninth tergite; *E*, clasper, lateral aspect.

dorsal process retained the more primitive, less curved condition. Representatives of this stage are *stenostyla* (Fig. 258) and *carletoni*. From the ancestor with long claspers arose a form in which the tenth tergite assumed a more ventral position, bringing it into direct contact with the apical band. A firm attachment developed between them at the point of contact, but the portion of the apical band beyond this point tended to become membranous. These details are illustrated in Figs. 262-64, which also illustrate other structures that have evolved. More complete illustrations are given by Kimmins (1953*b*). Seven species are known in this line, *alticola, procliva, styligera, spinalis, naviculata, cruciata, hamifera,* and *avicularis.* All are from the mountainous areas of China, Burma, and north India. The relationships of these species are shown in Chart 23.

The apex of evolutionary development in this line is reached in the species *avicularis* (Fig. 265). In this species the tenth tergite is reduced to a small bar forming part of the mechanism controlling the extrusion of the aedeagus, and the apex of the ninth segment has evolved into an articulated piece which now appears to perform the function of the original tergite. This resembles the supplanting of the cercus in the Hydrobiosinae by a new structure which has become cercus-like while the original cercus has become reduced to a minute button (see p. 114).

The distribution phenomena of this group are most intriguing. The most primitive form (*arnaudi*) is found in the western montane region of North America. Its close relative *lieftincki* is known from Java. All the others, which form a monophyletic, highly specialized line, are found in the montane area of eastern China and north Burma and India. There seems little doubt from this that the primitive ancestor of the group became widespread, and its range subsequently became divided into North American, Sundaland, and Himalayan segregates. From evidence now at hand the indications are that each of these segregates has remained isolated ever since and that the Himalayan segregate developed into a distinctive species flock.

*Nigrocephala Group.* The principal feature of this group is the evolution of a unique type of coupling between the tenth tergite and aedeagus. There are four distinctive points in the resulting structure (Fig. 266): (1) the apical band has become very narrow, and a membranous area extends beyond it; (2) dorsally, the apical band is hinged by membrane with the base of the anal sclerite; (3) the tergal strap is slender, attached at the base of the aedeagus, and has developed a flat process (called the sagittate process) anterior to its juncture with the apical band, and (4) a loose loop of membrane joins the *base* of the sagittate process with the ventral side or bottom of the apical band. In repose the sagittate process often lies appressed to the dorsum of the aedeagus and is easily overlooked. This unique type of structure is found in no other group, nor are any annectent forms known which indicate its origin. The simple structure of the apical band, however, indicates that it arose from a very simple ancestral type, and not from any of the specialized lines of Branch 9.

The group is confined to Asia (Chart 24) and contains fourteen known species. The most primitive line has retained the lateral processes of the aedeagus, and is represented by *remingtoni* (Fig. 270) from Japan, and two other very closely related species, *manuleata* from Siberia and *kawamurae* from Japan. The other line of the group lost the lateral processes and evolved into an ances-

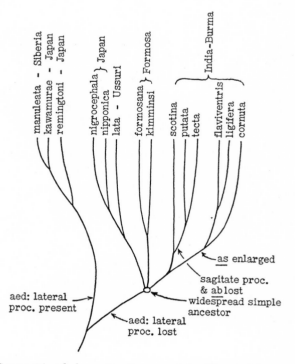

CHART 24. Phylogenetic diagram of the *Rhyacophila nigrocephala* group.

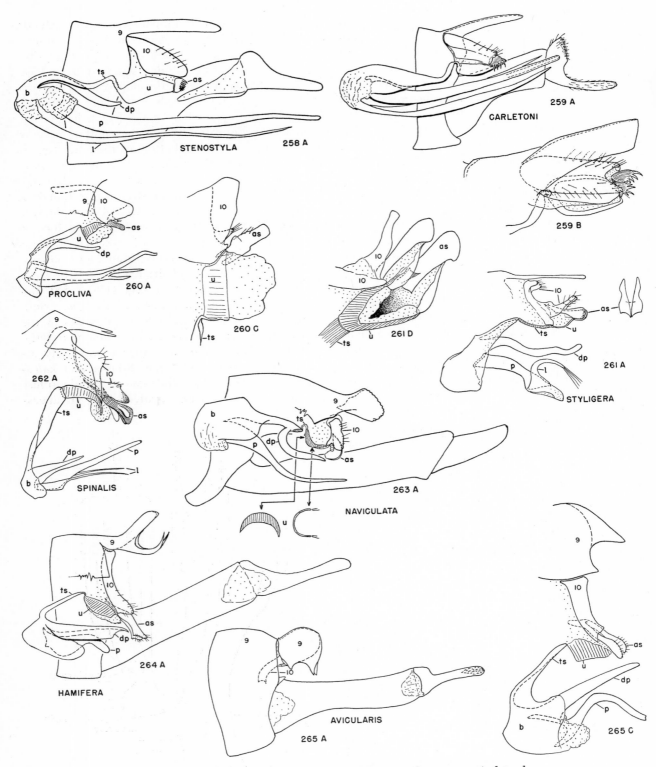

Figs. 258-65. Male genitalia of *Rhyacophila naviculata* group. *A*, lateral aspect; *B*, *C*, *D*, details of tenth tergite and anal sclerite, subdorsal, lateral, and lateroventral aspects, respectively.

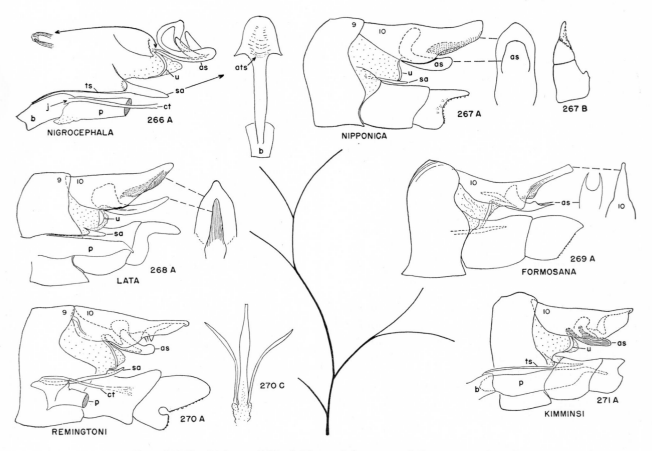

Figs. 266-71. Male genitalia of *Rhyacophila nigrocephala* group. *A,* lateral aspect; *B,* clasper, ventral aspect; *C,* aedeagus, ventral aspect. *sa,* sagittate process.

tral form much like *kimminsi* (Fig. 271) or *scotina.* This ancestral form seems to have given rise to several small complexes. One complex, characterized by the shape of the clasper and the broad ventral aspect of the anal sclerite, is known from the Japanese and Siberian species *nigrocephala* (Fig. 266), *lata* (Fig. 268), and *nipponica* (Fig. 267). Another complex is found in *formosana.* In the latter the tenth tergite is highly modified and the anal sclerite is bifurcate (Fig. 269). The remaining species are found in the north India–Burma region, and comprise three complexes: (1) *scotina,* very like the primitive widespread ancestor; (2) a pair of species, *tecta* and *putata,* in which the apical band is not discernible and the sagittate process is lost; and (3) a complex of three species *flaviventris, ligifera,* and *cornuta,* in which the anal sclerite has become greatly enlarged. These India–

Burma species have been illustrated by Kimmins (1953).

The absence of the apical band and the sagittate process in the species *tecta* and *putata* can be interpreted in two ways. Either these characters are atrophied and lost or these species represent a primitive stage in the evolution of the characters mentioned.

Because of the following reasons it seems more logical to assume these two characters became atrophied and lost. In the first place, the specialized apical band of the group probably arose from a broader type such as is found in less specialized groups; it is difficult to rationalize the complete disappearance of this primitive structure with its reappearance in closely related species in very nearly the same shape. In the second place, it seems more reasonable that the sagittate process would

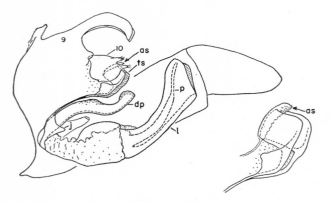

FIG. 272. Male genitalia of *Rhyacophila verrula*, lateral aspect, with enlarged view of anal sclerite.

have resulted from the specialization of some definitely sclerotized structure rather than from membrane. In the third place, the lateral processes of the aedeagus are indubitably a primitive attribute of this genus, and their presence in the *kawamurae* complex (which has a sagittate process) and their absence in the *tecta* complex would indicate that the latter was more specialized.

The *nigrocephala* group is another which apparently originated in Asia, became widespread within that area, and later fragmented into several local

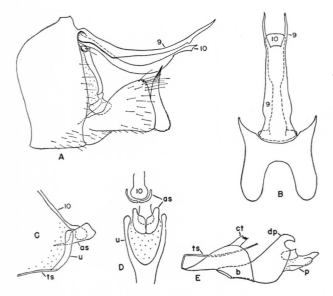

FIG. 273. Male genitalia of *Rhyacophila vagrita* (A and B) and *milnei* (C, D, E). A, B, lateral and dorsal aspects; C, anal sclerite assembly, lateral aspect; D, same, ventral aspect with inset of posterior aspect; E, aedeagus, lateral aspect.

groups. Each of these has undergone some species multiplication but little subsequent dispersion.

*Verrula Group.* A most unusual species, *verrula*, occurs in the western montane region of North America. The ninth tergite is produced into a pair of high, arched processes, and the tenth tergite is small (Fig. 272). The aedeagus has a large dorsal process, and the phalicata is simple, almost enclosed in a large, scoop-shaped ventral structure which probably represents the fused lateral processes. The unusual feature of the genitalia is the curious structure which has resulted from a complete fusion of the tergal strap, apical band, and anal sclerite, resulting (Fig. 272, *as*) in an inverted U-shaped apical portion which fits into a ventral cavity of the tenth tergite.

The affinities of this form are obscure, except that it probably does belong in some manner to Branch 9.

*Vagrita Group.* The two species, *vagrita* and *milnei*, placed in this group are known to inhabit only the western montane region of North America. The male genitalia of both these odd species (Fig. 273) has curious dorsal projections of both ninth and tenth tergites, but a very small, simple aedeagus. In this group there is a curious development of the apical band and anal sclerite. The lobes of the anal sclerite form a trough-shaped structure open from above; into the opening fits the ball-shaped ventral end of the tenth tergite, and the arms of the apical band articulate with the outer sides of the walls of the trough. In this species the end of the tenth tergite is completely separated from the apical band by the walls of the anal sclerite. This mechanism actually results in a remarkably efficient ball-and-socket articulation.

This group is so different in structure from its closest relative that it must be classed as an off-shoot, probably of Branch 9, which has evolved highly specialized characters of its own.

### Unplaced Species

There are numerous species described in *Rhyacophila* which I have been unable to study. Undoubtedly when adequately known these will contribute much to an understanding of the phylogeny and dispersal of the group. These species are listed on p. 122.

### Fossil Species

Three species of the genus *Rhyacophila* have been described from Baltic amber, *occulta, profusa,* and *laminata.* Illustrations of the male genitalia are available for the last two. It is plain that these two species are typical members of *Rhyacophila,* and that they represent two different groups or branches of the genus. It is difficult to place *laminata* (Fig. 274), but it appears to have a tenth tergite much as in some members of the *acropedes* group. It may therefore belong to Branch 3.

Illustrations for the other species, *profusa* (Fig. 275), show that the ventral aspect of the aedeagus and the general shape of the clasper are very similar to the condition found in the modern species *philopotamoides* or *glareosa.* Since no other modern groups resemble these two in the details illustrated, it is practically certain that the fossil species *profusa* represents a stage near the base of one of these lines, or their common ancestor (see Charts 16, 19). This assumes that the phalicata had a ventral process (see Figs. 198, 199), but the illustrations of *profusa* show no such structure. If it was present this situation would indicate either (1) that it was membranous, as it would be on the *glareosa* stem, or (2) that it was reduced, which would be indicative of the *philopotamoides* line.

### The Genus *Himalopsyche*

The twenty or more species in this genus exhibit a remarkable diversity of genitalic types in the males. In this diversity there are confusing combinations of what appear to be primitive and specialized characters. In some species there seems to be, for instance, an anal sclerite but no tenth tergite, or single-segmented claspers combined with a primitive set of tergal characters. It is impossible to rationalize the evolution of the genus as development along one or two pectinate branches. If, however, one considers the possibility that many independent phyletic lines arose from one or a few very primitive ancestors, and that each line developed peculiar specializations in some structures but remained little changed in others, then it is possible to construct a family tree for *Himalopsyche* which reconciles the apparently conflicting data. The primitive characters assumed to have been possessed by the ancestral form of *Himalopsyche* are:

1. A well-developed anal sclerite.
2. Tenth tergite sclerotized and simple, and with a pair of broad lateral lobes.
3. Claspers simple and 2-segmented.

It is interesting that no tergal strap or its apical band was developed in *Himalopsyche.* In some species of the *naviculata* group of *Rhyacophila* the veins have moved backward so that $R_4$ and $R_5$ are on either side of the wing point, as in *Himalopsyche.* These *Rhyacophila* species, however, arose long after the tergal strap and apical band had developed, and after some other parts of the genitalia had evolved peculiar modifications. Evidently the similarity in venation has come about by parallel evolution in unrelated groups.

From the progenitor of *Himalopsyche* possessing the characters listed above (see Chart 25, Ancestor A) four distinct lines or branches seem to have arisen.

### Branch 1

The first evolutionary change from the ancestral form was that the tenth tergite became membra-

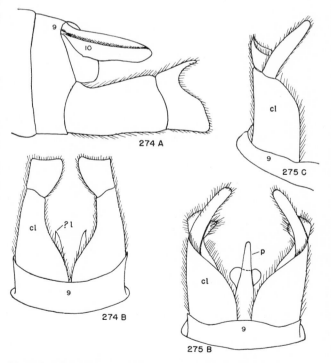

Figs. 274-75. Male genitalia of *Rhyacophila laminata* (274) and *profusa* (275). *A,* lateral aspect; *B,* ventral aspect; *C,* ventral aspect of a second specimen. (After Ulmer.)

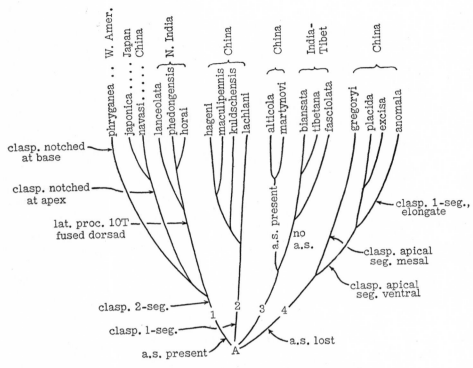

CHART 25. Phylogenetic diagram of *Himalopsyche.*

nous, although it retained about the same total area as before. The claspers of the *lanceolata* group (Fig. 276) are as simple as any found in the genus. In the *lanceolata* group the lateral lobes of the tenth tergite appear to have fused on the meson to form a cap over the membranous tenth tergite, and the anal sclerite is a small, hooked sclerite. The *lanceolata* group includes three species, *lanceolata, phedongensis,* and *horai.* After the *lanceolata* group diverged the line developed a mesal lobe on the clasper. From this ancestral form two groups arose. In one, containing *japonica* (Fig. 279) and the Chinese *navasi* (Fig. 278), the lateral lobes of the tenth tergite became narrow and curved mesad. In the other, containing only the western North American *phryganea* (Fig. 277), the lateral lobes of the tenth tergite became enlarged and the dorsal edge folded downward along the meson, the lobes completely hiding the anal sclerite from lateral view.

### Branch 2

In the progenitor of this branch the tenth tergite and anal sclerite changed little, but the claspers became deeply incised at the base and 1-segmented.

The most primitive species of this Asiatic branch is *lachlani* (Fig. 280); in the other three species of the branch (*hageni, maculipennis,* and *kuldschensis*) the ninth tergite is produced into a mesal process overhanging the tenth tergite (Fig. 282).

### Branch 3

In the early distinctive members of this branch, also known only from Asia, the ninth and tenth tergites became partially fused dorsally, and the lateral processes of the tenth tergite expanded and became cleft to form a bilobed structure. This branch gave rise to two complexes. In the *alticola-martynovi* complex (Fig. 281) the anal sclerite became cleft and the ninth and tenth tergites fused completely. In the *tibetana-biansata-fasciolata* complex (Fig. 283) the anal sclerite atrophied and the ninth and tenth dorsal areas remained relatively distinct.

### Branch 4

In this branch the anal sclerite atrophied, the apex of the tenth tergite became divided into a pair of downcurved points, and the lateral or dorsal margin of the basal clasper segment became elongate so that it reached the tip of the apical clasper segment (Fig. 285). In addition the lateral processes of the tenth tergite became elongate. In *gregoryi* these lateral processes are sinuate and cross the meson, and the apical segment of the clasper is imbedded in the mesal face of the basal segment. The *placida-excisa* complex has the base of

the lateral processes bulbous and the apex slender (Figs. 285, 287), and the apical segment of the clasper is apicoventral in position. This complex was the ancestor of the very odd species *anomala*, in which the apical portion of the lateral process of the tenth tergite is extremely long (Fig. 286); the clasper is equally long, and its dorsal edge is

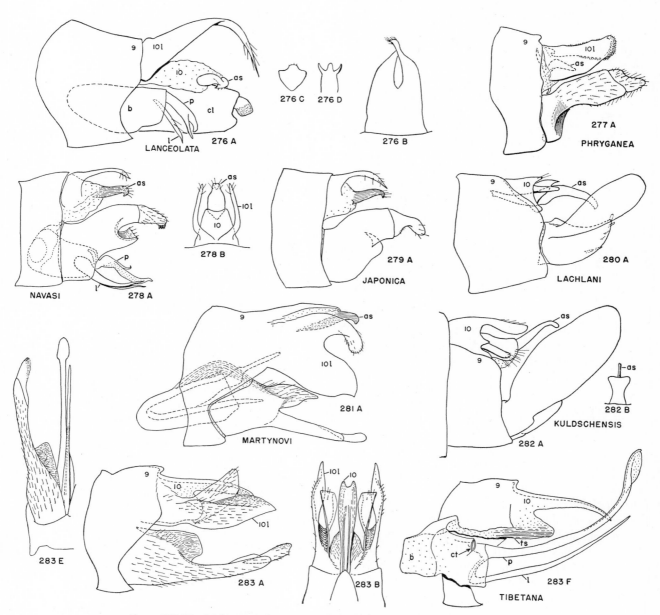

FIGS. 276-83. Male genitalia of *Himalopsyche*. A, lateral aspect; B, C, D, dorsal aspect of tenth tergite, anal sclerite, and aedeagus, respectively; E, ventral aspect; F, cut-away portion, lateral aspect. 10L, lateral lobes of tenth tergite.

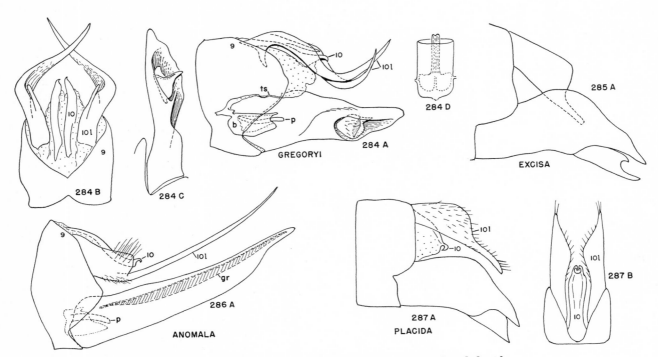

FIGS. 284-87. Male genitalia of *Himalopsyche*. *A, B,* lateral and dorsal aspects, respectively; *C,* clasper, ventral aspect; *D,* aedeagus, ventral aspect. *10L,* lateral lobes of tenth tergite; *gr,* groove on clasper into which fits lateral lobe of tenth tergite.

invaginated to form a narrow trough along the entire length of the clasper; in repose the lateral process fits perfectly into this trough. It is not surprising that the male of this species was originally described as an unusual female with an ovipositor like a grasshopper! The apical segment of the clasper is entirely gone. This branch is entirely Asiatic.

### Dispersal of the Genus

It is evident that *Himalopsyche* originated and developed in southern or southeastern Asia, with two lines developing in the Himalayan region of India and Tibet. One line, however, spread to North America and the species *phryganea* of its American progeny has survived in the western mountain ranges of Oregon and California. It is interesting that this is a relative of the only Asiatic form (*japonica*) occurring as far north as Japan. This situation suggests very strongly that the *japonica* complex has an ecological tolerance conditioned to lower elevations than other members of the genus. Unfortunately, specimens of *navasi* from China have

been erroneously identified as *japonica,* so that existing Chinese records of *japonica* actually refer to the related species *navasi.*

### Dispersal of the Rhyacophilinae

The two genera of this subfamily present a most unusual pattern of extreme isolation of distinctive groups. There are 44 such groups in *Rhyacophila* alone, summarized in Chart 16. With the exception of a few species such as *lieftincki* and *sumatrana* from Sundaland, none of the known forms has spread south of the equator. None of the subfamily has reached Africa, Australia, or South America.

The distribution of the group is principally montane, and the great bulk of the species are clustered in the montane areas of eastern North America, western North America, Europe, and Asia. In Asia there is apparent a subdivision into southern areas embracing the Himalayas, southern China, and southeastern Asia, and a northern area embracing the mountains north of the Gobi Desert and those of northeast Asia, with an area of overlap embracing Japan. Because of this overlapping, the entire

Asian area will be treated as a single distribution area.

Of the 43 species groups in *Rhyacophila,* 5 occur only in Europe, 15 only in Asia, 12 only in western America, and 5 only in eastern America; in all, 37 are confined each to a single region. Four groups occur in two adjoining regions, and 2 in more than two regions. No intermediate steps are known between several groups; it is thus impossible to be sure of the exact relationship of one group with another. In these cases no information can be extracted as to interregion dispersals or areas of origin. For those few cases in which phylogenetic details are available, we find evidence of five dispersals between Asia and America; two between Europe and western America, but with no known Asiatic representatives; two between Europe and eastern America with no known intervening representatives; and one between Asia and Europe, following an America-to-Asia dispersal. Essentially the same situation is seen in *Himalopsyche.*

This rhyacophiline pattern is at variance, to a certain extent, with that of the Philopotamidae, in which the distribution pattern reflects wide dispersal of several forms, although many philopotamid groups have persisted as isolated relics.

I believe that several sound conclusions may be drawn from the data shown in Chart 16:

1. The restriction of the groups is a function of the narrow ecological tolerance of the entire group, and its dependence on montane conditions.

2. The great morphological differences displayed by a large number of groups is indicative of considerable geologic age. If this amount of difference occurred in only a few groups it would carry less weight, but here it is the rule rather than the exception.

3. There is evidence, therefore, that the dependence on montane conditions is of equal age, and that it has probably been a characteristic of the great bulk of the subfamily since it became established as a distinct phyletic line.

These points may be summarized in another fashion, namely, that the Rhyacophilinae are a collection of species flocks of considerable age, which have only rarely spread from one circumscribed area to another.

The bulk of the evidence indicates that dispersal between the Nearctic and Palearctic regions has been across the Bering Bridge. The dispersal points indicated by "*a*" on Chart 16 are especially good evidence that this route was followed by many spreading populations. In the *sibirica* group there is evidence that allied forms spread and respread across this area at moderately regular intervals.

Pairs of related groups, one occurring in Europe and the other in eastern North America, keep alive the possibility of a past land connection between Labrador and northwest Europe, which might have been the avenue of dispersal for these forms. It is, of course, entirely possible that distribution patterns like those of the *stigmatica* and *glaberrima* groups represent only peculiarities in survival pattern. It is also possible that these groups actually occur in other areas but have not yet been discovered.

## The Subfamily Hydrobiosinae

This is the warm-adapted branch of the Rhyacophilidae, occurring primarily in the tropical and subtropical regions of Asia, Australia, and the New World. It is true, however, that all information indicates that most of the species require clear, rapid, cool streams, even though in tropical lands. Thus the restriction of the subfamily to tropical and subtropical regions may be simply an inability to survive prolonged frost conditions. If this is true, the group occupies a narrow ecological zone bounded on the one hand by need for cool, well-aerated water, and on the other by an inability to withstand icy water. Perhaps such a narrow ecological tolerance accounts for the small amount of intercontinental dispersal displayed by the group, and its marked preference for mountainous or hilly country.

The predaceous larvae are free-living, and possess chelate front legs quite unusual for the order (Fig. 158). In the adults many differences have evolved in venation and other nongenitalic parts, so that, unlike the species of the Rhyacophilinae, the species of Hydrobiosinae may be grouped into a number of well-marked genera.

As an extended account of the evolution and dispersal of the subfamily was published in 1951, only a summary of the results of that paper (Ross 1951*e*) as modified by later discoveries reported in Mosely and Kimmins (1953) is included here. Pages 123-26 contain the pertinent taxonomic comments.

Early in its history the subfamily divided into

two branches (Chart 26). In the *Apsilochorema* branch the male genitalia developed no new lobes above the filicerci and in many species the veins of the front wing moved forward so that M₁ was above the wing apex (Fig. 157) and the branches of Rs were all on the leading edge. In the *Hydrobiosis* line the wing veins remained normal in this respect, but the male genitalia developed an additional pair of appendages or lobes above the cerci and filicerci, called the paracerci (Figs. 289, 290). In some genera (e.g., *Notiobiosis*, Fig. 291) additional pairs of appendages evolved.

dispersal path as *Chimarra*, and probably spread with it from southeastern Asia. At the time of my earlier treatment of the group, there were no records available for Australia, a fact which became more and more puzzling as records for both *Chimarra* and *Agapetus* indicated that there had been a spread of many New Guinea genera into Aus-

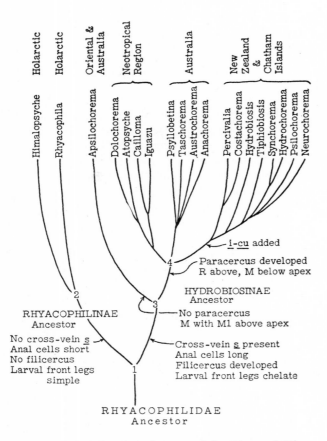

CHART 26. Phylogenetic diagram of the *Rhyacophilidae*.

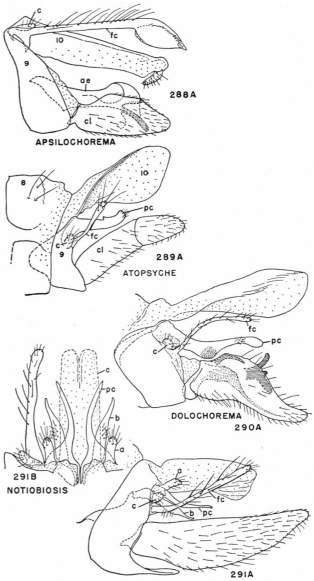

FIGS. 288-91. Male genitalia of Hydrobiosinae; *Apsilochorema malayanum* (288), *Atopsyche erigia* (289), *Dolochorema irregularis* (290), *Notiobiosis nigrita* (291). A, lateral aspect; B, dorsal aspect, with topmost part, the tenth tergite, shown by broken line. *c*, cercus; *cl*, clasper; *fc*, filicercus; *pc*, paracercus.

The *Apsilochorema* branch is represented by a single variable genus, *Apsilochorema*, known from Bukhara and India, through Malay, with a branch extending to Formosa, Japan, and South Ussuri, and another extending eastward through New Guinea to Australia and the Fiji Islands. In these two latter areas the genus has followed the same

tralia. The records of *Apsilochorema* from Australia given by Mosely and Kimmins clarify this point and indicate a unity of dispersal between several elements of the Australian caddisfly fauna. There is a question concerning the number of species involved in the dispersal. Although not enough species are yet known for us to be sure, nevertheless there is a definite possibility that several species of *Apsilochorema* spread simultaneously into the Pacific area, resulting in polyphyletic colonizations of Fiji and Australia.

The *Hydrobiosis* branch has developed into three groups of genera. Four genera are in the Neotropical Americas, four in Australia, and eight in New Zealand, as shown in Chart 26. The relationships within each group indicate that the cluster of genera in each area evolved independently from a similar primitive ancestor, and that since the original dispersal and isolation, there has been no respread of forms from one area to another. All three presumably are the result of the spread of a single ancestral species which was the progenitor of the whole series.

There seem to be only two alternatives to explain how *Apsilochorema* can today occupy a position between the surviving segments of the *Hydrobiosis*-line genera. The alternative suggested in the 1951 paper was that the ancestor of *Apsilochorema* was isolated in peninsular India by the Tethys Sea while the ancestor of the *Hydrobiosis*-line spread around the northern ring of the Pacific.

The only other reasonable alternative is that the *Hydrobiosis*-line ancestor spread across an Antarctic bridge to South America. This alternative is still very much of a possibility, although objections to it are raised by many investigators. This alternative is discussed at greater length in the following chapter.

## Ecological Zonation in the Rhyacophilidae

Species groups or genera of both subfamilies have been isolated and confined in their distribution to an unusual degree, and this circumstance has permitted us to gain considerable insight into their movements in the past.

Comparing the two subfamilies, it is seen that the more primitive Rhyacophilinae have spread throughout the cooler climatic zones and have been restricted completely to land masses of the Northern Hemisphere. The Hydrobiosinae, on the other

hand, have become adapted to and dependent on subtropical climates, and have spread into both Australasia and South America.

## SYSTEMATIC ACCOUNT

### KEY TO SUBFAMILIES

Front wing with anal cells short and with intercostal vein present, but with no cross-vein *s* (Fig. 154) .......................... **Rhyacophilinae**
Front wing with anal cell long, with no intercostal vein, and often having cross-vein *s* (Fig. 156) ....... .......................... **Hydrobiosinae**

### Subfamily Rhyacophilinae

#### KEY TO GENERA

Metascutellum with a pair of warts; front wing with veins curved posteriorly so that $R_5$ ends posterior to apex of wing (Fig. 155) ....... **Himalopsyche**
Metascutellum without warts; front wing usually with veins normal, so that $R_5$ ends at or anterior to apex of wing (Fig. 154) .......... **Rhyacophila**

### Genus **Rhyacophila** Pictet

*Rhyacophila* Pictet (1834:181). Type species: *Rhyacophila vulgaris* Pictet (subsequent designation of Ross 1944).

In this study I have attempted to determine the relationships between the various species of *Rhyacophila* for the purpose of arranging them in phylogenetic sequence. The results have been expressed in phyletic lines which I have designated as numbered branches. I have been unable to define the branches as convenient taxonomic units because of the difficulty of constructing keys for their identification, hence treat them in this list in the same arrangement used on previous pages.

Should it be desirable in the future to employ subgeneric terms for categories within the genus or as finer generic segregates, the following list of names is available:
*Doliocypta* Banks (1939b:502).

Type species: *Rhyacophila liliputana* Banks. Original designation.
*Trichophila* Kimmins (1952:359).

Type species: *Trichophila fletcheri* Kimmins. Original designation.
*Prosrhyacophila* Dohler (1950:274).

Type species: *Rhyacophila laevis* Pictet. Monobasic.

In addition Dohler (1950) has proposed the following four names based on larval characters:

*Hyperrhyacophila*: larva not identified with certainty, perhaps belonging to the *torrentium* group.

*Pararhyacophila*: for the *intermedia* formenkreis.

*Metarhyacophila*: possibly the *stigmatica* group.

*Hyporhyacophila*: for the *hirticornis* and *philopotamoides* groups.

Type species have not been designated for these four names.

For aid in the identification of species there are available a number of keys or synopses dealing with the fauna of a particular region. The following are especially useful: for Europe, McLachlan (1874-80); for northern Eurasia, Martynov (1934); for Japan, Tsuda (1942); for North America, Betten (1934), Ross (1944), and Denning (1948b).

## LIST OF SPECIES

### Branch 1

#### Lobifera Group

*Distribution*: North America.

**lobifera** Betten (1934:131). Central United States. Fig. 161.

#### Anatina Group

*Distribution*: Southern Asia.

**anatina** Morton (1900:6); Martynov (1935:95); Kimmins (1953b:528). Northern India.

**elongata** Kimmins (1953b:529). Northeastern Burma.

#### Alberta Group

*Distribution*: North America.

**alberta** Banks (1918:21); Ross (1950a:261). Western North America. Fig. 162, A-C.

*Rhyacophila mirus* Denning (1948a:21).

**tucula** Ross (1950a:261). Western North America. Fig. 162, D.

#### Torva Group

*Distribution*: North America.

**ecosa** Ross (1941:37). Western North America. Fig. 164.

**torva** Hagen (1861:296); Betten (1934:133). Eastern North America. Fig. 163.

*Rhyacophila terminata* Banks (1907:132).

*Rhyacophila vinura* Milne (1936:100).

#### Montana Group

*Distribution*: North America.

**montana** Carpenter (1933:42); Ross (1944:Fig. 121). North Carolina. Fig. 165.

#### Fletcheri Group

*Distribution*: Asia.

**fletcheri** (Kimmins), *Trichophila* (1952:359). Sikkim, India.

#### Glaberrima Group

*Distribution*: North America.

**glaberrima** Ulmer (1907b:85); Ross (1944:35). Eastern North America. Fig. 166.

*Rhyacophila fairchildi* Banks (1930a:130).

*Rhyacophila andrea* Betten (1934:127).

#### Stigmatica Group

*Distribution*: Europe.

**bonaparti** Schmid (1947:524). Switzerland.

**eatoni** McLachlan (1879:463). Pyrenees Mountains.

**furcifera** Klapalek (1904:719); Botosaneanu (1952a:247). Roumania.

**meyeri** McLachlan (1879:461); Schmid (1947:523). Switzerland.

**stigmatica** (Kolenati), *Crunophila* (1859:197); McLachlan (1879:461); Schmid (1947:523). Austria (Noric Alps). Fig. 167.

**vandeli** Despax (1933:625). Pyrenees Mountains.

### Branch 2

#### Nevadensis Group

*Distribution*: North America.

**jewetti** Denning (1954:57). Oregon.

**nevadensis** Banks (1924:443). California, Nevada. Fig. 168.

**vaefes** Milne (1936:96); Denning (1948b:105, 109). Oregon, Washington, British Columbia. Fig. 169.

*Rhyacophila vujuna* Milne (1936:99).

A restudy of the two holotypes shows that in the type of *vujuna* the tenth tergite was contracted at the corners, giving the dorsal aspect a triangular appearance. Treatment with weak, hot KOH solution relaxed the parts, making it possible to prove that the type of *vujuna* is virtually identical with the type of *vaefes*.

#### Vofixa Group

*Distribution*: Western North America.

**harmstoni** Ross (1944:268). Colorado, Utah. Fig. 171.

**iranda** Ross (1938a:103). Oregon, Washington.

**vobara** Milne (1936:94); Denning (1948b:106). British Columbia, Yukon Territory.

**vofixa** Milne (1936:95); Alberta and Washington, to Alaska. Fig. 170.

#### Tristis Group

*Distribution*: Europe.

**aquitanica** McLachlan (1879:457). France and the Tyrol. Fig. 172.

**tristis** Pictet (1834:184). Central and southern Europe. Fig. 173.

*Rhyacophila umbrosa* Pictet (1834:185).

*Rhyacophila angularis* Pictet (1834:186).

*?Rhyacophila biguttata* Pictet (1834:188).

### Branch 3

#### Curvata Group

*Distribution*: Asia.

**cameroni** Banks (1931a:403). Malaya. Fig. 174.

**curvata** Morton (1900:5); Kimmins (1953b:526). Assam (India).

**malayana** Banks (1931a:402). Malaya. Fig. 175.

**mishmica** Kimmins (1953*b*:516). Assam (India). Fig. 176.
**mortoni** Kimmins (1953*b*:526). Assam (India).
*Rhyacophila curvata* Martynov (1935:103), *nec* Morton.
**sinuata** Kimmins (1953*b*:527). Burma.
**sumatrana** Ulmer (1930:416). Sumatra.

### Divaricata Group

*Distribution*: Asia.
**apicalis** Kimmins (1953*b*:534). Northeastern Burma.
**assimilis** Kimmins (1953*b*:553). Northeastern Burma.
**bicolor** Kimmins (1953*b*:532). Northeastern Burma.
**discoidalis** Kimmins (1953*b*:536). Northeastern Burma.
**divaricata** Kimmins (1953*b*:552). Northeastern Burma.
**inconspicua** Morton (1900:7); Kimmins (1953*b*:534). Assam (India).
**labeculata** Kimmins (1953*b*:538). Northeastern Burma.
**manicata** Kimmins (1953*b*:531). Northeastern Burma.
**orientalis** Kimmins (1953*b*:530). Northeastern Burma.
**parva** Kimmins (1953*b*:536). Assam (India).
**rhombica** Martynov (1935:98). Bengal (India).
**uncata** Kimmins (1953*b*:538). Northeastern Burma.
**ungulata** Kimmins (1953*b*:548). Northeastern Burma.

### Acropedes Group

*Distribution*: Asia and North America.
**acropedes** Banks (1914:201). North America. Figs. 183, 185.
**articulata** Morton (1900:5); Tsuda (1940:132). Japan. Fig. 178.
*Rhyacophila towadensis* Iwata (1927*a*:204).
**gemona** Ross (1938*b*:117). Western North America.
**grandis** Banks (1911:350). Western North America. Fig. 182.
*Rhyacophila vohrna* Milne (1936:94).
**inculta** Ross and Spencer (1952:43). Western North America.
**lezeyi** Navas (1933*b*:94). Japan. Fig. 179.
**neograndis** Denning (1948*b*:110). California.
**sequoia** Denning (1950*b*:116). California.
**vao** Milne (1936:93). Western North America. Fig. 184.
*Rhyacophila vu* Milne (1936:93).
**vemna** Milne (1936:92). Western North America. Fig. 181.
**yamazakii** Tsuda (1941:159). Manchuria. Fig. 177.

### Rhyacophila vaoides new species

*Male*: Length 15 mm. Color dark brown, the venter slightly lighter than the dorsum, the wings deep smoky. General structure typical for the group. Genitalia as in Fig. 180. Ninth segment forming a nearly even ring, slightly incised just below the articulation of the tenth tergite, the apex of the ninth tergite forming a sharp angle slightly overhanging base of tenth. Lobes of tenth tergite moderately deep and fairly short, rounded at apex,

with a moderately sclerotized apical band on the membranous lobe beneath the base of the tergite. Clasper: basal segment only slightly incised ventrally; apical segment with the dorsal portion angulate and the ventral portion produced into a blunt angulation. Aedeagus as illustrated for *acropedes* (see Fig. 185).

*Holotype, male*: Nikko, Japan, July 19, 1931 (L. Gressitt). In the collection of the Museum of Comparative Zoology.

In shape of ninth and tenth tergites this species approaches most closely the North American *vao*, but differs from it in the less constricted basal segment of the clasper and in the wider dorsal portion of the apical segment of the clasper.

### Branch 4
#### Fuscula Group

*Distribution*: North America.
**fuscula** (Walker), *Phryganea* (1852:10); Betten (1934:130); Betten & Mosely (1940:3); Ross (1944:36). Eastern North America. Fig. 186.
**vuphipes** Milne (1936:99). Eastern North America. Fig. 187.
*Rhyacophila* sp. 2 Betten (1934:134).

#### Vulgaris Group

*Distribution*: Europe.
**acutidens** McLachlan (1879:441). Italy.
**adjuncta** McLachlan (1884:63). Portugal.
**albardana** McLachlan (1879:437). Central Europe.
**aliena** Martynov (1916:187; 1934:45). Southern Russia.
**appenina** McLachlan (1898:51). Italy.
**aurata** Brauer (1857:37); McLachlan (1879:448). Central Europe.
**casaci** Navas (1934:156); Schmid (1949:307). Italy.
**contracta** McLachlan (1879:449). Pyrenees.
**cupressorum** Martynov (1913*a*:40; 1934:46). Caucasus.
**denticulata** McLachlan (1879:443). Pyrenees.
**dorsalis** (Curtis), *Philopotamus* (1834:213). Western Europe.
*Rhyacophila obtusidens* McLachlan (1879:440).
*Rhyacophila persimilis* McLachlan (1879:440).
*Rhyacophila persimilis* form *integra* Despax (1944:272).
**evoluta** McLachlan (1879:438). Central Europe.
**fasciata** Hagen (1859*a*:153); McLachlan (1879:443). Europe. Fig. 188.
**forcipulata** Martynov (1926:22; 1934:46). Caucasus.
**fraudulenta** McLachlan (1879:450). Central Europe.
**furcata** Dziedzielewicz (1911:107). Eastern Carpathians.
**hageni** McLachlan (1879:447). Central Europe. Fig. 189.
**intermedia** McLachlan (1868:306; 1879:449). Central Europe.
**laufferi** Navas (1918*b*:7). Spain.

**lusitanica** McLachlan (1884:63). Portugal.
**martynovi** Mosely (1930b:242). France.
**meridionalis** Pictet (1865:101); McLachlan, (1879: 454). Pyrenees.
  *Rhyacophila adunca* Navas (1930a:165).
**mocsaryi** Klapalek (1898:437). Roumania.
**munda** McLachlan (1862b:309; 1879:455). Europe.
**nubila** (Zetterstedt), *Phryganea* (1840:1068); McLachlan (1879:441). Europe.
  *Rhyacophila paupera* Hagen (1859a:153).
**obliterata** McLachlan (1863:134; 1879:445). Western Europe.
**occidentalis** McLachlan (1879:438). Pyrenees.
**pallida** Mosely (1930a:171). Corsica.
**palmeni** McLachlan (1879:440). Central Europe.
**pascoei** McLachlan (1879:451). Central Europe.
  *Rhyacophila palazoni* Navas (1934:157).
**polonica** McLachlan (1879:446). Poland.
**praemorsa** McLachlan (1879:447). Western Europe.
**proxima** McLachlan (1880, supp. pt. 2:76). Central Europe.
**rectispina** McLachlan (1884:60). Northern Italy.
**relicta** McLachlan (1879:442). Pyrenees.
**rougemonti** McLachlan (1880, supp. pt. 2:77). Switzerland.
**rupta** McLachlan (1879:450). Pyrenees.
**septentrionis** McLachlan (1865:157; 1879:444). Europe.
**simulatrix** McLachlan (1879:453). Southern Europe.
**subnubila** Martynov (1934:42). Vladikavkaz.
**subovata** Martynov (1913a:5; 1934:45). Caucasus.
**torrentium** Pictet (1834:184); McLachlan (1879:436). Europe.
  *Rhyacophila armeniaca* Guerin (1837:396).
**trifasciata** Mosely (1930a:170). Corsica.
**vicaria** Martynov (1927a:119; 1934:42). Caucasus.
**vulgaris** Pictet (1834:182); McLachlan (1879:452). Europe.
  *Rhyacophila venusta* Hagen (1859a:154).

## Rotunda Group

*Distribution*: North America.
**basalis** Banks (1911:352). California.
**ebria** Denning (1949b:37). Montana.
**latitergum** Davis (1950:448). Washington.
**oreta** Ross (1941:39). Western North America. Fig. 191.
**norcuta** Ross (1938b:117). Western North America. Fig. 190.
  *Rhyacophila novarotunda* Ling (1938:61).
**rotunda** Banks (1924:443). Western North America.

### Branch 5

#### Viquaea Group

*Distribution*: North America.
**viquaea** Milne (1936:92). Oregon, Washington. Fig. 192.
  *Rhyacophila celina* Denning (1954:57). *New synonymy.*

#### Clemens Group

*Distribution*: Asia.
**clemens** Tsuda (1940a:124). Japan. Fig. 193.

### Branch 6

#### Rayneri Group

*Distribution*: North America.
**rayneri** Ross (1951a:66). Lower California. (Mexico). Fig. 194.

#### Invaria Group

*Distribution*: North America.
  **Invaria subgroup** (Eastern North America).
**banksi** Ross (1944:268). Northeastern North America.
**carpenteri** Milne (1936:98). Northeastern North America. Fig. 196.
**invaria** (Walker), *Polycentropus* (1852:101); Betten & Mosely, (1940:5). Northeastern North America.
  *Rhyacophila luctuosa* Banks (1911:351).
**mycta** Ross (1941:38). North Carolina.
**nigrita** Banks (1907:132). Eastern North America.
**parantra** Ross (1948:17). Indiana. Fig. 197.
**vibox** Milne (1936:101); Ross (1944:36). North Carolina and Northeastern North America.
  **Bifila subgroup** (Western North America).
**bifila** Banks (1914:201). Western North America.
**coloradensis** Banks (1905:10). Western North America. Fig. 195.
  *Rhyacophila stigmatica* Banks (1904:108). Preoccupied.
  *Rhyacophila anomala* Banks (1924:444).
**kernada** Ross (1950a:264). California.

#### Hyalinata Group

*Distribution*: North America and Europe.
**clavalis** Martynov (1913b:7; 1934:62). Caucasus. (Placed in this group with doubt; specimens not seen.)
**hyalinata** Banks (1905:10). Western North America. Fig. 198.
**sonoma** Denning (1948b:110). California.
**vocala** Milne (1936:100); Denning (1948b:106). British Columbia, Washington.

#### Glareosa Group

*Distribution*: Europe.
**glareosa** McLachlan (1867:62; 1879:459). Alps. Fig. 199.

#### Carolina Group

*Distribution*: North America.
**carolina** Banks (1911:353); Ross (1939a:66). Eastern North America.
  *Rhyacophila gordoni* Sibley (1926:79).
  *Rhyacophila carula* Denning (1947:660).
The type of *carula* was recorded from Puerto Rico in the original description. I have examined this type and find it to be identical in every point compared with specimens of *carolina* from North Carolina and Tennessee. I believe that the association of the locality label for Puerto Rico with the type of *carula* was an accident of labeling, and that the

type actually came from the southeastern United States. Should my surmise prove wrong, this would represent a most interesting range extension for *carolina*.

**fenestra** Ross (1938*a*:102). Illinois. Fig. 201.
**kiamichi** Ross (1944:37). Oklahoma.
**ledra** Ross (1939*a*:65). North Carolina and Northeastern North America. Fig. 200.
*Rhyacophila hardeni* Denning (1948*b*:101).
Series of specimens from several localities in Ohio indicate that the differences in shape of claspers originally thought to separate *ledra* and *hardeni* are extremes of variation found in the same populations.
**teddyi** Ross (1939*b*:628). North Carolina, Tennessee.

### Philopotamoides Group
*Distribution*: Europe.
**hirticornis** McLachlan (1879:464). Alps.
**orghidani** Botosaneanu (1952*b*:721). Roumania. Not seen, placement doubtful.
**philopotamoides** McLachlan (1879:463). Pyrenees. Fig. 205.
**pubescens** Pictet (1834:186); McLachlan (1879:458). Europe. Fig. 202.

### Pepingensis Group
*Distribution*: Asia.
**marcida** Banks (1947:103). Szechwan (China). Fig. 204.
**pepingensis** Ulmer (1933:39). China. Fig. 203.

### Castanea Group
*Distribution*: Asia.
**argentipunctella** Kimmins (1955:376). Sarawak.
**castanea** Hagen (1858:487). Ceylon. Fig. 206.
**davao** Ross (1950*b*:132). Philippine Islands. Fig. 207.
**lilliputana** Banks (1939*b*:502). Southern Kiangsi (China). Fig. 209.
**minuta** Banks (1939*b*:503). Hainan Islands (China). Fig. 208.

### Scissa Group
*Distribution*: Asia.
**bidens** Kimmins (1953*b*:521). Northeastern Burma and India.
**burmana** Kimmins (1953*b*:525).
**obscura** Martynov (1927*b*:163); Kimmins (1953*b*:520). Taschkent and Northern India.
**scissa** Morton (1900:5); Kimmins (1953*b*:518). Assam (India) and Northeastern Burma.
**scissoides** Kimmins (1953*b*:520). Assam (India).

### Branch 7
### Yosiiana Group
*Distribution*: Asia.
**kuramana** Tsuda (1942:247). Japan.
**ulmeri** Navas (1907:399). China. Fig. 213.
**yosiiana** Tsuda (1940*a*:119). Japan. Fig. 212.

### Rhyacophila kohnoae new species
*Male*: Length 11 mm. Color dark brown, the legs bearing coxae somewhat paler, nearly straw color. General structure typical for genus. Genitalia as in Fig. 211. Ninth segment with dorsal portion widest, central portion narrowest, widening slightly to the ventral margin. Tenth tergite from lateral view appearing short and stubby, the apex rounded; the ventral aspect at the base very wide, almost bulbous, narrowing to a spatulate and slightly incised apex. Clasper: basal segment fairly long and slender; apical segment only half as long and indented below the dorsal corner to make a shoe-shaped structure with a narrow dorsal heel and broad ventral toe. Aedeagus with basal cup chiefly membranous; the dorsum forms a sclerotized strap with which articulates the U-shaped apical band; phalicata narrow, its apex divided into a small pointed mesal lobe and a pair of slightly rounded lateral processes; lateral processes both ventral in position and bearing a scattering of about six large spines.

*Holotype, male*: Higas Yama, Japan, April 20, 1949 (Mitsuko Kohno). In the collection of the Illinois Natural History Survey.

This species is most closely related to *yosiiana*, differing in the shape of the tenth tergite.

This species is named in honor of Mitsuko Kohno, in recognition for her fine work on the aquatic insects of Japan.

### Rhyacophila tsudai new species
*Male*: Length 9 mm. Color moderately light brown. General structure typical for genus. Genitalia as in Fig. 210. Ninth segment widest at point of articulation of tenth tergite, narrowing below the meson and widening slightly toward the venter. Tenth tergite with the base widened and vasiform, the dorsum and posterior portion narrowed and excavated on the posterior face to form a deep wide groove. Clasper: basal segment short and nearly parallel-sided; apical segment much deeper, with a narrow cleft below the midline, and bearing on each side of this cleft an apical area of black spicules. Aedeagus with basal cup produced dorsally into a long tonguelike process with which the apical band articulates; phalicata quadrate and curved, the apex divided into an upturned narrow mesoventral lobe and a pair of winglike lateral processes; the two lateral processes of the aedeagus are elongate, ventral in position, and the apical two-thirds is armed with a scattering of long setae.

*Holotype, male*: Kibune, Kyoto, Japan, June 14, 1935 (M. Tsuda). In the collection of the Illinois Natural History Survey.

This species is most closely related to *kohnoae*, differing in the shape of the tenth tergite and the more ventral position of the cleft on the apical segment of the clasper.

This species is named in honor of Professor Tsuda who has done so much excellent work on the caddisflies of Japan.

### Sibirica Group

*Distribution*: Europe, Asia, and North America.
**abchasica** Martynov (1934:61). Abkhasia (Siberia). Fig. 216.
**atrata** Banks (1911:351); Ross (1938c:4). Fig. 220.
**belona** Ross (1948:19). Montana. Fig. 232.
**blarina** Ross (1941:36). Western North America. Fig. 227.
**depressa** Martynov (1910:420; 1934:57). Ussuri (Siberia). Fig. 218.
**kardakoffi** Navas (1926:57); Martynov (1934:54). Ussuri (Siberia). Not seen.
**kisoensis** Tsuda (1940a:132). Japan. Fig. 229.
**laevis** Pictet (1834:187); McLachlan (1879:466). Europe. Fig. 236.
  *Rhyacophila obfuscata* Pictet (1834:188).
  *Rhyacophila latipennis* Pictet (1834:189).
  ?*Rhyacophila flavipes* Pictet (1834:187).
**lenae** Martynov (1910:417; 1934:54). Siberia. Not seen.
**manistee** Ross (1938a:104). Northcentral and Northeastern North America. Fig. 225.
**melita** Ross (1938a:104). Northcentral and Eastern North America. Fig. 221.
**minora** Banks (1924:444). Eastern North America. Fig. 226.
  *Rhyacophila* sp. 1, Betten (1934:134).
**narvae** Navas (1926:57); Martynov (1934:53). Eastern Siberia.
**ophrys** Ross (1948:19). Montana. Fig. 215.
**oreia** Ross (1947:126). Wyoming. Fig. 214.
**pellisa** Ross (1938b:118). Western North America. Fig. 224.
  *Rhyacophila doddsi* Ling (1938:61).
**producta** McLachlan (1879:460). Carinthia (Austria). Fig. 235.
**sibirica** McLachlan (1879:465). Northwestern Siberia. Fig. 228.
**transquilla** Tsuda (1940a:131). Japan. Fig. 231.
**unimaculata** Denning (1941:198). British Columbia. Fig. 234.
**valuma** Milne (1936:100). Western North America. Fig. 223.
**velora** Denning (1954:58). California.
**vepulsa** Milne (1936:96). Western North America. Fig. 230.
**vetina** Milne (1936:91). Western North America. Fig. 233.
**visor** Milne (1936:101). Western North America. Fig. 217.
**yukii** Tsuda (1942:248). Japan.

### Rhyacophila amicis new species

*Male*: Length 10 mm. Color moderately dark brown above, paler below. General structure typical for genus. Genitalia as in Fig. 222. Ninth segment widest dorsally, narrowed abruptly below junction with tenth tergite and of about equal width from there to venter. Tenth tergite short, broad, shallow, its apical margin produced to form a pair of short processes, one on each side of the meson. Clasper elongate, nearly parallel-sided and with the apical segment almost completely fused with the basal one. Aedeagus with the basal cup bearing a dorsal process composed of a broad, flat basal projection, and an apical produced portion pointed at apex and bearing a single large preapical dorsal knob; phalicata narrow and spinelike, ventral process elongate and deeply divided to form a short basal portion and a pair of very long slender apical processes.

*Holotype, male*: Black Mountain, North Carolina, May 20, 1952 (Cornelius Betten). In the collection of Dr. Betten, Asheville, North Carolina.

This species is most closely related to *atrata* from which it differs in the fused segments of the clasper. This was first noticed by Dr. Betten who kindly sent me the specimen for inclusion in this report.

### Rhyacophila rickeri new species

*Male*: Length 11 mm. Color light brown, wings only faintly smoky. General structure typical for genus. Genitalia as in Fig. 219. Ninth segment widest on dorsal half, and bearing a short blunt dorsal projection extending over the tenth tergite. Tenth tergite very short, small, divided into a pair of small earlike lateral lobes and a pair of approximate smaller lobes on each side of the meson. Anal sclerites represented by a pair of small dorsal lobes and a pair of apparently detached small sclerotized bars set in the anal membrane. Apical band attached to aedeagus cup. Clasper with basal segment fairly long and narrowing toward apex, apical segment narrower and set at a slight angle to basal segment. Aedeagus with a short cup bearing a long, wide dorsal process expanded at apex; phalicata long and rodlike, with a dorsal hump at base;

lateral process of aedeagus fused to form an extensile membranous base surmounted by an oval cluster of spines.

*Holotype, male*: Babine River at slide, 50 miles north of Hazelton, British Columbia (W. E. Ricker). *Paratypes*: Reed Creek, below Snow Bird Mine, Talkeetna Mountains, near Palmer, Alaska, Oct. 12, 1950 (D. A. Sleeper), 2♂. In the collection of the Illinois Natural History Survey.

This species is most closely related to *atrata*, differing from it in the smaller tenth tergite, shape of the clasper, and many other characters of the male genitalia.

### Branch 8
#### Bilobata Group
*Distribution*: Asia.
**bilobata** Ulmer (1907a:84). Japan. Fig. 238.
**diffidens** Tsuda (1940a:128). Japan.
**pacata** Tsuda (1940a:121). Japan. Fig. 237.

#### Quieta Group
*Distribution*: Asia.
**angulata** Martynov (1910:414; 1934:52). Ussuri (Siberia).
**quieta** Tsuda (1940a:126). Japan. Fig. 239.

#### Betteni Group
*Distribution*: North America.
**betteni** Ling (1938:59). California. Fig. 242.
**chilsia** Denning (1950b:116). Alberta. Fig. 241.
**fenderi** Ross (1948:18). Oregon. Fig. 240.
**karila** Denning (1948b:109). California.
**malkini** Ross (1947:126). Oregon. Fig. 244.
**perda** Ross (1938a:105). Western North America. Fig. 243.
**vaccua** Milne (1936:94). Western North America.
*Rhyacophila complicata* Ling (1938:60).
*Rhyacophila bruesi* Milne & Milne (1940:154).
**vedra** Milne (1936:97); Denning (1948b:105). Western North America. Fig. 245.
*Rhyacophila californica* Ling (1938:60).

#### Truncata Group
*Distribution*: Asia.
**annulicornis** Kimmins (1953b:522). Northeastern Burma. Fig. 246.
**truncata** Kimmins (1953b:523). Northeastern Burma.

### Branch 9
#### Vobara Group
*Distribution*: North America.
**iranda** Ross (1938a:103). Western North America. Fig. 247.
**vobara** Milne (1936:94); Denning (1948b:106). Western North America.

#### Willametta Group
*Distribution*: North America.
**willametta** Ross (1950a:261). Oregon. Fig. 248.

#### Angelita Group
*Distribution*: North America.
**angelita** Banks (1911:352); Denning (1948b:97). North America. Fig. 249.
*Rhyacophila bipartita* Banks (1914:201).
**vuzana** Milne (1936:97); Denning (1948b:109). Oregon, British Columbia.
**perplana** Ross & Spencer (1952:44). British Columbia.

#### Retracta Group
*Distribution*: Asia.
**retracta** Martynov (1914a:4; 1934:66). Eastern Asia. Fig. 250.
*Rhyacophila uenoi* Tsuda (1940a:123).

#### Alexanderi Group
*Distribution*: North America.
**alexanderi** Denning (1950b:115). Montana. Fig. 251.

#### Hingstoni Group
*Distribution*: Asia.
**hingstoni** Martynov (1930:67); Kimmins (1953b:545). Tibet and Northern India. Fig. 252.
**hobsoni** Martynov (1930:69); Kimmins (1953b:546). Tibet.
**sinensis** Martynov (1931:1). Szechwan (China). Fig. 253.

#### Naviculata Group
*Distribution*: Asia and North America.
**alticola** Kimmins (1953b:544). Tibet.
**arnaudi** Denning (1948b:97). Western North America. Fig. 254.
**avicularis** Kimmins (1953b:550). Northeastern Burma. Fig. 265.
**bifida** Kimmins (1953b:541). Northeastern Burma. Fig. 257.
**carletoni** Banks (1931b:69). Northern India. Fig. 259.
**cruciata** Forsslund (1935:2). China.
**falita** new name. Tonkin. Fig. 256.
*furcifera* Navas (1932a:930). Preoccupied.
**hamifera** Kimmins (1953b:551). Northeastern Burma. Fig. 264.
**lieftincki** Ulmer (1951:44). Java. Fig. 255.
**naviculata** Morton (1900:7); Kimmins (1953b:549). India. Fig. 263.
**procliva** Kimmins (1953b:542). Northeastern Burma. Fig. 260.
**spinalis** Martynov (1930:69); Kimmins (1953b:540). Tibet. Fig. 262.
**stenostyla** Martynov (1930:70); Kimmins (1953b:540). Tibet. Fig. 258.
**styligera** Kimmins (1953b:547). Northeastern Burma. Fig. 261.

#### Nigrocephala Group
*Distribution*: Asia.
**cornuta** Kimmins (1953b:514). Northeastern Burma.

**flaviventris** Kimmins (1953b:514). Northeastern Burma.
**formosana** Ulmer (1927:173). Formosa. Fig. 269.
**kawamurae** Tsuda (1940a:130). Japan.
**lata** Martynov (1922:434; 1934:66). Ussuri (Siberia). Fig. 268.
**ligifera** Kimmins (1953b:516). Northeastern Burma.
**manuleata** Martynov (1934:69). Ussuri (Siberia).
**nigrocephala** Iwata (1927a:204). Japan. Fig. 266.
*Rhyacophila modesta* Tsuda (1940a:129).

This synonymy was expressed in a letter from Dr. Tsuda, to whom I am greatly obliged for the information.

**nipponica** Navas (1933b:93). Japan. Fig. 267.
**putata** Kimmins (1953b:512). Northern India.
**scotina** Kimmins (1953b:513). Northern India.
**tecta** Morton (1900:4); Kimmins (1953b:511). Northern India and Northeastern Burma.

## Rhyacophila kimminsi new species

*Male*: Length 12 mm. Color dark brown above, slightly lighter brown below; wings dark smoky. General structure typical for genus. Genitalia as in Fig. 271. Ninth segment forming a nearly regular ring slightly wider just below middle. Tenth tergite elongate, the apex with the ventral portion excavated and bearing a dark tooth within this excavation. Anal sclerites evenly sclerotized but fairly short and rounded at apex. Clasper short and deep, the apical segment with a shallow incision just below the dorsal point. Aedeagus with short basal cup, its sagittate process well-developed and spade-like at apex; phalicata tubular, constricted to a narrow sinuate portion at apex.

*Holotype, male*: Urai, Formosa, April 1, 1933 (L. Gressitt). In the collection of the Museum of Comparative Zoology.

This species is most closely related to *nigrocephala* from which it differs in details of the tenth tergite and claspers.

## Rhyacophila remingtoni new species

*Male*: Length 10 mm. Color dark brown, the legs slightly lighter, the wings medium smoky. General structure typical for genus. Genitalia as in Fig. 270. Ninth segment with dorsal portion moderately long, middle and ventral portion much longer. Tenth tergite elongate, the ventral margin with the apical portion sinuate to produce a slender apex which is excavated ventrally; the excavation contains sclerotized teeth. Anal sclerite with a fairly broad base and a slightly bulbous rounded apex. Clasper with basal segment constricted in middle, flattened at apex; apical segment large and having

on its posterior margin a circular incision below the midline; the mesal surface of the apical segment with a scattering of short, blunt, black teeth. Aedeagus with small basal cup, the sagittate process well-developed and with a spear-shaped head; aedeagus tubular, tapering to a slender apex; lateral processes of aedeagus simple and of moderate length.

*Female*: Length 11 mm. Color and general structure as for male. Terminal abdominal segments slender and tapering without unusual structures.

*Holotype, male*: 5 mi. west of Sapporo, Hokkaido, Japan, Oct. 28, 1945 (C. L. Remington). *Allotype, female*: same data. *Paratypes*: Same data as for holotype, 1♂; Higashiyama, Fukushima, Japan, Nov. 20, 1949 (M. Kohno), 6♂, 1♀. All in the collection of the Illinois Natural History Survey.

This species is most closely related to *kawamurae*. From it, it differs in the curious shape of the apical segment of the claspers, and in details of the tenth tergite.

### Verrula Group

*Distribution*: North America.
**verrula** Milne (1936:90). Western North America. Fig. 272.
*Rhyacophila oregonensis* Ling (1938:62).

### Vagrita Group

*Distribution*: North America.
**milnei** Ross (1950a:264). Alberta. Fig. 273, *C, D, E.*
**vagrita** Milne (1936:91); Denning (1948b:105). British Columbia. Fig. 273, *A, B.*

### Fossil Species

All from Baltic amber, Germany.
**laminata** Ulmer (1912:32).
**occulta** Hagen and Pictet (1856:120); Ulmer (1912:30).
**profusa** Ulmer (1912:31).

### Unplaced Species

**aberrans** Martynov (1913b:5; 1934:62). Northern India.
**ancestralis** Martynov (1935:93). Northern India.
**andorrana** Navas (1917a:177). Spain.
**arcangelina** Navas (1932b:32). Italy.
**atlantica** Navas (1936b:93). Morocco.
**atomaria** Navas (1936a:125). China.
**baibarana** Matsumura (1931:1136). Japan.
**brevicephala** Iwata (1927a:205). Japan.
*Rhyacophila lacrymae* Tsuda (1940a:125).
**chesa** Navas (1918b:9). Spain.
**choprai** Martynov (1935:97). Northern India.

**confinis** Navas (1920:23). Spain.
**coreana** Tsuda (1940a:122). Korea.
**dilatata** Martynov (1935:96). Northern India.
**excavata** Martynov (1909:305). Kham, India.
**extensa** Martynov (1928:493; 1934:49). Turkestan.
**flava** Klapalek (1898:437). Hungary.
**formosae** Iwata (1928:341). Japan.
**gemella** Navas (1923:21). Spain.
**germana** Navas (1923:22). Spain.
**gigantea** Navas (preoccupied) (1925a:20). Samarkand.
**grahami** Banks (1940:197). China.
**hokkaidensis** Iwata (1927a:203). Japan.
**hungarica** Satori (1938:42). Hungary.
**impar** Martynov (1914a:77; 1934:50). Altai.
  *Rhyacophila tacita* Tsuda (1940a:127).
**isolata** Banks (1934:573). Borneo (♀ only).
**javanica** Ulmer (1951:47). Java (♀ only).
**kirvillei** Navas (1929:41). France.
**linguata** Navas (1932b:33). Italy.
**mainensis** Banks (1911:354). Maine (♀ only).
**melli** Ulmer (1926:26). China.
**nigra** Martynov (1930:72). Formosa.
**niwae** Iwata (1927b:392). Japan.
**obtusa** Klapalek (1894:492). Bulgaria.
**oreina** Navas (1936b:94). Morocco.
**pacifica** Banks (1895:316). Washington.
**perdita** Banks (1938:234). Pahang.
**pieli** Navas (1933c:19). China.
**rhombica** Martynov (1935:98). Northern India.
**shikotsuensis** Iwata (1927a:204). Japan.
**sicorensis** Navas (1917b:1). Spain.
**sociata** Navas (1916b:10). Spain.
**soror** Provancher (1878:135). Quebec.
**spinulata** Martynov (1913b:4; 1934:58). Caucasus.
**stankovici** Radovanovic (1932b:162). Balkans.
**talyshica** Martynov (1938:65). Nakitshevan.
**thyridata** Navas (1935:42). Italy.
**verecunda** Tsuda (1940a:120). Japan.
**viduata** Navas (1918b:8). Spain.
**yamanakensis** Iwata (1927a:205). Japan.

## Genus **Himalopsyche** Banks

*Himalopsyche* Banks (1940:197). Type species: *Rhyacophila tibetana* Martynov (original designation).

*Himalophanes* Banks (1940:201). Type species: *Himalopsyche* (*Himalophanes*) *anomala* Banks (original designation).

*Distribution*: Asia and North America.

### List of Species

**alticola** Banks (1940:200). Szechwan (China).
**anomala** Banks (1940:201). Szechwan (China). Fig. 286.

Originally described as females with long ovipositor, the types prove to be males having extremely long tenth tergal processes and claspers, grooved to fit together in respose like blades of an ovipositor.

**auricularis** (Martynov), *Rhyacophila* (1914b:324). Szechwan (China). Not studied.
**biansata** Kimmins (1952:351). Tibet.
**digitata** (Martynov), *Rhyacophila* (1935:102). India. Not studied.
**elegantissima** (Forsslund), *Rhyacophila* (1935:3). Southern Kansu (China). Known only from female.
**excisa** (Ulmer), *Rhyacophila* (1905b:37). Tibet. Fig. 285.
**fasciolata** Kimmins (1952:352). Northeastern Burma.
**gigantea** (Martynov), *Rhyacophila* (1915:404; 1934:51). Siberia. Known only from the female.
**gregoryi** (Ulmer), *Rhyacophila* (1933:41). Southwestern China. Fig. 284.
**hageni** Banks (1940:197). Szechwan (China).
**horai** (Martynov), *Rhyacophila* (1936:306). Northern India.
  *Rhyacophila pallida* Martynov (1935:100). Preoccupied.
**japonica** (Morton), *Rhyacophila* (1900:3). Japan. Fig. 279.
**kuldschensis** (Ulmer), *Rhyacophila* (1927:172); Kimmins (1952: 357). Turkestan and Tibet. Fig. 282.
**lachlani** Banks (1940:198). Szechwan (China). Fig. 280.
**lanceolata** (Morton), *Rhyacophila* (1900:2); Kimmins (1952:354). Northern India. Fig. 276.
**maculipennis** (Ulmer), *Rhyacophila* (1905a:108). Kuku-Nor (Western China). Not studied.
**martynovi** Banks (1940:199). Tibet. Fig. 281.
**maxima** (Forsslund), *Rhyacophila* (1935:4). Southern Kansu (China). Known only from the female.
**navasi** Banks (1940:200). Southern China. Fig. 278.
  *Rhyacophila japonica* Ulmer (1926:23) *nec* Morton.
**phedongensis** Kimmins (1952:356). Northern India.
**phryganea** (Ross), *Rhyacophila* (1941:40). Western North America. Fig. 277.
**placida** Banks (1947:101). Szechwan (China). Fig. 287.
**tibetana** (Martynov), *Rhyacophila* (1930:65); Kimmins (1952:348). Tibet. Fig. 283.

## Subfamily Hydrobiosinae

Several recent publications (McFarlane 1939 and 1951, Ross & King 1952, and Mosely & Kimmins 1953) summarize the fauna of this subfamily so that there is no need here to make a detailed report of the genera. It is possible to clarify the status of a few genera and species not previously treated in detail, and this is done to explain points that would otherwise be confusing as inferred from Chart 39.

A complete list of the species in all of the endemic Australian and New Zealand genera is given by Mosely and Kimmins (1953). The only known species from New Caledonia, *Xanthochorema caledon,* is described by Kimmins (1935a). Below I have therefore listed only species from genera occurring in other areas.

### Genus **Apsilochorema** Ulmer

*Bachorema* Mosely, in Mosely & Kimmins (1953: 493). Type species: *Bachorema obliqua* Mosely (original designation). *New synonymy.*

The type species resembles *malayanum* Banks (Fig. 288), *indicum* Ulmer from India, and *banksi* Mosely from the Fiji Islands. It would appear, therefore, that *obliqua* represents at most a small species complex within the genus.

In both *obliqua* and *malayanum* the front wing is primitive for the genus in having $M_1$ ending at

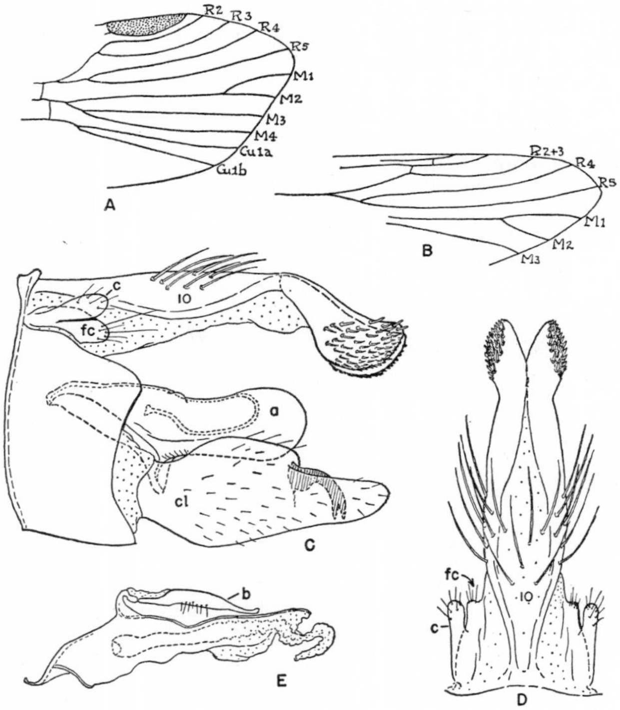

FIG. 292. Parts of Hydrobiosinae. A, B, *Iguazu aculeatum,* apical portion of wings. C, D, *Psilochorema diffinis,* male genitalia, lateral and dorsal aspects, respectively. E, *Notiobiosus nigrita,* aedeagus, lateral aspect. *a,* aedeagus; other abbreviations as in Figs. 288-91.

or just below the wing apex rather than above it as in most other species of the genus.

#### LIST OF SPECIES

**annandalei** Martynov (1935:110). India.
**banksi** (Mosely), *Achorema* (1941:373). Fiji Islands. Fig. 159.
**burgersi** Ulmer (1938:398). New Guinea.
**diffinis** Banks (1920:362). Ceylon. Fig. 292 C, D.

The illustrations in Figure 292 C, D, are drawn from a paratype which has been compared carefully with a cleared preparation of the lectotype. This species is peculiar in that the filicercus has apparently retrogressed and is represented by a mere stub. In venation the species is primitive in that the front wing has $M_1$ only as far forward as the wing apex.

**excisum** Ulmer (1927:174). Formosa.
**gisba** (Mosely), *Bachorema* (Mosely & Kimmins 1953: 494). Australia (Victoria).
**indicum** (Ulmer), *Psilochorema* (1905b:38); Martynov (1927b:173). India.
　Subsp. **turanicum** Martynov (1934:71). Bukhara.
**malayanum** Banks (1931a:403). Malay (Pahang). Fig. 288.
**mancum** Ulmer (1951:49). Java.
**moselyi** Ross (1951d:181). Fiji Islands.
**obliqua** (Mosely), *Bachorema* (Mosely & Kimmins 1953:494). Australia (Queensland).
**sutshanum** Martynov (1934:72). Siberia (S. Ussuri) and Japan.
　*Psilochorema japonicum* Tsuda (1942:243).
　I wish to thank Dr. Tsuda for apprising me of this synonymy in correspondence.
**zimmermani** Ross (1951d:179). Fiji Islands.

### Genus **Allochorema** Mosely

The sole species known in this genus, *tasmanica,* to date collected only in Tasmania, seems impossible to place with certainty in a phylogenetic position. It could be a primitive *Apsilochorema* with highly modified claspers, or a genus representing an offshoot of the line leading to *Hydrobiosis* and its allies. The simple venation favors the latter view. If true, this would indicate *Allochorema* as the most primitive known member of its line. Due to uncertainty regarding its relationships I have not indicated this genus in Chart 39.

### Genus **Ulmerochorema** Mosely

This genus, also not indicated in Chart 39, is known only from a female. It appears to be a close relative of *Anachorema* Mosely, and may eventually prove to be the same. Knowledge of the males will be needed to verify this surmise.

### Genus **Percivalia** McFarlane

The intercubital cross-vein of the front wing marks this genus as belonging to the endemic group of hydrobiosine genera typical of and restricted to New Zealand. Although considered as a synonym of *Notiobiosis* by Mosely and Kimmins (1953), I believe *Percivalia* constitutes a separate generic entity and that it should be taken from synonymy.

### Genus **Notiobiosis** Banks

When Banks (1939*b*) described this genus, he designated as the type species *pallescens* Banks, from West Australia, and included another species, *nigrita* Banks from North Queensland. The former is known only from the female type. The type of *nigrita* is a male, of which the genitalia are illustrated in Fig. 291. This species resembles the type species *pallescens* in the primitive front wing venation, but differs in having $R_{2+3}$ branched in the hind wing. The male genitalia of *nigrita* have three pairs of dorsal processes in addition to the cerci and filicerci; the ventral pair of these three is attached more intimately to the base of the aedeagus than to the tenth tergite.

### Genus **Dolochorema** Banks

This genus contains only the type species *irregularis* Banks (1913:240), known only from Cuzco, Peru. The wings in general (Fig. 293A, B) resemble those of *Atopsyche* Banks, although the front wing venation shows many freakish characters. The male genitalia (Fig. 290, 293C—E) are also of the same general pattern as *Atopsyche*, but with many highly modified features in the claspers. The genus would therefore appear to be an offshoot from the base of the *Atopsyche* line.

### Genus **Iguazu** Ross

In addition to the type species, *ulmeri* Ross, this genus probably includes *Macronema aculeatum* Blanchard (1851:138), described from Chile. We were able to study the type specimen, in the Paris Museum. Only a front and a hind wing remain, which match well those of *ulmeri* except for the unbranched $R_{2+3}$ in the hind wing and other slight differences in both wings. Our sketches of the apical portions of the type wings are shown in Fig. 292A, B.

A paratype female in the Paris Museum proves

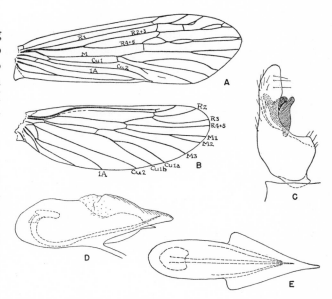

FIG. 293. Parts of *Dolochorema irregularis*. A, B, wings; C, clasper, ventral aspect; D, E, aedeagus, lateral and dorsal aspects, respectively.

to belong to another family; it appears to be a female of *Notiomyia*.

### Genus **Cailloma** Ross

This genus was erected for *brunosa* Ross from Peru and *lucidula* (Ulmer) from Argentina. The following third species has been collected in Chile.

#### **Cailloma pumida** new species

*Male*: Length 10.5 mm. Head and body various shades of light brown, antennae and mouthparts the same color; pleurae, coxae, and femora straw color; wings uniformly light brown with brown hair. General structure typical for genus. Sixth and seventh sternites each with a short mesal process on apical margin. Genitalia as in Fig. 294. Ninth segment narrow dorsally and widest near middle. Cercus small; filicercus fairly long, narrow at base, the apex forming an elongate triangle set with long setae. Central membranous lobe of tenth tergite elongate and somewhat cylindrical; between its base and each filicercus is situated a short ovate process. This process articulates dorsally with the tenth tergite and ventrally with the base of the filicercus at the points indicated by small circles (*x* and *y*) in Fig. 294A. Actually, the articulations are not as delineated but are fusions of membrane. Clasper single-segmented, fairly short, round at apex, and bowed so that it is concave ventrally; its ventral aspect is elongate and narrow, with the

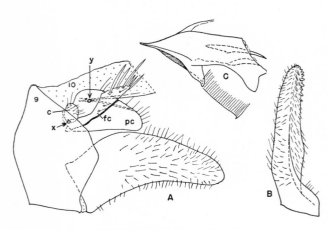

Fig. 294. Male genitalia of *Cailloma pumida*. *A,* lateral aspect; *B,* clasper, ventral aspect; *C,* aedeagus, lateral aspect. Abbreviations as in Figs. 288-91.

mesal margin only slightly angulate. Aedeagus short, its apical margin angled slightly ventrad, forming a notched process; internally it bears a short, sharp rod which can be exserted.

*Holotype, male:* 5 mi. west of LaJunta, Coquimbo, Chile, Dec. 7, 1950, E. S. Ross & Michelbacher. *Paratypes:* Same data, 9♂. Holotype and six paratypes in collection of the California Academy of Sciences, three paratypes in collection of the Illinois Natural History Survey.

This species differs from *brunosa* in the shorter lateral process of the tenth tergite, the incised ventral angle of the aedeagus, and the almost straight mesal margin of the clasper.

### Genus **Atopsyche** Banks

The species of this American genus were revised by Ross and King (1952). Since then additional species have been described and fitted into a phylogenetic explanation of the development of the genus (Ross 1953*a* and 1953*b*).

chapter five  # THE FAMILY GLOSSOSOMATIDAE

## EVOLUTION AND DISPERSAL

The larvae of the Glossosomatidae make saddle-like cases, and without exception inhabit cool or cold, rapid streams. Some groups such as *Agapetus* live chiefly in spring-fed rills or brooks; others such as *Protoptila* and *Glossosoma* subgenus *Ripaeglossa* live in cold rapid rivers of moderate size. Both adults and larvae are relatively uniform in appearance throughout the family, but there is a considerable range in size, from *Glossosoma* species measuring 10 mm. in length to some of the smaller *Protoptila* species which are less than 3 mm. long. Both larvae and adults possess a number of different characteristics by which generic diagnosis may be made and relationships established. Within each genus the adults, primarily the males, exhibit differences in secondary sexual characters which permit the deduction of the major phyletic lines.

The genus *Anagapetus* is the most primitive member of the family. It has a complete wing venation (Fig. 295A), with no marked modifications, and in addition has a transverse suture separating the upper and lower parts of the mesepisternum. The male genitalia are simple, but the cerci have apparently been lost.

The other genera all have the two parts of the mesepisternum separated by a constriction. This may indicate that the *Anagapetus*-like ancestor (Chart 27, Ancestor 1) gave rise to a form (Ancestor 2) primitive in venation and genitalia, but specialized in regard to this mesothoracic character, and that from this form the remainder of the genera diverged. These other genera represent three well-marked lines:

1. *Glossosoma*: Specialized in the forward migration of the front legs of the larva to the anterior corner of the pronotum, and, in the adults, the alignment of $R_5$ with Rs and $R_{4+5}$ to make a straight vein. Otherwise *Glossosoma* has changed little from Ancestor 2.

2. *Catagapetus* to *Agapetus*: A line marked by the loss of $R_{1a}$ in the front wing, so that $R_1$ is simple (Fig. 295B), and the progressive reduction of the branches of Rs and $R_1$ in the hind wings (Fig. 296, D-I).

3. *Protoptila* and its allies: A distinctive line of small forms in which the anal claws in the larva are many-toothed, the front tibial spurs and venation in the adults are much reduced.

Each of these three groups has specialized characters which indicate that it could not have been the parent of the other two. It follows that all three arose independently either from Ancestor 2, or, less likely, from Ancestor 1 with a parallel evolution in the mesopleural sclerites. This is illustrated in Chart 27.

*Anagapetus*, *Glossosoma*, and the *Agapetus* line form a compact taxonomic unit and are grouped together as three tribes (*Anagapetini*, *Glossosomatini*, and *Agapetini*) of a single subfamily Glossosomatinae. *Protoptila* and its allies form such a distinctive unit that they are regarded as a separate subfamily, the Protoptilinae.

### The Tribe Anagapetini

The only known representatives of this primitive group are four closely related species grouped in the genus *Anagapetus*. The larval and adult struc-

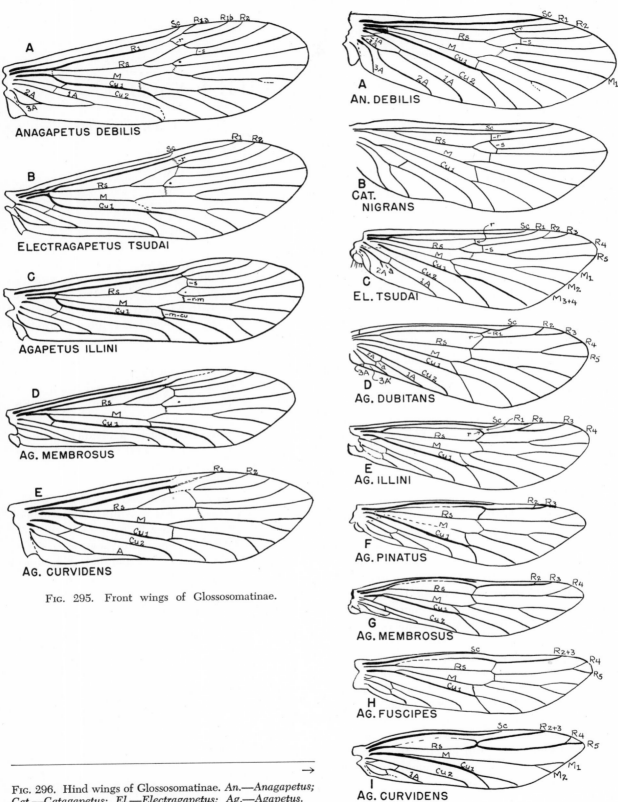

FIG. 295. Front wings of Glossosomatinae.

FIG. 296. Hind wings of Glossosomatinae. *An.—Anagapetus;*
*Cat.—Catagapetus; El.—Electragapetus; Ag.—Agapetus.*

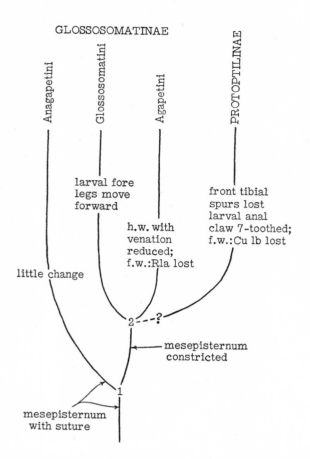

GLOSSOSOMATINAE

Anagapetini

Glossosomatini

Agapetini

PROTOPTILINAE

larval fore
legs move
forward

front tibial
spurs lost
larval anal
claw 7-toothed;
f.w.:Cu 1b lost

h.w. with
venation
reduced;
f.w.:R1a lost

little change

2 ---?

mesepisternum
constricted

1

mesepisternum
with suture

CHART 27. Phylogenetic diagram of the *Glossosomatidae*.

tures are little changed from what we would deduce as the characteristics of Ancestor 1 in Chart 27.
The only exception is in the male genitalia, which
have lost the cerci, but this is a frequent occurrence in various caddisfly groups and would appear to be only a minor change. We may regard
*Anagapetus* as a virtual living fossil, the product
of a line which has continued for a considerable
period of geologic time with little change while
offspring lines have evolved at a faster rate.

The four species of *Anagapetus* are, as we have
said, closely related, and can be resolved into a
simple scheme of relationships. The most primitive
is *chandleri*, with the apex of the clasper only
slightly incised. The other three represent two
groups, one with a row of clubbed hairs on the
middle of the posterior margin of the ninth segment, including *bernea* and *hoodi*, the other with-

out this row of hairs, including only *debilis* (Fig.
297).

All four species are confined to the western montane region of North America. The first three species are from the western mountain ranges of the
region, and *debilis* is fairly widespread through the
more eastern mountain ranges. Unfortunately we
have only scattered records for these forms, especially for the more western species which appear
either to be confined to the slopes of some of the
higher mountains or to be extremely local in occurrence. Even so, I believe we can put forward two
suggested conclusions from these data:

1. That, judging by their basic similarity, all
our species arose from a single surviving line arising from Ancestor 1, and result from a speciation
pattern occurring within fairly recent times.

2. That this single line probably survived in the
western ranges of the region, and from this line a

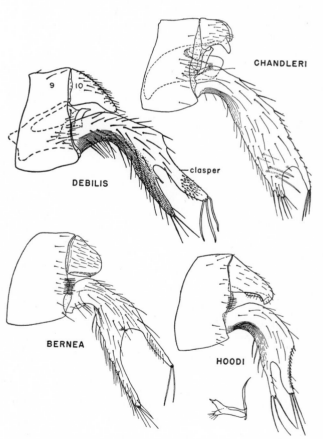

FIG. 297. Male genitalia of *Anagapetus*, lateral aspect.

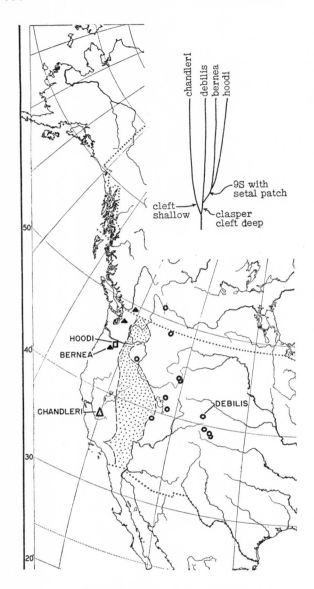

CHART 28. Phylogenetic diagram of *Anagapetus*.

single form spread into the eastern ranges to produce the species *debilis*.

These suggestions are outlined in Chart 28.

### The Tribe Glossosomatini

This tribe contains about 45 species which display pronounced differences in male genitalia and one or two other male characters, but which are remarkably similar in wing venation and female genitalia. Several distinctive types of male genitalia have evolved, but, fortunately, enough primi-

tive species still survive to permit us to piece together a cohesive picture of the changes which have occurred. Because of similarity in wing venation and the continuous nature of the evolutionary pattern, all species in the tribe are placed in one genus, *Glossosoma*.

The most primitive known species of the genus is *taeniatum* (Fig. 298), which has very simple genitalia, including the aedeagus, and differs from *Anagapetus* chiefly in having $R_2$ and $R_5$ aligned with their parent veins in the front wings. From an ancestral form similar to *taeniatum*, all three di-

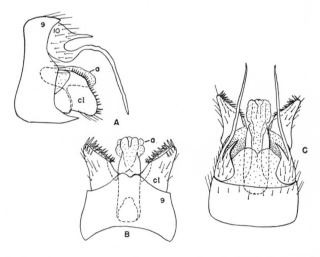

FIG. 298. Male genitalia of *Glossosoma taeniatum*. A, lateral aspect; B, ventral aspect; C, dorsal aspect. *a*, aedeagus; *cl*, clasper.

vergent evolutionary lines of the genus can be traced, Chart 29, with the possible exception of the *Ripaeglossa* line as explained below.

### The Ripaeglossa Line

The large streams of the western montane region of North America abound in a curious group of *Glossosoma* found in no other area. This group is the subgenus *Ripaeglossa*, characterized by the hooded type of male genitalia, caused by a prolongation of the lateral margins of the ninth segment into broad, blinder-like rigid flaps (Fig. 299). No intermediate types are known suggesting connections with other lines of *Glossosoma*. The best clue to their relationship appears to be the structure of the aedeagus. In its simplest form (Fig. 299) it is a simple tube arising from a shallow

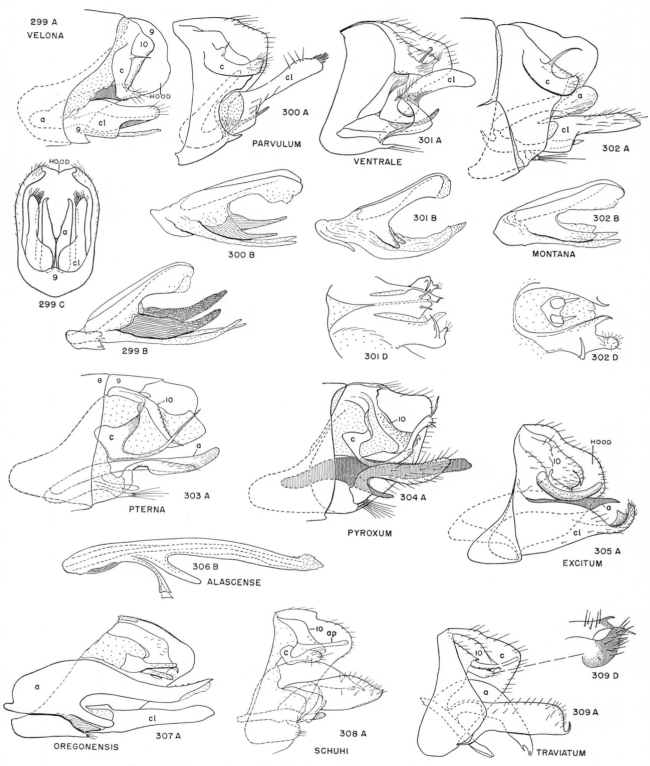

FIGS. 299-309.  Male genitalia of *Glossosoma* subgenus *Ripaeglossa*. *A*, lateral aspect; *B*, aedeagus, lateral aspect; *C*, ventral aspect; *D*, details of tenth tergite, dorsolateral aspect. *a*, aedeagus; *c*, cercus; *cl*, clasper.

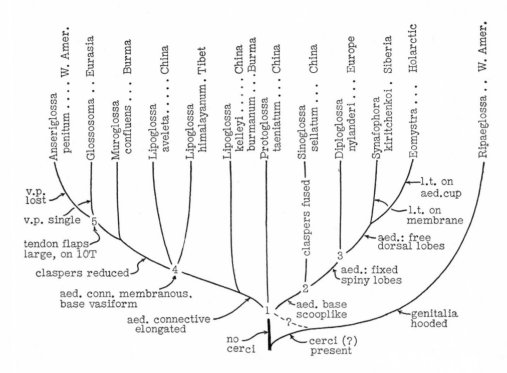

CHART 29. Phylogenetic diagram of *Glossosoma*.

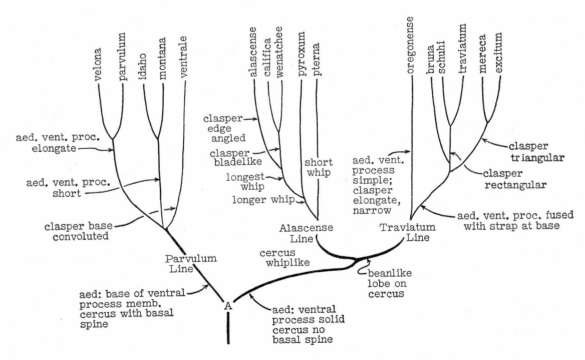

CHART 30. Phylogenetic diagram of *Glossosoma* subgenus *Ripaeglossa*.

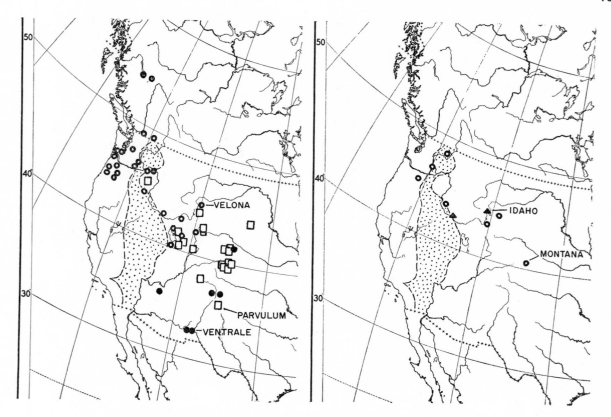

Fig. 310. Known distribution of species of the *parvulum* line of *Ripaeglossa*.

cuplike structure which is firmly attached to one end of a band whose other end attaches to the bases of the claspers. The apical tube articulates with the cup by means of short membranous folds, so that a little movement is possible between tube and cup. This is almost the same general structure which we find at the base of all the large phyletic lines in *Glossosoma,* and apparently represents a condition very close to the primeval one for the genus.

*Ripaeglossa* could therefore be a North American offshoot from a primitive form such as Ancestor 1 (Chart 29). There is another possibility. At the base of the tenth tergite are a pair of lateral processes which I have called cerci in the past, and which practice I am continuing for the sake of uniformity of terminology. These may actually prove to be secondary processes and not homologous with the cerci as found in *Sortosa.* If so, our surmise above will hold. If, however, they prove to be true cerci, they would mark *Ripaeglossa* as a branch of *Glossosoma* more primitive than all the

others, and indicate that *Ripaeglossa* branched from the *Glossosoma* stem before the evolution of Ancestor 1.

Regardless of its exact point of origin, it is clear that *Ripaeglossa* resulted from an early spread of a primitive *Glossosoma* species to North America. There are no known species illustrating the steps in the changes which took place in the evolution of the specialized male genital capsule of *Ripaeglossa* from that of its primitive ancestor. But we do have evidence of a burst of species after this point was reached. To date 15 species are known and they portray the evolution of three distinctive species groups with each of these again dividing into about five species. This is shown in Chart 30.

The ancestral form of *Ripaeglossa* which gave rise to the existing species groups had already evolved a curious ventral projection near the base of the aedeagus. This form gave rise to two lines. In the *parvulum* line the ventral process of the aedeagus was membranous at the base and gave rise to a pair of membranous processes (Fig. 300B), and the

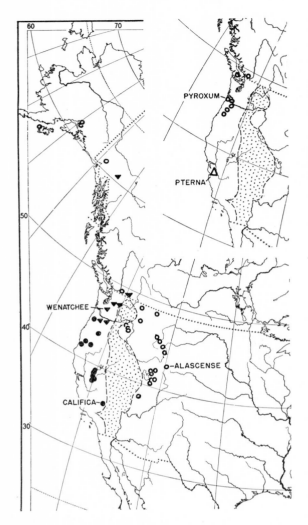

Fig. 311. Known distribution of species of the *alascense* line of *Ripaeglossa*.

cercus was a simple lobe with a stout seta near the base (Fig. 300A). In the *alascense-traviatum* line the ventral process of the aedeagus was a rigid, single sclerotized projection (Fig. 306B), and the cercus was either without a basal seta or had it highly modified. This latter line again divided to form the *alascense* line, with a whiplike cercus (Fig. 303A), and the *traviatum* line, with a curious swollen structure on the cercus (Fig. 305). Whether this curious structure, labelled *ap* in Fig. 308, is a modified basal seta or an added, special lobe is difficult to determine.

Species of the *parvulum* line seem to have arisen in a trident fashion from an ancestral form much

like *montana,* possessing (1) a detached dorsal sclerite in the membrane between the lobes of the tenth tergite, and (2) an aedeagus much like that shown in Fig. 301, having a basoventral membranous lobe and a more apical ventral sclerotized lobe, both bifid at the apex. One of the three branches changed only in the apicoventral process of the aedeagus, which became membranous (Fig. 302B); this branch is represented by two closely related species, *montana* and *idaho.* In a second branch, containing only *ventrale* (Fig. 301), the dorsal plate enlarged and fused with the bases of the tenth tergite lobes, and the basoventral process of the aedeagus enlarged. In the third branch the dorsal plate of the tenth tergite became reduced and finally lost, and the apicoventral lobe of the aedeagus developed into a pair of long, sclerotized, articulated processes (Fig. 300B). This branch contains two known species, *parvulum* in which the aedeagal processes are slender (Fig. 300B), and *velona* in which they are sturdy and unusually long (Fig. 299B).

The *alascense* line appears to have followed a series of changes involving increases in the length of the whiplike cercus. An early stage is shown in *pterna* (Fig. 303) and later stages by *pyroxum* (Fig. 304) and *wenatchee.* At this point a branch arose giving rise to *alascense* in which the ventral edge of the clasper is angled like a reinforcing bar on a piece of metal.

The *traviatum* line has given rise to the most distinctive set of species in *Ripaeglossa.* All members of the line have the cercus set with short hairs at the apex, and bearing a bean-shaped, smooth process at its base. The most primitive species is *oregonense* (Fig. 307), in which the claspers are slender and elongate, and the ventral process of the aedeagus is much as in *pterna.* The base of the aedeagus, however, is fused more closely with the basal strap than is that of *pterna,* so that even by manipulation the two cannot be separated to any great extent. In the line continuing beyond the point of separation of *oregonense,* this type of fusion seems to have progressed to the point that most of the ventral process of the aedeagus and the aedeagus below it became rigidly fused with the basal strap. From such an ancestor two branches arose. In one, containing *schuhi, traviatum,* and *bruna,* the tip of the ventral process of the aedeagus became produced as a free lobe extending between the bases of the claspers (Fig. 309), and the claspers themselves became nearly rectangular. In the other branch, the ventral process of the aedeagus has no free tip and is practically unidentifiable as such, and the clasper has become triangular (Fig. 305); it contains only *mereca* and *excitum.*

An examination of the known distribution data of the species of *Ripaeglossa* underscores some intriguing speculation. The three primitive members of the *parvulum* line occur only in the southern portion of the Rocky Mountains proper; the two most specialized occur in the Rocky Mountains to the north and also in the Cascade ranges to the west (Fig. 310). This would indicate that the line arose in the eastern portion of the western montane region and that only in comparatively recent times has it spread into the western mountain ranges.

In both the *alascense* line and the *traviatum* line, however, the primitive members occur only in the *western mountain ranges* of the montane region, with only one or two species occurring in the eastern ranges. In the *alascense* line (Fig. 311), all four primitive members are so far known only from western ranges, the last and most advanced species (*alascense*) occurring in the eastern ranges

south of Canada and in the western ranges of Alaska. In the *traviatum* line (Fig. 312) the first three species occur solely, and the other three chiefly, in the western ranges; for two of these specialized forms, *traviatum* and *excitum,* only an occasional record is known to the east. From this it would be deduced that the ancestral forms of both the *alascense* and *traviatum* lines arose in western ranges of the montane region, and that only in fairly recent times have any of their members spread to more eastern areas. Since this appears true for both, it follows as logically for the common ancestor of the two.

Reconstructing both phylogeny and distribution, it appears highly likely that the first great division of *Ripaeglossa* was into two populations, one in a more eastern montane area, developing into the *parvulum* line, and another in a more western montane area developing into the *alascense-traviatum* line. Further, these divergent sections of the subgenus appear to have remained apart geographically until a late point in their evolution.

It must be reiterated that these surmises, although apparently sound, are based only on the data in available collections. More collections are highly desirable and will be necessary before this and similar problems can be resolved.

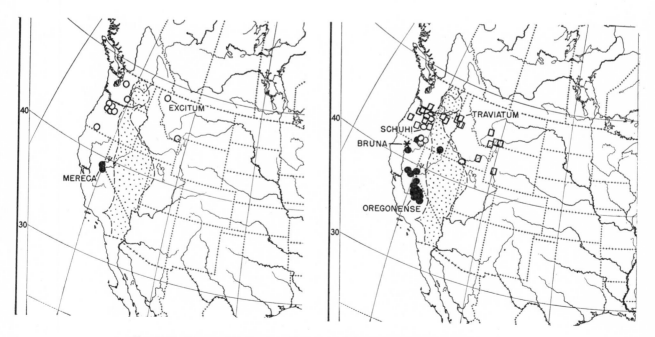

FIG. 312. Known distribution of species of the *traviatum* line of *Ripaeglossa.*

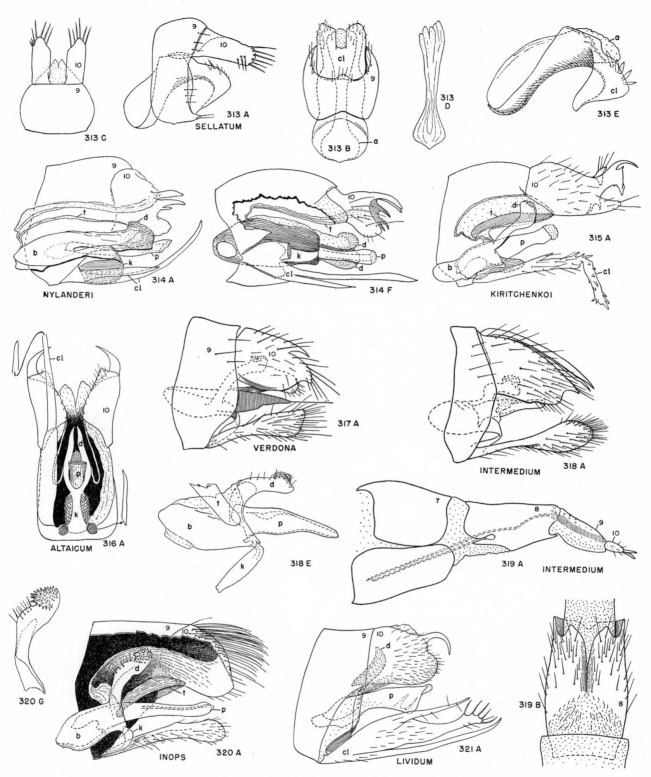

313 C

313 A
SELLATUM

313 B

313 D

313 E

NYLANDERI    314 A

314 F

315 A
KIRITCHENKOI

316 A
ALTAICUM

317 A
VERDONA

318 A
INTERMEDIUM

318 E

319 A    INTERMEDIUM

319 B

320 G

INOPS    320 A

321 A
LIVIDUM

FIGS. 313-21. Male genitalia of *Glossosoma* of the *Eomystra* line, except 319 which is the female genitalia. *A*, lateral aspect; *B*, ventral aspect; *C*, dorsal aspect; *D*, *E*, details of aedeagus, dorsal and ventral aspects, respectively; *F*, genital capsule, lateroventral aspect; *G*, dorsal lobe of aedeagus. *b*, base of aedeagus; *cl*, clasper; *d*, dorsal lobe of aedeagus; *k*, keel; *p*, phalicata; *t*, tendon.

The question of dating these suggested events is dealt with in Chapter 6.

### The Eomystra Line

In the second extensive line in the genus *Glossosoma*, leading from the primitive deduced Ancestor 1 to *Eomystra*, the bottom of the aedeagus forms a sclerotized runner, shaped somewhat like a shoehorn with the handle bent over and fused with the ninth sternite where the claspers join it. An early step in this process is seen in *sellatum* (Fig. 313). It is interesting to note that *sellatum* preserves also very primitive lobes of the tenth tergite, but has the claspers fused mesally at the base and in this respect is highly specialized.

From a primitive form (called Ancestor 2) having the *sellatum* type of aedeagus, arose the *Eomystra* line. The bent "handle" of the shoehorn became a keel, and the internal runner-like piece became more vasiform, and the intromittent part of the structure developed into a sclerotized tube or phalicata (Fig. 314, *p*). Associated with this was the development of a pair of spiny dorsal lobes (*d*) at the apex of the vasiform structure, together with a strengthening of the membrane (*t*) connecting the vasiform portion of the aedeagus to the tenth tergite. Such an ancestor is represented in Chart 29 by No. 3. A species at this stage is *nylanderi,* which has the aedeagus as described but has the claspers bifid and thus is individually specialized (Fig. 314). This is the subgenus *Diploglossa*, of which only this one species is known.

The next step of which we have record in this line has two modifications (Fig. 315): (1) the apicodorsal processes of the aedeagus cup (*d*) are free flaps, projecting nearly dorsad, and with definite freedom of movement; and (2) a sclerotized ribbon-like band has developed between the aedeagus cup and the tenth tergite (*t*), joined directly to the latter and to the membrane just above the apex of the aedeagus cup. These structures, in combination with the sclerotized, elongate and vasiform phalicata, typify the subgenus *Synafophora*.

*Synafophora* is known only from a pair of closely related Siberian species having curiously shaped claspers and tenth tergite. The male also has one of the apical tibial spurs of the hind leg modified. The aedeagotergal tendon (*t*) appears to be a new structure in this line. Apparently this tendon made one more adjustment, becoming connected closely

to the sides of the aedeagus cup, and this latter condition typifies the subgenus *Eomystra*, which is at the end of its phyletic line. In *Eomystra* the tendon is attached to the aedeagus cup with a membranous hinge (Fig. 317E), the two tendons and hinges, one on each side, forming part of a complicated mechanism which regulates the partial extrusion and retraction of the whole aedeagus, cup and all. Presumably the actual extrusion is powered by hydrostatic pressure of the blood, and the main function of the tendons would be in regulating the position of the aedeagus and its withdrawal.

*Eomystra* contains eight known species which present some intriguing questions about dispersal. Before studying these it is necessary to explore the phylogeny of the species. The subgenus is divided first into two groups (Chart 31), the *lividum* group in which the male has oddly cleft claspers (Fig. 321) and the female has a simple, ringlike, eighth segment; and the *intermedium* group in which the male has simple claspers but the female has an elongate, tapered eighth segment (Fig. 319). The females of *inops* and *ussuricum* are not known, but these two species have claspers and aedeagus so like *intermedium* that there is no doubt of their close relationship. Both groups must have arisen from a form with simple structures in both sexes. It will be interesting to see if *inops* and *ussuricum*, which have extremely simple genitalia for this group (Fig. 320), have the female genitalia of a more primitive type and fit this deduced ancestor.

The *lividum* group contains two closely related species, *nigrior* and *lividum*, confined to eastern North America, the two differentiated by details of the genitalia; and a third species *dulkejti* from Siberia which appears to be a very close relative of *nigrior*. I have not seen specimens of this species but Martynov (1934) gives illustrations of the claspers and tenth tergite that leave no doubt as to this relationship.

The *intermedium* group contains three species complexes. The first contains two northern Asiatic species *inops* and *ussuricum*, which have a very simple tenth tergite. The second complex contains two species: *verdona*, restricted to the Rocky Mountains of North America, and which usually has a short dorsal process on each lobe of the tenth tergite (Fig. 317); and *intermedium*, a Holarctic species which has a long dorsal process on the tenth tergite lobe and is obviously an offshoot of *verdona*

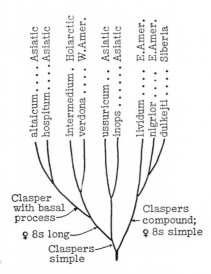

CHART 31. Phylogenetic diagram of *Glossosoma* subgenus *Eomystra*.

(Fig. 318). The third complex contains the Japanese species *hospitum* and the northern Asiatic species *altaicum,* the two charcterized by the greatly elongate, tapering claspers (Fig. 316).

Considering the Eurasian distribution of all primitive members of the *Eomystra* line—*sellatum nylanderi, kiritchenkoi,* and the pair *inops-ussuricum*—there is practically no doubt that the group originated in the Palearctic region and there developed its major morphological features. On this basis it would seem that an early branch of *Eomystra* spread to North America and developed into the *lividum-nigrior* group; and that a form ancestral to *nigrior* spread back to Asia, the North American population developing into *nigrior,* the Asiatic into *dulkejti.* A later branch of *Eomystra* also spread to North America and developed into the *verdona* group; this gave rise to the specialized species *intermedium* which has become widespread throughout the Holarctic region.

### The Anseriglossa Line

The third great branch of *Glossosoma* culminated in those species having the curious, asymmetrical male genitalia found in the subgenus *Anseriglossa.* As did the *Eomystra* branch, this one began also from a simple form such as *taeniatum,* that is, from Ancestor 1. The first step was the retraction of the base of the aedeagus into the cavity of the apical segments, possibly much as in *minutum* (Fig. 322). The next step was the thinning of the ventral ten-

don joining the base of the aedeagus with the base of the claspers, and the constriction of the aedeagus into a basal cuplike portion (cup) and an apical portion (phalicata) extending beyond it. Simultaneously with the reduction of the ventral tendon, there appeared tendons joining the dorsum of the aedeagus cup with specialized areas or plates where the ventral corner of the tenth tergite joined the ninth segment. Examples of this stage are illustrated by *himalayanum* and *aveleta* (Figs. 323, 324). Next the claspers became much reduced, as in *confluens,* and definite sclerites, the tendon flaps (*tf*), formed where the dorsal tendons of the aedeagus were attached (Fig. 325).

A most singular change seems to have occurred at this point. The tendon flaps appear to have enlarged and moved beneath the tenth tergite, to which they now seem to belong (Fig. 327). The dorsal tendons at this point are wide, strong bands, but membranous. The ancestral form represented here, Ancestor 5, appears to have spread to North America, for two diverse types developed further, one in Eurasia and one in North America.

In the Eurasian group, which evolved into the subgenus *Glossosoma* (Figs. 327-35), the area between the original but now atrophied claspers developed into a long, asymmetrical tongue. The aedeagus became asymmetrical, and was exserted always to the left side of the ventral tongue. Whereas in *confluens* the aedeagus had a pair of ventral processes, in the subgenus *Glossosoma* these fused to form a single structure. The dorsal tendon remained membranous.

Several distinct lines can be traced within the subgenus (Chart 32). The most primitive known species is *atrichum,* in which the lobes of the tenth tergite are simple and symmetrical, and the ventral process on the aedeagus is nearly symmetrical and bilobed (Fig. 327).

The next advance is illustrated by *caudatum,* in which the tenth tergite lobes are divided by a crease into dorsal and ventral portions (Fig. 328) and the ventral process of the aedeagus is single, extensile, and capped with a cone of dense, stout setae.

Beyond this point there arose a form in which the tenth tergite lobes each had a dorsal point and ventral lobe, and the two tendon flaps were entirely different from each other. From some such ancestor the remaining species of the genus seem to

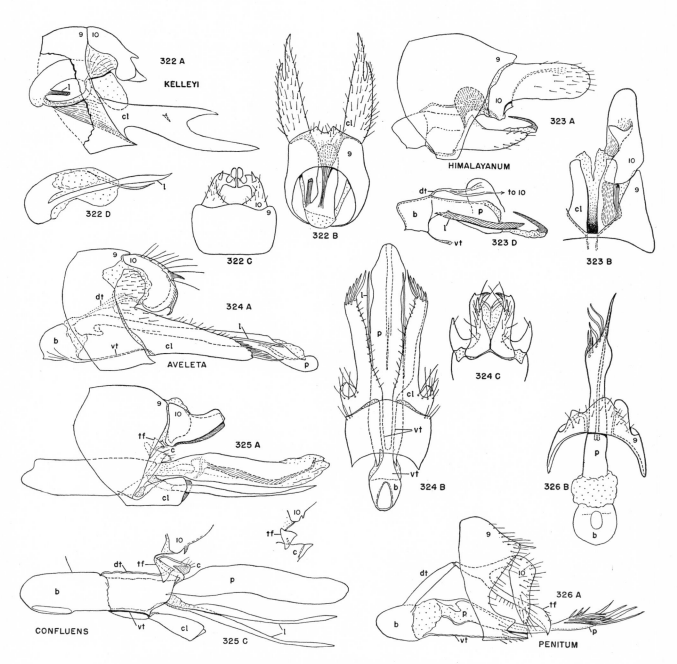

FIGS. 322-26. Male genitalia of *Glossosoma* of the *Anseriglossa* line. A, B, C, lateral, ventral, and dorsal aspects, respectively; D, aedeagus and its connections, lateral aspect. *b*, base of aedeagus; *cl*, clasper; *dt*, dorsal tendon; *l*, lateral process of aedeagus; *p*, phalicata; *tf*, tendon flap; *vt*, ventral tendon.

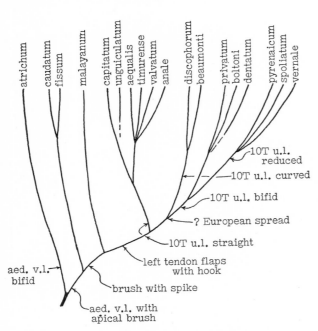

CHART 32. Phylogenetic diagram of *Glossosoma* subgenus *Glossosoma*.

have arisen. These species belong to five well-marked but small groups, and they appear to have evolved steplike, one after another, in this fashion:

1. At first the tendon flaps were simple at the base, with no hooklike sclerotized areas (Fig. 329). At the same time the dorsal process of the tenth tergite lobe became slender and finger-like. A species representing this step is *malayanum*.

2. Next, the membranous fold at the base of the tendon flap became sclerotized to form a thickened, hooklike area (Fig. 331G) which fitted against the inside of the tenth tergite lobe. The dorsal process of this lobe appears to have become sharp and pointed. A cluster of seven known species, *capitatum* (Fig. 330), *aequale, orientale, moselyi, timurense, valvatum,* and *anale* (Fig. 331), speciated from a branch representing this point in development. The Caucasian species *unguiculatum* may belong near *capitatum,* but on the basis of Martynov's illustrations I cannot be sure of its affinities.

3. A pair of species, *discophorum* and *beaumonti,* are fundamentally very similar to the five listed above, but differ in that the dorsal processes of the tenth tergite lobes curve mesad more than they extend posteriad. They appear to represent the third step in this progression.

4. The fourth step was the bifurcation or doubling of the dorsal process of the tenth tergite lobe. In all these "double" species, the processes are short and curve mesad more than posteriad, hence it seems logical to suppose that this doubled dorsal process arose from a form in which the process was already curved mesad, as in group 3 above. Two described species, *privatum* and *boltoni,* represent this fourth step.

5. In an apparent offshoot from the base of the fourth step, two changes occurred in the tenth tergite lobe: the dorsal pair of processes became very reduced, and the ventral lobe became attenuated, then curved upward. The species *spoliatum* and *dusmeti* represent the base of this branch, with the ventral lobe turned only slightly at the apex (Figs. 333, 334); *vernale,* the third species in the group, represents the end of the line, and has the ventral lobe turned up much more at the apex (Fig. 332).

The curious species *dentatum* is difficult to place. It has no dorsal process on the tenth tergite lobe, and the ventral process of the ninth sternite has a large, blunt, lateral tooth (Fig. 335). It could have come about by reduction of the dorsal process from a form ancestral to *aequale,* but at present this is strictly a surmise.

The American branch which arose from Ancestor 5 gave rise to a form highly modified by a remarkable specialization of the tendon flaps. Each of these developed into an elongate structure (Fig. 326) connected dorsally with the tenth tergite by a narrow, long band, and forming an articulated joint with the basal part of the tendon. The ninth sternite is asymmetrical but produced only slightly. The lobes of the tenth tergite are elongate, divergent, and downpointed, usually resting on the outside of the tendon flaps. The aedeagus has lost its ventral process and its apex bears a cluster of long spines. Only a single species, *penitum,* is known representing this line, and it is placed in a separate subgenus *Anseriglossa.* Its range extends over much of the western mountain region.

This completes the account of the known members of the third large branch of *Glossosoma.* In essential respects it parallels the evolution of the *Eomystra* branch, in that the base of the branch rises from an Asiatic species, its early development can be followed through *Asiatic* species, and the largest specialized cluster of species arising at the

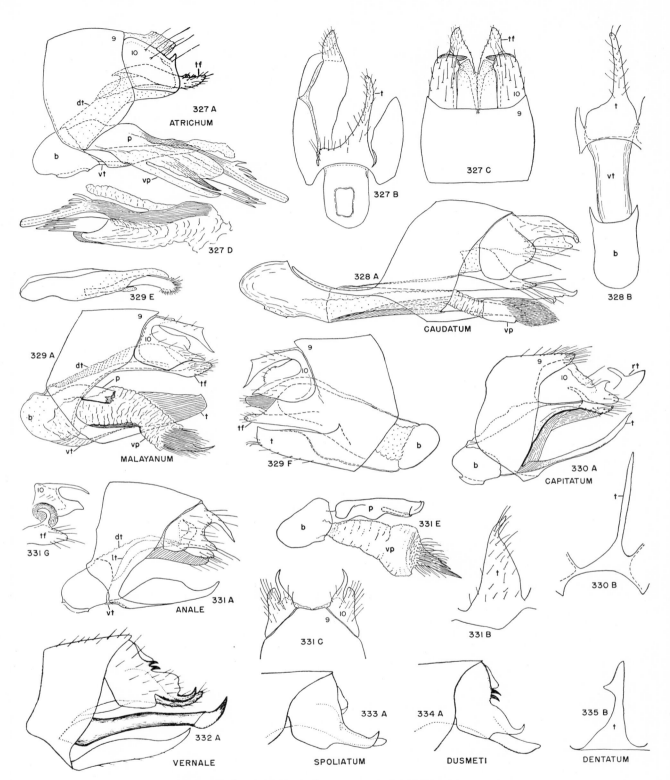

FIGS. 327-35. Male genitalia of *Glossosoma* subgenus *Glossosoma*. *A, F,* lateral aspect, left and right sides, respectively; *B,* ventral aspect; *C,* dorsal aspect; *D,* aedeagus, right side, *E,* aedeagus, left side; *G,* mesal aspect of lobe of tenth tergite, *b,* base of aedeagus; *dt,* dorsal tendon; *p,* phalicata; *t,* ventral tongue; *tf,* tendon flaps; *vp,* ventral process of aedeagus, *vt,* ventral tendon.

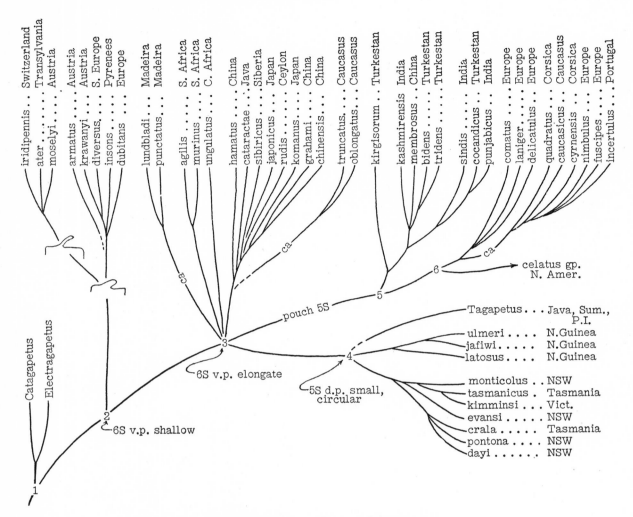

CHART 33. Phylogenetic diagram of the *Agapetini*.

end of a branch (*Glossosoma s. st.*) has its primitive steps documented by Asiatic species. The circumstantial evidence is overwhelming that this branch arose and developed in Asia. It is evident that only one branch spread to and succeeded in surviving in North America, the subgenus *Anseriglossa*.

Reviewing the story of *Glossosoma*, on Chart 29, we see that there is doubt as to the earliest history of the genus and the origin of the primitive *Ripaeglossa* branch which spread to North America. The remainder of the genus certainly originated and speciated in Asia to give rise to two large Asiatic branches. From each of these a branch spread to North America, and one (*Eomystra*) spread back and forth again. Only a few specialized branches

became established in Europe. None has yet been found in South America, Australia, or Africa, indicating the continued cool-adapted nature of the group.

## The Tribe Agapetini

The Agapetini are not primarily a montane group. While all require clear, rocky, cool streams, most of them occur in hilly country, although several species are found in the mountains. In this fashion they form a sort of fringe or peripheral group in relation to the typically mountain forms, and offer a valuable comparison from the viewpoint of dispersal patterns.

For this purpose it has been profitable to deal chiefly with the distribution and relationship of the distinctive groups of species. Little effort has been made to delve into the phylogeny of the species within these groups, except for evidence which would bear on the question of their monophyletic origin. Certain conclusions have been drawn from this analysis. Not mentioned later is the added conviction that additional records and integration of the species within these groups will yield equally interesting results on different aspects of the subject.

As indicated on Chart 27, the Agapetini probably arose from the glossosomatid Ancestor 2, which had

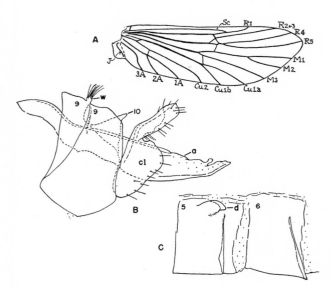

FIG. 336. Parts of male *Catagapetus nigrans*. A, hind wing; B, genitalia, lateral aspect; C, fifth and sixth sternites, lateral aspect. *a*, aedeagus; *cl*, clasper; *d*, dorsal process; *w*, wartlike process of ninth segment.

a primitive venation. The first point which we can define on the Agapetini line, shown in Chart 33, is documented jointly by the two genera *Catagapetus* and *Electragapetus*. These two genera have in common the loss of $R_{1a}$ in the front wing (Fig. 295B) and the reduction of the discal cell in the hind wing; also in the hind wing, the occasional or habitual forking of $R_{4+5}$ beyond cross-vein *s*.

*Catagapetus* is known only from a single European species *nigrans*; in its hind wing (Fig. 296B) the anal veins are well separated and complete, but Sc joins $R_1$, and $R_{2+3}$ is unbranched. The hind wing of *Electragapetus* (Fig. 296C) has vein 2A at least partially atrophied, but Sc is free to its apex and

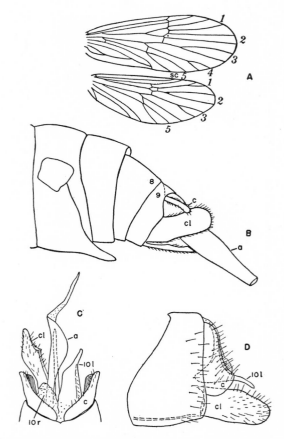

FIG. 337. Parts of male *Electragapetus, scitulus* (A, B) and *tsudai* (C, D). A, wings; B, D, genitalia, lateral aspect; C, genitalia, dorsal aspect. *a*, aedeagus; *c*, cercus; *cl*, clasper; *l*, left; *r*, right. (A, B, after Ulmer.)

$R_{2+3}$ branches near the wing margin. The hind wing of Ancestor 1 in Chart 33 undoubtedly combined the primitive features of both, and had a complete set of anal veins, $R_{2+3}$ branching near the wing margin, and Sc extending as a free vein. The genitalia of existing species of both genera are highly modified. Those of *Catagapetus nigrans* (Fig. 336) have the cerci either absent or represented only by a pair of small dorsal warts (*w*), and the lobes of the tenth tergite have been reduced to a pair of small, semimembranous triangles. In existing species of *Electragapetus* the cerci are short but extremely broad at the base, extending for some distance along the margin of the ninth segment (Fig. 337C, D); the lobes of the tenth are less reduced in one species but in *tsudai* one lobe is almost atrophied. Only in the fossil *Electragapetus scitulus* (Fig. 337B) do we find a cercus

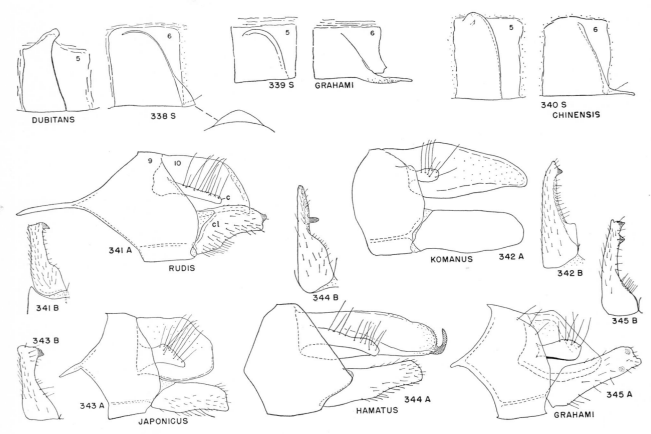

FIGS. 338-45. Parts of male *Agapetus*. *A*, genitalia, lateral aspect; *B*, clasper, ventral aspect; *S;* fifth and sixth abdominal sternites, lateral aspect. *c*, cercus; *cl*, clasper.

like that in *Agapetus*. It is probable, therefore, that Ancestor 1 had a genital capsule resembling that of this fossil species more than it does the living forms of *Electragapetus* and *Catagapetus*.

Ancestor 1 apparently gave rise to two branches. One in turn branched to produce *Catagapetus,* in which the hind wing and veins remained primitive and the branches of R changed, and *Electragapetus* in which the opposite occurred. The second branch from Ancestor 1 changed in two more hind wing characters (Fig. 296D). Cross-vein *s* disappeared entirely, in conjunction with a moving of fork $R_{4+5}$ toward the wing margin; and the anal veins became crowded together to form narrow rectangular cells. This point in the evolution of the line marks the development of the ancestral form of *Agapetus*. Other important differences in the hind wing included the shortening of Sc, and the curving of $R_1$ into it just beyond cross-vein *r* so that the apical

portion of $R_1$ looks like a cross-vein. This ancestral form had male genitalia much like those of Ancestor 1.

## The Genus Agapetus

The phylogeny of *Agapetus* has been difficult to deduce because *Agapetus* is a large, widespread genus with relatively few distinctive types of genitalic structures. I tried first to devise a scheme of relationships based on the continued reduction in venation which occurs in certain species. This reduction of hind wing pattern consists of (1) the gradual atrophy of the cross-veinlike apex of $R_1$, (2) further shortening of Sc, (3) alignment of the base of $R_1$, *r*, and the apical portion of $R_{2+3}$ to form a serial vein with scarcely an irregularity, (4) movement of the branches of Rs and $M_{1+2}$ toward the wing margin, and (5) some atrophy in the anal veins. Steps in these processes can be followed in

Figs. 296D to I. This approach proved untenable because it became evident that several different lines had paralleled each other in some or all of these developments, which appeared to be correlated more with a decrease in size than with a pectinate phylogenetic advance.

Later a curious, internal pouchlike organ was noticed in the fifth abdominal segment of the males in some species. When examining types in 1952 I noticed also that certain other male structures had been developed on these segments. Using these structures in addition to venation and male genitalic characters, it is possible to construct a phylogenetic scheme that appears to follow the actual path of evolutionary development.

The ancestral *Agapetus* male apparently had on the fifth abdominal sternite an unmodified lateral ridge as in Fig. 339, and on the sixth sternite a short, broad apicomesal process (Fig. 338). The genitalia were simple, with long, many-haired cerci. The most primitive forms existing today comprise the *dubitans* group. These resemble the deduced ancestor in having Sc and $R_1$ primitive, the sixth sternite process short and broad (Fig. 338), and the cerci ovate, but the fifth sternite has evolved a curious dorsal projection from the top of the lateral ridge (Fig. 338). In the species *dubitans, insons, diversus,* and *krawanyi* this process is thumblike; in *ater, iridipennis,* and *moselyi* the process is longer and more slender (Fig. 338). These latter three species evidently represent a separate twig of the *dubitans* group, a twig that has given rise to three species.

The first specialization of what we might call the progressive line seems to have been the elongation of the mesal process of the sixth sternite, and a narrowing of its base. At this point there evolved a form (Ancestor 3 on Chart 33) resembling *rudis* or *komanus,* primitive except for the longer and narrower process of the sixth segment, as in Fig. 340. This ancestor became widespread, then later its range was disrupted and the isolated species so produced gave rise to all the more specialized groups in the genus. Species still little changed from this ancestral type are found today in Ceylon (*rudis,* Fig. 341), Japan (*japonicus,* Fig. 343, and *komanus,* Fig. 342), Java (*cataractae*), and others in Burma, China, India, and Siberia. Each of these is known from a very small area, in spite of considerable collecting in intervening localities.

An Asiatic group which arose from a primitive ancestor is characterized in the male by a sclerotized, upturned process arising from the tip of the clasper (Fig. 344). Known members of the group include *hamatus* (Fig. 344) from southeastern China and *albomaculatus, incurvatus, foliatus,* and *mitis* from Burma.

A population of this early ancestor became isolated on Madeira, developing into the *punctata* line. In this line the cerci atrophied.

*New Guinea and Australian Fauna.* One segregate of Ancestor 3 certainly occurred in the eastern portion of ancient Sundaland and gave rise to the *monticolus* group known from New Guinea and Australia. The males of this group developed a curious blister-like protuberance on the dorsal margin of the fifth sternite, detached from the ridge (Fig. 353). The three New Guinea species (*jafiwi, ulmeri,* and *latosus*) bear no marked resemblance to the Australian species, which appear to belong to distinctive units. This indicates that the first distinctive ancestor of the *monticolus* group spread into both areas, became segregated into New Guinea and Australian populations, and the progeny of these populations have not redispersed from one area to the other since that time.

The three known New Guinea species can be grouped into two units or complexes. In one the cerci are short and thick (*ulmeri* and *jafiwi,* Figs. 346, 347), in the other the cerci are long, unusually slender, and slightly clavate (*latosus,* Fig. 348). These represent collections made by Mr. Harry Hoogstraal from only two localities, Dorema and Hollandia. How many more unknown species might be discovered if extensive collections were made in these South Pacific Islands!

The seven Australian species form three well-marked complexes, based on male genitalia.

1. The first complex consists of *crala, pontona,* and *dayi* (Fig. 350), in which the anterior margin of the ninth segment is angulate or produced near the midlateral line, the claspers have mesal teeth reminiscent of primitive Oriental species such as *grahami,* and other characters are little modified from the same type. This seems to represent the most primitive complex of *Agapetus* in Australia.

2. The second complex consists of a single species *evansi* in which the clasper has a curious setose process at its base (Fig. 349, *sp*).

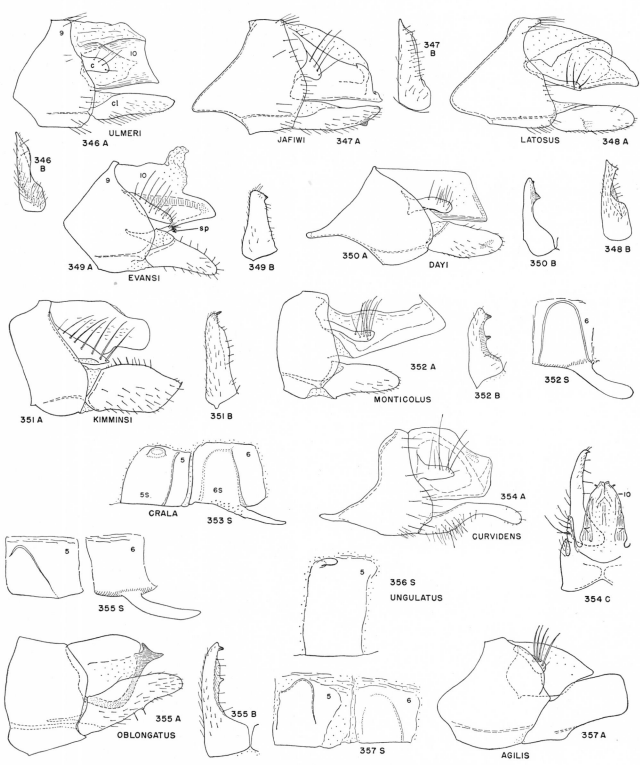

FIGS. 346-57. Parts of male *Agapetus*. A, genitalia, lateral aspect; B, clasper, ventral aspect; C, genitalia, dorsal aspect; S, abdominal sternites. *c*, cercus, *cl*, clasper; *sp*, setate process at base of clasper.

3. In the three species of the third complex, the anterior and posterior margins of the ninth segment are nearly parallel. In one of these species (*montanicolus*) the tenth tergite is elongate and has a dorsal point (Fig. 352), in the other two (*tasmanicus* and *kimminsi*) the tenth tergite is simple but the base of the cercus is greatly broadened (Fig. 351).

There is apparently a hit-and-miss variation in the shape of the process of the sixth sternite. In some species it is short and pointed, in others it is long and pointed, and in still others it is long and clavate as in *montanicolus* (similar to Fig. 355S).

On the basis of our present knowledge, this entire aggregation of Australian species is restricted to the montane areas of southeastern Australia and Tasmania. The two Tasmanian species each belong to a different complex, and each is indubitably related to a mainland species. Other than demonstrating that speciation of the montane fauna has occurred in the region, few definite conclusions can be drawn from the known fauna. If other species exist in the other hill or mountain areas of Australia, their discovery will add material of great interest in the interpretation of past changes in continental conditions. Certain it is that *Agapetus* species have traversed the Australian continent in past times in order to reach the areas in which they are now found. It should not be forgotten that additional material from the New Guinea and Sunda Islands region will be equally necessary as either explanatory or confirmatory evidence concerning the evolution of this genus in Australia.

*African Groups.* Two groups of *Agapetus* occur in montane areas of Africa, the *ungulatus* group in Uganda and the *agilis* group in South Africa. The first contains only the one species *ungulatus,* in which the cerci and the ventral process of the sixth segment are atrophied, but the anterodorsal corner of the fifth sternite has a curious thumblike process and the tenth tergite has very peculiar lobes. The *agilis* group contains two species, *agilis* and *murinus.* In these the fifth sternite is simple, cerci are present, and in *murinus* the sixth sternite has a simple process.

Each group has characters which ally it with some ancestral form such as *rudis.* The inference is that these African groups also originated from the dispersal of the same ancestral form which gave

rise to the *montanicolus* and *rudis* groups. In the present state of our knowledge it is impossible to say whether both African groups originated from the same dispersal, or whether the *agilis* group arose from an earlier one and the *ungulatus* group from a later spread.

*Caucasian Group.* Two Caucasian species, *oblongatus* and *truncatus,* are also closely allied to the primitive *rudis* group, differing chiefly in lacking cerci on the male genitalia. We have here another offshoot of a primitive ancestral form, but again it is difficult to even hazard a guess as to its origin in relation to other branches.

. . . . .

Up to this point we have discussed the more primitive forms of *Agapetus* which constitute the subgenus *Synagapetus.* Two other more highly specialized lines arose, designated as the subgenera *Tagapetus* and *Agapetus.*

### The Subgenus Tagapetus

There occurs in Sundaland and the Philippines the curious subgenus *Tagapetus* containing two very small species, *abbreviatus* and *curvidens.* The male fifth sternite has lost its ridge and has no distinctive structures. The male sixth sternite has a fairly short, sharp point, and the male genitalia (Fig. 354) are simple, bearing much resemblance to those of such primitive types as *grahami.* In *Tagapetus* the hind wing has undergone additional reduction, with M only 2-branched, but with Sc still fairly long (Fig. 296I). This little subgenus must therefore have originated from a primitive species which spread into the south Pacific island area, or from a branch of the *monticolus* group.

After its genetic segregation, *Tagapetus* seems to have become adapted to either warmer water, larger streams, or both, because it is found in the Philippine Islands in company with moderately warm-adapted genera of Psychomyiidae and Leptoceridae. In this region *Tagapetus* behaves much like the Protoptilinae in the Americas, being collected at lights in goodly numbers.

### The Subgenus Agapetus

The most distinctive line of *Agapetus* developed an invaginated pouch on the fifth sternite of the male. This unusual structure began as an invagination under the edge of the posterodorsal portion of

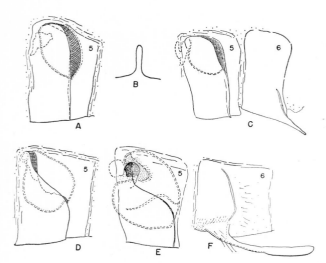

FIG. 358. Abdominal sternites of *Agapetus*, all lateral aspect except *B*, which is ventral aspect of process of fifth sternite. *A, B, kirgisorum; C, cocandicus; D, pinatus; E, F, caucasicus.*

the primitive sclerotized ridge (Fig. 358A, C). Later the pouch became larger (Fig. 358D) and the opening became sinuate and completely membranous, and finally there developed a round opening at the anterodorsal point (Fig. 358E). This entire group comprises the subgenus *Agapetus*.

The original ancestor of the subgenus (Ancestor 5, Chart 33) was similar in all other respects to the ancestor of the *rudis* group, with the exception that in the hind wings Sc was a little shorter and the apical portion of $R_1$ was weak. It is highly likely that subgenus *Agapetus* arose from Ancestor 3 (Chart 33).

The first division of Ancestor 5 was into the *bidens* group, in which the pouch remained simple but dorsal sclerotized rods developed on the lobes of the tenth tergite; and into Ancestor 6, which developed a more complex pouch (Fig. 358D) but retained a primitive type of male genitalia. Ancestor 6 in turn gave rise to two groups, a North American branch which shows little advance over Ancestor 6, and a European branch which has given rise to even more advanced types.

The *bidens* group has subsequently evolved into three well-marked complexes or subgroups, all of them known only from the mountainous area stretching from Turkestan to southern China. The most primitive is the *kirgisorum* subgroup, which has ovate cerci and simple claspers (Fig. 359). The tenth tergite, however, is unusually long. I have

seen specimens of only the Turkestan species *kirgisorum,* but Martynov's illustrations indicate that *triangularis* from India and *jakutorum* from Siberia belong with it.

The two other complexes of the *bidens* group arose from a common ancestral form in which the cerci became reduced to small protuberances and bore only one or two setae (Figs. 360, 362). In other characters this ancestral form must have been much like *kirgisorum.* Two groups evolved from this ancestor. In one the claspers became divided into two or three lobes (Fig. 360), and both claspers and tenth tergite became shorter. This group

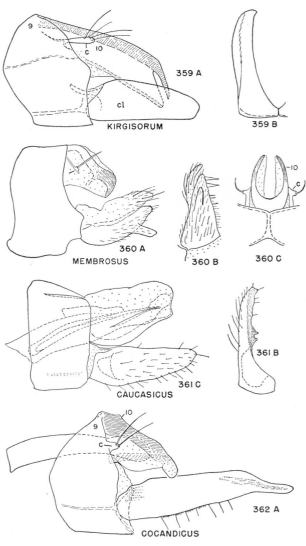

FIGS. 359-62. Male genitalia of *Agapetus*. *A*, lateral aspect; *B*, clasper, ventral aspect; *C*, dorsal aspect. *c*, cercus; *cl*, clasper.

contains *kashmirensis, membrosus, bidens,* and *tridens.* In the other group first the claspers and tenth tergite became moderately elongate (as in *sindis*) and subsequently the first branch of the radial sector in the front wing moved close to its point of separation from $R_1$. The two known species representing this advanced type are *cocandicus* and *punjabicus.*

The restricted distribution of all known forms of the *bidens* group leads to the conclusion that its ancestor arose in the Himalayan region and that the evolution of the entire group has taken place in that area.

The American branch arising from Ancestor 6 has spread to the mountain and hill country of temperate North America and developed into about 25 species. All have the intermediate type of fifth sternite pouch (Fig. 358D); many have a faint indication of the tip of $R_1$ in the hind wing (Fig. 296E); all have well-developed cerci; and all have a small process on the male sixth sternite. From this it follows that since its isolation in North America the group has very nearly stood still in an evolutionary sense except for developing differences in details of male genitalia as speciation progressed. Its unity of characters indicates that the American branch is monophyletic, or if not—that it originated from a few very similar species.

The European branch apparently first added specializations to the fifth sternite pouch. It became more convoluted internally and developed a complex opening at the anterior corner (Fig. 358E). At the same time the apex of $R_1$ in the hind wing was lost, and the serial vein $R_1+r+R_{2+3}$ became almost straight (Fig. 296H). The *comatus* group, containing *comatus, laniger* and *delicatulus,* represents this stage in the evolution of the group. The next and final stage was the loss of the cerci and the atrophy of $R_2$, resulting in the *fuscipes* group. In this group the process of the male sixth sternite became elongate, often clavate, and situated near the middle of the segment. This is a fairly large group, embracing six species (Fig. 361).

### Agapetine Dispersal

In reviewing the distribution on Chart 33, it is seen that the early ancestral forms, *Catagapetus* and *Electragapetus,* center in Eurasia, the most primitive *Agapetus* group (*dubitans*) is confined to Europe, and the next series of groups related to the *rudis* group appear to radiate from an Asiatic

center. It seems highly likely from this that the Agapetini originated as a European segregate, giving rise to a primitive branch which evolved into a European *Catagapetus-Electragapetus* branch and to the first true *Agapetus,* Ancestor 2, also European. Judging from the occurrence of a primitive type of *Electragapetus* in the Baltic amber of Germany, it would appear that a member of this group spread to Asia at a later time. Ancestor 2 in turn evolved into a little-changed line which remained in Europe and evolved into the *dubitans* group, and into a more specialized, widespread form, Ancestor 3. This progenitor spread to Sundaland, to Africa and probably to all parts of Asia as well as to Madeira. "Pseudopods" of the range of this ancestral form became isolated in the New Guinea–Australia area and in two parts of Africa, where each developed into a distinctive group. A population apparently reached Madeira and has persisted there with little change.

The pouch-bearing subgenus *Agapetus* seems also to have arisen in Asia. The present distribution can be explained by several hypothetical dispersal patterns, but the facts seem to require that the ancestor of the subgenus arose in south central Asia, and gave rise to a Himalayan segregate which developed into the *bidens* group, and to a more northern Ancestor 6. Ancestor 6 could readily have developed in northern Asia, become Holarctic, then been broken into two units, a North American and a Eurasian. A second alternative would be that Ancestor 5 spread directly to North America, and Ancestor 6 evolved in the New World, later spreading either (A) across an Atlantic bridge into Europe, or (B) back across Asia and into Europe.

These alternatives highlight a pair of extremely puzzling biogeographic problems. Alternative 2A brings up the question of an Atlantic bridge. Alternatives 1 and 2B bring up the question as to what happened to many northern populations in Asia, especially warm temperate forms, which appear to have spread across this area at some time in the past, but are not known there now. These questions will be discussed in Chapters 6 and 7.

### Subfamily Protoptilinae

The Protoptilinae are small in size, ranging from about 2.5 to 5 or 6 mm. in length. Along with this size reduction there has been a marked change in certain other characters. The wing veins have lost some of their branches, notably $Cu_{1b}$ and $M_{3+4}$ in the front wing and $R_{2+3}$ in the hind wing. The preapical spurs of the front tibiae are reduced to hairs, or are absent, and the male genitalia have lost the cerci.

Species of this subfamily are seldom found in company with other members of their family. They

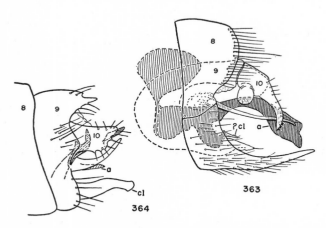

FIGS. 363-64. Male genitalia of Protoptilinae, lateral aspect. 363, *Protoptila lega;* 364, *Matrioptila jeanae.* a, aedeagus; *cl,* claspers.

frequent a definitely warmer type of stream and often abound in some of the large, cool rivers. Apparently clear water during most of the year is a prerequisite for their existence, as is also a fairly rapid flow.

Ecologically this subfamily has no place in this report, but the Protoptilinae do raise a few pertinent questions and offer a possible answer to one nagging question regarding the evolution of the family. Consequently I am giving here a very brief outline of those points which have a bearing on the case at hand.

The Protoptilinae are restricted to the Americas but are widespread in that area, occurring from southern Canada to central Chile. The two most primitive genera (*Matrioptila* and *Antoptila*) occur in southeastern North America and central South America, respectively. These two genera also represent the two major phyletic lines of the subfamily. In *Matrioptila* males (Fig. 364) the ninth and tenth segments are simple and recognizably glossosomatid in general structure. The ninth segment forms a moderately regular ring, the tenth tergite is divided into a pair of simple lobes, and the claspers are elongate and distinct, although more firmly

attached to the aedeagus than to the ninth sternite. This latter point, however, is not unusual in other Glossosomatidae. The front wing has $Cu_1$ and $Cu_2$ separate and distinct for their entire length, and $Cu_1$ is a strong vein in comparison with M. The hind wing lacks many vein branches but has $Cu_1$ branched, and in this character is quite primitive. No other close relative is known.

In *Antoptila* and its allies the male genitalia (Fig. 363) have undergone such extensive change that many parts have not yet been homologized with certainty. The ninth segment appears to consist chiefly of an arcuate portion with little dorsal or ventral extent, but the whole is invaginated deeply into the eighth and seventh segments. The claspers are unidentifiable as such, but are undoubtedly represented by some of the small processes associated with the ventral articulation of the aedeagus.

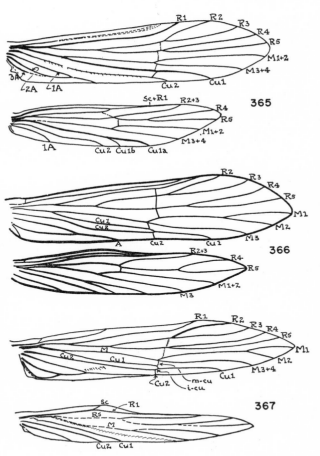

FIGS. 365-67. Wings of Protoptilinae. 365, *Matrioptila jeanae;* 366, *Antoptila brasiliana* (after Mosely); 367, *Protoptila erotica.*

In *Antoptila* Cu₁ is branched in the hind wing, in this primitive character resembling *Matrioptila*, but M has retained three branches in both wings (2 in *Matrioptila*). The characteristics of Cu in the front wing have changed profoundly (Figs. 366, 367). Cu₂ runs close to Cu₁ some distance from the wing margin, and Cu₁ basad of this point has become a weak vein subordinated to the stem of M. The basal part of Cu₂, the apical part of Cu₁, and the cross-vein which connects them are arranged to form what appears to be a continuous vein. The weak basal part of Cu₁ appears as a piece distinct from the serial vein below it. In addition, the short setae situated in *Matrioptila* on Cu₂, appear in the *Antoptila* series to have moved to the area between Cu₂ and 1A, where they form a short row (Fig. 367). Both the venational arrangement of Cu₂ and Cu₁, and the movement of the setae are most unusual in the Trichoptera.

Unlike the solitary genus *Matrioptila*, *Antoptila* represents a point near the base of an extensive evolutionary branch which has culminated in the genus *Protoptila*. The species of this genus extend from central South America to northern Ontario in North America.

In the earlier part of this chapter it was pointed out that the subfamily Protoptilinae was an offshoot of Ancestor 2 in Chart 27. It is therefore quite conceivable that *Matrioptila* is an archaic genus representing the first discovered step in protoptiline evolution. This would imply that the subfamily arose in North America, and that an early form spread to South America, giving rise to the *Antoptila* line. *Matrioptila* would then represent the most primitive known remnant of this widespread protoptiline ancestor.

### Early Glossosomatid Dispersal

Let us review the indications of origin for the main lines of the Glossosomatidae, that is, the three known descendants of Ancestor 2 in Chart 27. *Glossosoma* presumably arose in Asia or North America. Certainly its great development stemmed from an Asiatic ancestor. The Agapetini certainly arose in Eurasia, probably in Europe. The Protoptilinae probably arose in North America, or at least from an American offshoot from Ancestor 2.

Conditions which would bring these postulated areas of origin into harmony with the family tree diagrammed in Chart 2 are readily postulated. *Ana-*

*gapetus*-like Ancestor 1 was probably a North American form, then as now restricted to relatively high montane areas. Ancestor 2, which arose from it, became widespread over Eurasia and parts of North America. When its range contracted, it left in Europe an element which became the Agapetini, and possibly in the southern part of North America an element which became the Protoptilinae.

A third element, ultimately to become *Glossosoma*, may have had a range embracing either northeastern Asia or northwestern North America, or both. Whichever actually may have happened, the possibilities are obvious that some such situation could readily account for either an intercontinental break in a widespread population of primeval *Glossosoma*, or an extension of its range into another continent, to produce a pre-*Ripaeglossa* population in North America, and an ancestral form for the remainder of the genus in Asia.

## SYSTEMATIC ACCOUNT

The family Glossosomatidae is readily diagnosed in the larval stage on the basis of the curious anal leg, in which sclerite *s* is large and the claw is small (Fig. 9F, G). On the venter of the prothorax the larva has a pair of large semisclerotized plates which extend between the coxae and make a bridge posterior to the head. In the adult the mouthparts are similar in both sexes, the maxillary palps are 5-segmented, the ocelli are distinct and situated some distance from the eye, and the dorsal warts of the pronotum are separated by a distance equal to the long measurement of one of them.

In subdividing the family a strictly dichotomic system is difficult to apply because of the identification problems involved. It seems best to segregate *Protoptila* and its allies as a separate subfamily, the Protoptilinae, because of the distinctness exhibited by all stages of the life history. The remainder form a compact unit, the Glossosomatinae, which can be divided into tribes on the basis of the distinct phylogenetic lines they form (see Chart 27).

### Key to Subfamilies

Adult with front tibiae having a pair of apical spines which are prominent and sclerotized. Larva with anal claw having only 1 large and 1 small tooth . . . . . . . . . . . . . . . . . . . . . . . **Glossosomatinae**
Adult with front tibiae having only hairlike apical spines

or none. Larva with anal claw divided into about
7 teeth .......................Protoptilinae

## Subfamily Glossosomatinae

Three tribes are erected to accommodate the
three distinct phylogenetic divisions of this subfamily. These include (1) the primitive genus *Anagapetus,* (2) the genus *Glossosoma,* and (3) the
line ending with *Agapetus.*

### KEY TO TRIBES

1. Mesepisternum divided by a short, transverse suture...................... ... **Anagapetini**
   Mesepisternum divided by a central constriction of
   its anterior and posterior sutures......  2
2. Hind wing with cell 1st R$_3$ small (Fig. 296B) or
   absent (Fig. 296D), vein R$_{2+3}$ either unbranched or branched beyond cross-vein *s*..
   ............................. **Agapetini**
   Hind wing with cell 1st R$_3$ larger (as in Fig. 296A),
   vein R$_{2+3}$ branched before cross-vein *s*.....
   ...................... **Glossosomatini**

### Tribe Anagapetini

The tribe contains only the genus *Anagapetus*
Ross (1938a:109), with *debilis* (Ross) the type
species. Only four species are known, all occurring
in the western portion of North America; revised
by Ross (1951b), and illustrated in Fig. 297.

**bernea** Ross (1947:131). Oregon, Washington.
**chandleri** Ross (1951b:142). California.
**debilis** (Ross), *Agapetus* (1938a:108); Denning
   (1948b:113). Colorado, Montana, Oregon, Utah,
   Wyoming; British Columbia.
**hoodi** Ross (1951b:143). Oregon.

### Tribe Glossosomatini

Contains a single genus *Glossosoma,* which is
divided into a large number of subgenera on the
basis of differences in the male sex. To date, characters have not been discovered to define these groupings in the female sex.

### Genus **Glossosoma** Curtis

#### KEY TO SUBGENERA

1. Lateral margins of ninth segment produced into
   large lateral flaps making a hoodlike arrangement enclosing most of the male genitalia (Fig.
   299) .......................**Ripaeglossa**
   Lateral margins not produced into lateral flaps cov-
   ing genitalia ........................  2
2. Claspers either absent (Fig. 326) or represented by
   a single mesal process (Figs. 325, 327)...  3
   Claspers present, the two usually separate to base

(Fig. 322), but in one species fused on the
   basal half (Fig. 313)..................  5
3. Ninth sternite bearing a single, long sclerotized
   process which is always asymmetrical (Fig.
   327) ...................**Glossosoma s. st.**
   Ninth sternite at most with short asymmetrical processes as in Fig. 326.....................  4
4. Aedeagus with a single pair of slender ventral
   processes; no large flap below lobes of tenth
   tergite (Fig. 325)..............**Muroglossa**
   Aedeagus with no ventral process; a large pair of
   ribbon-like flaps below and extending beyond
   lobes of tenth tergite (Fig. 326)..**Anseriglossa**
5. Claspers with basal halves fused on the ventromeson
   (Fig. 313) ....................**Sinoglossa**
   Claspers fused only at extreme base, or not at all   6
6. Aedeagus with a pair of dorsal clavate processes
   (*d*) capped with a spinose area (Fig. 314)   7
   Aedeagus without dorsal spinose processes   9
7. Spinose processes confluent with dorsal margin of
   aedeagus (Fig. 314); clasper composed of a
   pair of long, slender, hairless processes separate
   to base ....................**Diploglossa**
   Spinose processes projecting dorsad and connected
   to body of aedeagus by a membranous articulation (Fig. 315); claspers various.....  8
8. Spinose processes with narrow base and large head;
   lateral tendon with its base attached to a
   membrane (Fig. 315)..........**Synafophora**
   Spinose processes with base stout (Fig. 320) or
   head narrow (Fig. 317); lateral tendon with
   its base attached to the side of the aedeagus
   cup...........................**Eomystra**
9. Both aedeagus and claspers short, the former with
   no external processes (Fig. 298)..**Protoglossa**
   Both aedeagus and claspers more elongate, the
   aedeagus with either one stout external process
   (Fig. 323) or a pair of slender, inconspicuous
   processes (Fig. 324)...........**Lipoglossa**

### **Ripaeglossa** new subgenus

Type species: *Glossosoma parvulum* Banks.

*Diagnosis:* Male with anal area of front wing
bearing a large, opaque and thickened sensory
area. Hind tibia with spurs sharp and simple. Male
genitalia with lateral margin of ninth segment forming hoodlike posterior side pieces within which the
other parts of the genitalia are withdrawn in repose; claspers present and simple; tenth tergite divided into two lobes, each bearing laterally a
cercus-like process; aedeagus articulating by a solid
strap with the ninth sternite near the base of the
claspers, the basal and apical parts of the aedeagus
joined firmly or practically fused.

This subgenus is restricted in range to the mountains of western North America, and includes all

the species of the genus found there except *peni-tum* and two species of the subgenus *Eomystra*.

KEY TO SPECIES

1.  Cercus with a sharp, preapical sclerotized spine (Fig. 299) (*Parvulum Group*)... ................................ 2
Cercus with no spine, but in some species with a swollen, beanlike process near apex (Fig. 308)............... 6

2(1).  Base of clasper convoluted (Fig. 301)..... ...................... ventrale
Base of clasper straight or slightly curved, never with a spiral convolution (Fig. 300)...................... 3

3(2).  Aedeagus bearing a pair of heavily sclerotized, ventral rods as long as the body of the aedeagus (Fig. 299), in addition to a pair of inconspicuous membranous processes .................... velona
Aedeagus with sclerotized rods much shorter, but the pair of thin, membranous processes little different (Figs. 300-302)   4

4(3).  Clasper elongate and slightly thickened at apex (Fig. 300)........... parvulum
Clasper shorter, and not thickened at apex (Fig. 302).................... 5

5(4).  Sixth and seventh sternites having mesal processes; basal spine on cercus as long as cercus, base of clasper twice as wide as apical portion, in lateral view...... ...................... montana
Sixth and seventh sternites without mesal processes; basal spine on cercus only half dorsal length of cercus; base of clasper only slightly wider than apical portion.................... idaho

6(1).  Cercus long and whiplike (Fig. 303) (*Alascense Group*) ................. 7
Cercus short and bearing near apex a swollen, bean-shaped projection (Fig. 308) (*Traviatum Group*) ................. 11

7(6).  Cercus exceedingly long, bearing a band of minute spines along apical fourth... 8
Cercus shorter, bearing at most a small patch of spines near apex (Figs. 303, 304) 10

8(7).  Ventral edge of clasper angled mesad to form a wide, flat, ventral flange (Ross & Spencer 1952, Fig. 4)....... alascense
Ventral edge of clasper thin, like a knife edge ............................ 9

9(8).  Clasper with apex narrowed to a long point, and with ventral margin very concave (Denning 1948b, Fig. 27)...... califica
Clasper with apex rounded and ventral margin straight or convex (Ross & Spencer 1952, Fig. 3) ................. wenatchee

10(7).  Sclerotized portion of tenth tergite lobes massive; clasper only gradually narrowed near base; cercus with small "heel" near base, and a thickened portion bearing spines at apex (Fig. 304)..... pyroxum
Sclerotized portion of tenth tergite forming only a shallow strap; clasper constricted to form a stemlike neck near base; cercus having a large "heel" near base, the apex narrow, bearing no spines except for an unusually long apical spine (Fig. 303).. ........................ pterna

11(6).  Aedeagus very similar to that of *pterna* (Fig. 307) having a slender, tubular basal projection and a curved ventral arm some distance from base......... oregonense
Aedeagus shorter and bowed, partially or wholly fused with the runner-like set of long basal rods.................. 12

12(11).  Clasper short and triangular; aedeagus with ventral process completely fused with ventral bands (Denning 1948b, Fig. 28) ........................... mereca
Clasper elongate (Fig. 308); base of ventral process of aedeagus fused with ventral bands, but in some species its apex projecting beyond the clasper base as a sclerotized process (Fig. 309)...... 13

13(12).  Clasper having a large broad base tapering gradually to apex where its ventral margin is twisted mesad (Fig. 305). excitum
Clasper having only a small ventral enlargement at base.................... 14

14(13).  Clasper markedly sinuate (Denning 1954, Fig. 4) ..................... bruna
Clasper nearly straight (Figs. 308, 309).. 15

15(14).  Apex of clasper truncate, the ventral corner forming a stout spine curved mesad (Fig. 309) ....................... traviatum
Apex of clasper tapering to a triangular apex, the apical spine small (Fig. 308). schuhi

LIST OF SPECIES

Parvulum Group

idaho Ross (1941:41). Idaho, Montana.
montana Ross (1941:42). Utah to Washington. Fig. 302.
parvulum Banks (1904:108). New Mexico to Idaho. Fig. 300.
velona Ross (1938a:109). Utah to Oregon. Fig. 299.
ventrale Banks (1904:109). Arizona to south central Wyoming. Fig. 301.

Alascense Group

alascense Banks (1900:472); Ross & Spencer (1952: 49). Utah to Alaska. Fig. 306.
califica Denning (1948b:114). California, Oregon.
pterna Ross (1947:130). California. Fig. 303.
pyroxum Ross (1941:42). Oregon, Washington. Fig. 304.
wenatchee Ross & Spencer (1952:45). British Columbia, Oregon, Washington.

### Traviatum Group

**bruna** Denning (1954:59). California.
**excitum** Ross (1938a:109). Oregon to Montana. Fig. 305.
**mereca** Denning (1948b:114). California.
**oregonense** Ling (1938:62). California, Oregon. Fig. 307.
**schuhi** Ross (1947:130). Oregon to Idaho. Fig. 308.
**traviatum** Banks (1936:266). Oregon to Montana. Fig. 309.

### Protoglossa new subgenus

Type species: *Glossosoma taeniatum* Ross & Hwang.

*Diagnosis*: Venation, spurs, and general body structure as in *Ripaeglossa*. Male genitalia extremely simple (Fig. 298); claspers separate and short; aedeagus composed of a simple short tube joined to base of claspers by a curved sclerotized strap. Female unknown.

Contains only the type species:
**taeniatum** Ross & Hwang (1953:8). Szechuan, China. Fig. 298.

### Sinoglossa new subgenus

Type species: *Glossosoma sellatum* Ross & Hwang.

*Diagnosis*: Venation, spurs, and general body structure as in *Ripaeglossa*. Male genitalia distinctive (Fig. 313); lobes of tenth tergite simple; claspers short, the ventral margins fused more than halfway to apex resulting in a two-lobed, single structure; aedeagus elongate vasiform, without processes, recessed within the large, hollowed ventral strap which is shoehorn-shaped.

Contains only the type species:
**sellatum** Ross & Hwang (1953:8). Szechuan, China. Fig. 313.

### Subgenus Diploglossa Martynov

*Diploglossa* Martynov (1934:85). Type species: *Glossosoma nylanderi* McLachlan (monobasic).

Contains only the type species:
**nylanderi** McLachlan (1879:474); Martynov (1934:86). Finland to Siberia. Fig. 314.

### Subgenus Synafophora Martynov

*Synafophora* Martynov (1927b:165). Type species: *Synafophora kiritshenkoi* Martynov (original designation).

Contains two species from Asia, revised in Martynov 1934:
**kiritshenkoi** (Martynov) (1927b: 167; 1934:83). Turkestan. Fig. 315.
**minutum** (Martynov) (1927b:166; 1934:83). Turkestan.

### Subgenus Eomystra Martynov

*Mystrophora* Klapalek (1892:19). Type species: *Mystrophora intermedia* Klapalek (monobasic). Preoccupied.
*Eomystra* Martynov (1934:84). Type species: *Eomystra dulkejti* Martynov (monobasic).
*Mystrophorella* Kloet & Hincks (1944:97). N. n. for *Mystrophora* Klapalek, 1892, *nec*. Kayser, 1871.

This subgenus is characterized by a modified outer apical tibial spur on the hind leg of the male. In most species this spur is short and broad, with a pointed and hooklike apical process; in *dulkejti* this spur has the apex bifid to produce two slender apical processes instead of one; and in *ussuricum* it is simple but curved.

The subgenus is Holarctic. I have been able to place the following nine described species in the subgenus.

#### KEY TO SPECIES

1. Clasper having a long slender process arising from the base of, and extending nearly as far posteriorly as the main body of, the clasper (Fig. 321) . . . . . . . . . . . . . . . . . 2
   Clasper having only a very short basal process (Fig. 316) or none . . . . . . . . . . . . . . . 4
2(1). Lobe of tenth tergite with an irregularly serrate, narrow downcurved process overhanging the main body of the lobe (Fig. 321) . . . . . . . . . . . . . . . . . . . . . . . .**lividum**
   Lobe of tenth tergite without a long dorsal process . . . . . . . . . . . . . . . . . . . . . . . . 3
3(2). Outer apical spur of hind tibia bifid at tip, having 2 slender, apical processes (Martynov 1934, Figs. 47, 48) . . . . . . . . . . .**dulkejti**
   Outer apical spur of hind tibia with a single apical process angled over end of spur (Betten 1934, Pl. 8, Figs. 4-6, Pl. 9, Figs. 1-5) . . . . . . . . . . . . . . . . . . . . . .**nigrior**
4(1). Clasper enlarged in middle and tapering to a very narrow apex; cercus with apex incised and clawlike from lateral view (Fig. 316) . . . . . . . . . . . . . . . . . . . . . 5
   Clasper thickest near apex; apex of cercus not clawlike . . . . . . . . . . . . . . . . . . . . . 6
5(4). Tapered end of clasper longer than thicker basal portion (Fig. 316) (Tsuda 1940b, Fig. 2) . . . . . . . . . . . . . . . . . . . . .**altaicum**

Tapered end of clasper only about a third of the clasper (Tsuda 1940*b*, Fig. 3) . . . . . . . . . . . . . . . . . . . . . . **hospitum**

6(4). Lobe of tenth tergite with apicodorsal corner produced into a short, sharp point (Fig. 317) . . . . . . . . . . . . . . . . . . . . . . 7
Lobe of tenth tergite with apicodorsal corner rounded (Fig. 320) or quadrate . . . . . 8

7(6). Lobes of tenth tergite with a pair of long, slender processes between them (Fig. 318) . . . . . . . . . . . . . . . . . . . . . . **intermedium**
Lobes of tenth tergite without processes between them, sometimes each lobe with a short process midway on the dorsal margin (Fig. 317) . . . . . . . . . . . . . . . . . **verdona**

8(6). Lobe of tenth tergite subtriangular; with no definite posterior margin (Fig. 320) . . . **inops**
Lobe of tenth tergite subquadrate, the posterior margin sinuate and the apicodorsal corner nearly square (Martynov 1934, Fig. 48) . . . . . . . . . . . . . . . . . . . . . . . **ussuricum**

### LIST OF SPECIES

**altaicum** (Martynov), *Mystrophora* (1914*a*:1; 1934: 76). Eastern Asia, Japan.
*Mystrophora lauta* Tsuda (1940*b*:191). Fig. 316.
This synonymy was kindly provided by Dr. Tsuda.
**dulkejti** (Martynov), *Eomystra* (1934:84). Great Shanter Island, Siberia.
**hospitum** (Tsuda), *Mystrophora* (1940*b*:192). Japan (Honshu).
**inops** (Tsuda), *Mystrophora* (1940*b*:193). Japan (Honshu). Fig. 320.
**intermedium** (Klapalek), *Mystrophora* (1892:19). Holarctic, northern. Fig. 318.
**lividum** (Hagen), *Tinodes* (1861:295). Northeastern North America. Fig. 321.
*Glossosoma americanum* Banks (1897:31).
*Mystrophora* sp., Betten (1934:141).
The types of Hagen's and Bank's names are both females, externally indistinguishable from females of *nigrior*. The two differ slightly in characters of the internal genitalia, those of *lividum* having the spermatheca more heavily sclerotized and vasiform, those of *nigrior* having the spermatheca little sclerotized and irregular in shape. A careful comparison of the two types involved has demonstrated that they belong to the same species and are distinct from *nigrior*. A series of both sexes from Quebec shows that the New York male described without a name in 1934 by Dr. Betten belongs to this species.
**nigrior** Banks (1911:355); Betten (1934; 140), as *Mystrophora americana*. Eastern North America.
*Eomystra unica* Denning (1942:46).
**verdona** Ross (1938*a*:110). Utah, Wyoming. Fig. 317.
**ussuricum** (Martynov), *Mystrophora* (1934:79). South Ussuri, Siberia.

## Subgenus **Lipoglossa** Martynov

*Lipoglossa* Martynov (1930:72). Type species: *Lipoglossa himalayana* Martynov (monobasic).

I am including in this subgenus three Asiatic species which are unlike in a large number of particulars, but have in common the retraction of the aedeagus cup into the abdomen.

### KEY TO SPECIES

1. Clasper incised at apex to form a pair of sharp, triangular points (Fig. 322) . . . . . . . . . **kelleyi**
Clasper with apex undivided . . . . . . . . . . . . . . 2
2. Clasper shorter than lobe of tenth tergite and without terminal large spines (Fig. 323) . . . . . . . . . . . . . . . . . . . . . . . . . . . . **himalayanum**
Clasper much longer than lobe of tenth tergite (Fig. 324) . . . . . . . . . . . . . . . . . . . . . . . . . . . 3
3. Aedeagus bearing a pair of slender lateral spines; clasper surmounted by a brush of about 6 long, wide spines (Fig. 324) . . . . . . . . . . . . **aveleta**
Aedeagus bearing only a single stout, lateral spine, much as in Fig. 323D; clasper with only slender hair at tip (Kimmins 1953*d*, Fig. 7) . . . . . . . . . . . . . . . . . . . . . . . . . . . . . **burmanum**

### LIST OF SPECIES

**aveleta** Ross & Hwang (1953:8). Szechuan, China. Fig. 324.
**burmanum** Kimmins (1953*d*:172). Burma.
**himalayanum** (Martynov), *Lipoglossa* (1930:72); Kimmins (1953*d*:174). Tibet. Fig. 323.
**kelleyi** new name. Szechuan, China. Fig. 322.
*Glossosoma minutum* Banks (1947:104). Preoccupied.

## **Muroglossa** new subgenus

Type species: *Glossosoma confluens* Kimmins.

*Diagnosis*: Diagnosed primarily on the basis of the male genitalia (Fig. 325). Tenth tergite composed of simple lobes; both claspers reduced to a single, short mesal flap. Aedeagus with a pair of elongate, slender ventral processes each articulating by means of a membranous base; the sheath surrounding the basal part of the aedeagus is joined to the tenth tergite by a curious, small, folded sclerite (*tf*) shown in Fig. 325C.

Contains only the type species:
**confluens** Kimmins (1953*d*: 169). Burma, Fig. 325.

## Subgenus **Glossosoma** Curtis

*Glossosoma* Curtis (1834:216). Type species: *Glossosoma boltoni* (monobasic).

This contains the assemblage of Eurasian forms

which have no discernible claspers, but a single, large, ventral, asymmetrical projection. In copulation the aedeagus is exserted to the left of this process.

The key to species given below must be considered as provisional, especially with regard to the *vernale* complex, because the status of many names will not be certain until the species concept is clarified within the complex. I hope it will be of some service, at least in orienting existing names and assisting in arriving at a tentative identification. Martynov's species *unguiculatum* is omitted from the key because of lack of material.

KEY TO SPECIES

1.     Ventral process of ninth segment with a large, lateral, triangular tooth near apex (Fig. 335) . . . . . . . . . . . . . . . . . . . . . . . . . 2
       Ventral process without any lateral tooth.   3
2(1).  Lobe of tenth tergite deeply incised, so that its dorsal process is nearly as long as the ventral one (Kimmins 1953d, Fig. 5) . . . . . . . . . . . . . . . . . . . . . . . . . . . **moselyi**
       Lobe of tenth tergite with dorsal process very short, ventral process very long (McLachlan 1879, Pl. 49) . . . . . . . **dentatum**
3(1).  Ventral process of aedeagus consisting of a bilobed, membranous, scoop-shaped flap (Fig. 327, *vp*) . . . . . . . . . . . . . .**atrichum**
       Ventral process of aedeagus consisting of an extensile membranous tube ending in a dense cluster of stout setae (Fig. 328A) . . . . . . . . . . . . . . . . . . . . . . . . . . . . 4
4(3).  Lobe of tenth tergite very large (Fig. 328A) divided by a crease into a large, irregular ventral area and a deep, tapering dorsal area . . . . . . . . . . . . . . . . . . . .**caudatum**
       Lobe of tenth tergite smaller, with at least one narrow or finger-like process (Figs. 329-34) . . . . . . . . . . . . . . . . . . . . 5
5(4).  Ventral process of ninth segment elongate and extremely slender (Fig. 330) .**capitatum**
       Ventral process of ninth segment broader, tapering gradually to apex . . . . . . . . 6
6(5).  Lobe of tenth tergite with a long dorsal process which may curve ventrad but little mesad (Figs. 329, 331) . . . . . . 7
       Lobe of tenth tergite either with dorsal processes short (Fig. 332) or the processes (1 or 2) curve sharply mesad . . . . . . 12
7(6).  Dorsal process of tenth tergite lobe thick and parallel-sided to near apex, and curved markedly ventrad (Ulmer 1926, Figs. 11-14) . . . . . . . . . . . . . . . . .**valvatum**
       Dorsal process of tenth tergite lobe projecting nearly directly posteriad (Fig. 329) or slender for most of its length . . . . 8

8(7).  Dorsal process of tenth tergite lobe sharply truncate at apex (Fig. 329) .**malayanum**
       Dorsal process pointed at apex . . . . . . . . 9
9(8).  Ventral process of tenth tergite lobe with apex square (Banks 1940, Fig. 66) . .**aequale**
       Ventral process of tenth tergite lobe with apex pointed or rounded (Fig. 331) . . . . . 10
10(9). Ventral process of tenth tergite lobe bearing a preapical, mesal shoulder much as in Fig. 329A (Kimmins 1953d, Fig. 4) . . . . . . . . . . . . . . . . . . . . . . . . . **orientale**
       Ventral process of tenth tergite lobe without a preapical shoulder (Fig. 331A) . . . . 11
11(10). Ventral process of ninth sternite nearly triangular, its apex not curved (Martynov 1934, Fig. 50) . . . . . . . . . . . . .**timurense**
       Ventral process of ninth sternite with apex slender and curved markedly laterad from axis of process (Fig. 331) . . .**anale**
12(6). Lobe of tenth tergite with a single, long, curved dorsal process . . . . . . . . . . . . 13
       Lobe of tenth tergite with two smaller processes, either curved mesad or minute . . . . . . . . . . . . . . . . . . . . . . . . . 14
13(12). Tenth tergite lobe with dorsal and ventral processes well separated at base and nearly parallel . . . . . . . . . .**discophorum**
       Tenth tergite lobe with dorsal and ventral processes close together at base and more divergent (Schmid 1947, Fig. 39) . . . . . . . . . . . . . . . . . . . . . . **beaumonti**
14(12). The 2 dorsal teeth of tenth tergite lobe appearing to be divisions of a common basal process . . . . . . . . . . . . . . . . . . 15
       The 2 dorsal teeth of tenth tergite lobe appearing to arise independently from the lobe itself. . . . . . . . . . . . . . . . . . . . . 16
15(14). Ventral process of tenth tergite lobe extending only slightly beyond dorsal teeth (McLachlan 1879, Pl. 49) . . . .**boltoni**
       Ventral process extending at least half its own length beyond dorsal teeth (McLachlan 1884, Pl. 7) . . . . . . . . . . . . . .**privatum**
16(14). Ventral process of tenth tergite lobe with apical point long and upturned, and preceded by a sharp shoulder of the lobe (Fig. 332) . . . . . . . . . . . . . .**vernale**
       Ventral process shorter or less upturned, the preceding edge of the lobe not shoulder-like . . . . . . . . . . . . . . . . . . . . . . . 17
17(16). Dorsal teeth of tenth tergite lobe prominent and placed above midpoint of lobe, whose ventral portion narrows gradually to near apex (Fig. 334) . . . . . . .**dusmeti**
       Dorsal teeth of tenth tergite lobe minute and placed below midpoint of lobe which narrows suddenly at this spot (Fig. 333) . . . . . . . . . . . . . . . . . . . . . . **spoliatum**

## List of Species

**aequale** Banks (1940:200). China.
**anale** Martynov (1931:2). China. Fig. 331.
**beaumonti** Schmid (1947:527). Switzerland.
**boltoni** Curtis (1834:216); McLachlan (1879:471). Europe, widespread.
**capitatum** Martynov (1913a:10). Caucasus. Fig. 330.
**caudatum** Martynov (1931:3). China. Fig. 328.
   subspecies **fissum** Martynov (1935:106). Northern India.
**dentatum** McLachlan (1875:43); Martynov (1934, Fig. 54). Turkestan. Fig. 335.
**discophorum** Klapalek (1902:165). Balkans.
**dusmeti** Navas (1920:24); Schmid (1949, Fig. 10). France, Spain. Fig. 334.
   *Glossosoma pyrenaica* Mosely (1935a:560). *New synonymy.*
**malayanum** Banks (1934:569). Malay. Fig. 329.
**moselyi** Kimmins (1953d:172). Kashmir.
**orientale** Kimmins (1953d:170). Burma.
**privatum** McLachlan (1884:65). Portugal, Spain.
   *Glossosoma lingulatum* Navas (1922:114).
**spoliatum** McLachlan (1879:473); Schmid (1949, Fig. 9). Pyrenees. Fig. 333.
   *Glossosoma loustaloti* Navas (1932c:97).
**timurense** Martynov (1927b:169). Turkestan.
**unguiculatum** Martynov (1925:124). Transcaucasia.
**valvatum** Ulmer (1926:28). China (Kuangtung).
**vernale** (Pictet), *Rhyacophila* (1834:189); McLachlan (1879, Pl. 50); Schmid (1949, Figs. 6-8). Europe. Fig. 332.
   ?*Rhyacophila decolorata* Pictet (1834:191). Doubtful ♀.
   *Glossosoma fimbriata* Stephens (1836:161).
   *Tinodes obscurus* Stephens (1836:164).
   *Glossosoma guayentinum* Navas (1925b:137). *New synonymy.*
   *Glossosoma aestivum* Navas (1930b:54). *New synonymy.*
   *Glossosoma serotinum* Navas (1930b:54).
   *Glossosoma biarcuatum* Navas (1930a:166).

### Glossosoma atrichum new species

*Male*: Length 9 mm. Specimen various shades of light brown. (The specimen was preserved in alcohol and later pinned, so that in life it was probably a much darker brown.) General structure typical for genus. Front wing with only one anal cell; it is elongate and triangular and the membrane is raised and opaque for the basal two-thirds, except for a very narrow anterior strip which is membranous and undoubtedly represents the anterior edge of the true cell 2A. Spurs all long and sharp. Sixth sternite with a moderately wide flap pointed at apex, seventh sternite with a stout, pointed projection about half as long as that on the sixth.

Genitalia as in Fig. 327. Ninth segment with lateral and dorsal portions long, ventral portions produced into a long, narrow, asymmetrical tongue. Tenth tergite divided into (1) a somewhat incised large mesal membranous lobe and (2) a pair of rectangular sclerotized lateral lobes each with a stout apical tooth projecting mesad. To the mesal side of each lateral lobe is attached an elongate, sinuate flap, whose base is attached by a membranous foot to the aedeagal cup. Aedeagus with relatively short cup attached by the short membrane to the ninth sternal region; phalicata with a broad, deeply divided, scooplike ventral process; the body of the phalicata is itself composed of several parts, including a dorsal membranous finger, a long and sinuate and heavily sclerotized process bearing four or five teeth near its apex, and a central membranous tube from which extrudes a sclerotized process divided at the apex into many sharp points; between the phalicata and the ventral process (visible only from the right side) is a moderately long, curved, sharp sclerotized process.

*Holotype, male*: Marie Parie, Kinabalu, Borneo, 5,000 ft. elevation, May 2. In the collection of the Museum of Comparative Zoology.

This species is readily distinguished from all others in the genus by the bifid, membranous ventral lobes of the aedeagus.

### Anseriglossa new subgenus

Type species: *Glossosoma penitum* Banks.

*Diagnosis*: General structure typical for genus, with unmodified tibial spurs in the male. Male genitalia diagnostic for the species (Fig. 326). Tendon flaps greatly elongated, attached by a narrow dorsal band to inner margin of tenth tergite lobes, and articulating by a well-defined membranous joint with basal part of dorsal tendon. Claspers absent, apex of ninth sternite asymmetrical but produced only slightly.

Contains only the type species, which is confined to the western montane region of North America:
**penitum** Banks (1914:202). Western North America. Fig. 326.

. . . . .

### Unplaced Species

**Glossosoma javanicum** Ulmer (1930:418). Java.
   This record, based only on the female, is the

only one of the genus from the East Indies. It will be most interesting to obtain a knowledge of its relationships within the genus when the male is discovered.

**Glossosoma furcatum** Navas (1932a:931). Tonkin.

The female type in the Paris Museum has $R_3$ fused with $R_4$ for a considerable distance in the front wing (Fig. 368), a character it shares with *confluens*.

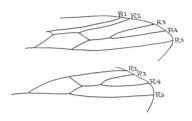

FIG. 368. Apical portions of wings of *Glossosoma furcatum*.

## Tribe Agapetini

### KEY TO GENERA

1. Hind wing with sectorial cross-vein (*s*) present (Fig. 296B) . . . . . . . . . . . . . . . . . . . . . . . 2
   Hind wing with sectorial cross-vein absent (Fig. 296D) . . . . . . . . . . . . . . . . . . . . . . **Agapetus**
2. Hind wing with $R_{2+3}$ undivided, $R_1$ fused with Sc, and 2A complete (Fig. 296B) . . . **Catagapetus**
   Hind wing with $R_{2+3}$ divided near apex, $R_1$ free, and 2A completely atrophied or represented by only a short stub (Fig. 296C) . . **Electragapetus**

## Genus **Catagapetus** McLachlan

*Catagapetus* McLachlan (1884:68). Type species: *Catagapetus nigrans* McLachlan (monobasic). Contains only the type species. The tenth tergite (Fig. 336) is represented by a pair of symmetrical, appressed, membranous lobes.

**nigrans** McLachlan (1884:68). Mountains of Italy. Fig. 336.

## Genus **Electragapetus** Ulmer

This genus is known from one Baltic amber and two Recent species. The Baltic amber species is placed in a separate subgenus.

### KEY TO SUBGENERA

Cercus digitate, projecting free from narrow base (Fig. 337B) . . . . . . . . . . . . . . . . . . . **Electragapetus**
Cercus low, with basal attached portion very long; apical edge with a row of fine setae (Fig. 337D) . . . . . . . . . . . . . . . . . . . . . . . . . . . **Eoagapetus**

### Subgenus **Electragapetus** Ulmer

*Electragapetus* Ulmer (1912:33). Type species: *Electragapetus scitulus* Ulmer (monobasic). Contains only the type species:

**scitulus** Ulmer (1912:34). Baltic amber. Fig. 337A, B.

### Subgenus **Eoagapetus** Martynov

*Eoagapetus* Martynov (1934:94). Type species: *Eoagapetus praeteritus* Martynov (monobasic).

Contains two species from eastern Asia, revised by Ross (1951c):

**praeteritus** (Martynov), *Eoagapetus* (1934:94). Siberia (South Ussuri).

**tsudai** Ross (1951c:353). Japan (Honshu). Fig. 337C, D.

## Genus **Agapetus** Curtis

I have been unable to study some dozen Old World species in this genus. On the basis of descriptions in the literature it has been possible to place many of these in their correct phylogenetic groups, and thus serve the primary purpose of this investigation. In the matter of identification keys, however, I feel in a less fortunate position, since many of the more detailed characters I would like to employ in a key are frequently not well shown in available illustrations. It seems the better course to key out the groups and to give in the list of species references to the available illustrations. At the end of the genus is appended a list of species which I have been unable to place definitely in a group.

### KEY TO SUBGENERA AND MAJOR SPECIES GROUPS

1. Fifth abdominal sternite with an internal pouch on each side near dorsal margin (Fig. 358) . . . . Subgenus **Agapetus**—2
   Fifth abdominal sternite without an internal pouch . . . . . . . . . . . . . . . . . . . . . . 7
2(1). Tenth tergite with dorsal margin of lobes sclerotized and rodlike, the ventral portions of the lobes membranous (Fig. 359); frequently the cercus reduced to a small knob or bar bearing only one or two long setae (Figs. 360, 362) . . . . . . . . . . . . . . . . . . . . . . . . . **bidens group**—3
   Tenth tergite with ventral margin of lobes more heavily sclerotized than dorsal margin . . . . . . . . . . . . . . . . . . . . . . . 5
3(2). Cercus ovate, with several setae (Fig. 359) . . . . . . . . . . . . . . **kirgisorum subgroup**
   Cercus small (Fig. 362) or straplike (Fig.

4(3). 360) with only 1 or 2 setae....... 4
Cercus small and knoblike, attached to or near edge of ninth segment; clasper simple but elongate, its end hooked or slender and curved mesad (Fig. 362)........
............... **cocandicus subgroup**
Cercus straplike, set in membrane of tenth tergite; clasper short, but bearing finger-like processes (Fig. 360)............
................... **bidens subgroup**

5(2). Cerci absent (Fig. 361).....**fuscipes group**
Cerci present ..................... 6

6(5). Palearctic species ..........**comatus group**
Nearctic species ...........**celatus group**

7(1). Hind wing with $M_{3+4}$ absent (Fig. 296I); cerci present......**Subgenus Tagapetus**
Hind wing with $M_{3+4}$ present (Fig. 296D) or cerci absent..**Subgenus Synagapetus**—8

8(7). Center of dorsal margin of fifth sternite forming a thumblike dorsal process projecting above sternite and curving posteriad (Fig. 338S)...........**dubitans group**
Center portion of dorsal margin of fifth sternite not so produced (Figs. 339, 356) 9

9(8). Dorsal margin of fifth sternite with a central hump or anterior process........ 10
Dorsal margin of fifth sternite without such structures, at most with a curved ridge (Fig. 340) .................... 11

10(9). Fifth sternite with a central hump just below dorsal margin; in a cleared specimen the hump appears as a clear, round or oval area (Fig. 353)......**monticolus group**
Anterodorsal corner of fifth sternite with a thumblike projection which lies over the surface of the sternite and does not project above it (Fig. 356); cerci absent ................. **ungulatus group**

11(9). South African species, the front wing usually with Cu$_1$ branching just beyond *m-cu*.. .................... **agilis group**
Palearctic species, the front wing usually with Cu$_1$ branching at or before *m-cu*.... 12

12(11). Cerci present ...............**rudis group**
Cerci absent ..................... 13

13(12). Ventral process of sixth sternite fairly short but thin and narrow, or minute.......
.................. **punctatus group**
Ventral process of sixth sternite elongate and slightly clavate.......**oblongatus group**

## Subgenus **Synagapetus** McLachlan

*Synagapetus* McLachlan (1879:484). Type species: *Synagapetus dubitans* McLachlan (subsequent designation of Mosely 1935b:16).

*Pseudagapetus* McLachlan (1879:485). Type species: *Pseudagapetus insons* McLachlan (original designation). *New synonymy.*

*Myspoleo* Barnard (1934:388). Type species: *Myspoleo agilis* Barnard (original designation). *New synonymy.*

*Lanagapetus* Mosely (1938b:5). Type species: *Lanagapetus lundbladi* Mosely (original designation). *New synonymy.*

*Afragapetus* Mosely (1939:34). Type species: *Afragapetus ungulatus* Mosely (original designation). *New synonymy.*

### LIST OF SPECIES

#### Dubitans Group

**armatus** (McLachlan), *Pseudagapetus* (1879:486); Mosely (1935b, Figs. 1, 7-8). Austria.

**ater** (Klapalek, *Synagapetus* (1905:11). Transylvanian Alps.

**diversus** (McLachlan), *Pseudagapetus* (1884:67). Portugal and Spain.
*Pseudagapetus placidus* Navas (1918d:47).

**dubitans** (McLachlan), *Synagapetus* (1879:484); Mosely (1935, Figs. 4-6). Central Europe. Figs. 296D, 338.

**insons** (McLachlan), *Pseudagapetus* (1879:487). Pyrenees, France and Spain.
*Pseudagapetus serotinus* Navas (1919:31).
*Pseudagapetus rotundatus* Navas (1930a:166).

**iridipennis** (McLachlan), *Synagapetus* (1879:484); Mosely (1935b, Figs. 2, 3, 10-12). Switzerland.

**krawanyi** (Ulmer), *Synagapetus* (*in* Ulmer & Krawany 1938:307). Austria.

**moselyi** (Ulmer), *Pseudagapetus* (*in* Ulmer & Krawany 1938:310). Austria.

#### Punctatus Group

**lundbladi** (Mosely), *Lanagapetus* (1938b:5). Madeira.

**punctatus** Hagen (1859a:163); McLachlan (1879, Pl. 51). Madeira.

There is a possibility, as stated by Mosely in the original description, that *lundbladi* is an anomalous specimen of *punctatus*. Certainly the male genitalia of the two are virtually identical. If they are different species, then *lundbladi* is characterized only by the reduction in wing venation listed and illustrated by Mosely (1938).

#### Agilis Group

This group embraces the two South African species for which Barnard erected the genus *Myspoleo*.

**agilis** (Barnard), *Myspoleo* (1934:388). Mountains of South Africa. Fig. 357.

**murinus** (Barnard), *Myspoleo* (1934:390). Mountains of South Africa.

#### Ungulatus Group

Originally proposed as the genus *Afragapetus* Mosely, this group includes only a single known African species. In addition to characters mentioned in the key, this species possesses two unusual characters, well illustrated by Mosely—the hind tibia has only a single preapical spur which is thickened at the base and angled at the apex, and the tenth tergite is divided into a pair of curious, twisted, knobbed apical projections.

**ungulatus** (Mosely), *Afragapetus* (1939:34). Ruwenzori Mountains, Uganda, Africa. Fig. 356.

### Rudis Group

The species placed in this group may be divided into two categories, the typical *rudis* subgroup in which the tenth tergite is composed of simple lobes (Figs. 341-43), and the *mitis* subgroup in which the lobes of the tenth tergite each bear an upcurved process arising either at the end of the lobe (Fig. 344) or from the base of the ventral margin.

*Rudis Subgroup.*

**cataractae** Ulmer (1951:54). Java.

**chinensis** (Mosely), *Pseudagapetus* (1942:359). China (Foochow). Fig. 340.

**dentatus** (Kimmins), *Synagapetus* (1953d:180). Northeastern Burma.

**excisus** Kimmins (1953d:177). Northeastern Burma.

**japonicus** (Tsuda), *Synagapetus* (1940b:194). Japan (Honshu). Fig. 343.

**komanus** (Tsuda), *Synagapetus* (1942:252). Japan (Honshu). Fig. 342.

**ohiya** Kimmins (1953d:178). Ceylon.

**rudis** Hagen (1859b:211). Ceylon. Figs. 341, 369A, B.

**sibiricus** Martynov (1922:49). Siberia (Minoussinsk).

## Agapetus grahami new species

*Male*: Length 4 mm. Color dark brown. General structure typical for genus. Wings broken so that details of venation can not be made out with certainty. Fifth sternite with simple, arcuate ridges, sixth sternite with moderately long and narrow mesal process (Fig. 339). Genitalia as in Fig. 345.

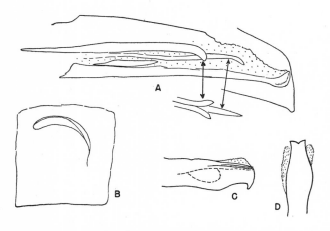

FIG. 369. Parts of male *Agapetus*. *A,* tip of aedeagus, and *B,* fifth sternite, of *rudis; C, D,* lateral and ventral aspects, respectively, of tip of aedeagus of *dayi.* Below *A* is shown the dorsal aspect of the parts indicated.

Ninth segment of moderate length, its anterior margin produced into a short but sharp point. Tenth tergite with lobes moderately broad, deep but short, with a ventral margin fairly heavily sclerotized but without points or processes of any sort. Cercus moderately long and broad, constricted at base, the apical half bearing an irregular dorsal row of long scattered setae. Clasper with lateral aspect nearly rectangular, the extreme apicoventral corner produced into a small area; ventral aspect with base wide and triangular, apical portion narrow and bearing on the mesal surface two sclerotized cones, one at apex and one just below it. Aedeagus simple in structure, much as in *rudis* (Fig. 369A).

*Holotype, male*: Beh Luh Din, 30 mi. N. Chengtu, Szechwan, China, April 1-15, 1935 (D. C. Graham). In the collection of the United States National Museum.

In most respects this species is closely related to *rudis* (Fig. 341) and *japonicus* (Fig. 343), differing from them in having two rather than one sclerotized comblike area on the mesal aspect of the clasper.

*Mitis Subgroup.*

**albomaculatus** (Kimmins), *Synagapetus* (1953d:179). Northeastern Burma.

**foliatus** (Kimmins), *Synagapetus* (1953d:181). Northeastern Burma.

**incurvatus** (Kimmins), *Synagapetus* (1953d:181). Northeastern Burma.

**mitis** (Kimmins), *Synagapetus* (1953d:182). Northeastern Burma.

## Agapetus hamatus new species

*Male*: Length 4 mm. Color dark brown. General structure typical for genus. Hind wings with $R_{2+3}$ unbranched, and with the apex of $R_1$ indistinct. Anal veins complete but only partially sclerotized. Fifth sternite with little indication of the lateral ridges. Sixth sternite with a long apical process (Fig. 370C). Genitalia as in Figs. 344, 370. Ninth segment with anterior margin produced only slightly into a wide, blunt angle, posterior margin produced much more to form a fairly sharp angle where the claspers attach. Tenth tergite with elongate lobes, each with the ventral margin sclerotized and with the apex produced into a heavily sclerotized, upturned hook. Seen from dorsal view (Fig. 370B) the thickening of the base of these hooks appears to be attached by some sort of articulation with sclerotized thickenings on the wall of the ventral margin of the tergite. Cerci long and slender, bearing long setae in an irregular pattern along the entire dorsal margin. Clasper with lateral aspect blunt; ventral aspect with basal portion wide, apical portion narrow and bearing a single prominent peglike process. Aedeagus consisting of a central sclerotized rod cleft into a broad Y at apex, with a central narrow mesal process extending beyond this; these surrounded by membrane and associated with the pair of ventral sclerotized rods which attach to the base of the hooks of the tenth tergite lobes. Due to the delicacy of the specimen and the fact that I have only one available for study, I have not felt at liberty to dissect this specimen further, but it is evident that there is some connection in this species between the parts of the aedeagus and those of the tenth tergite, which is unusual for the genus.

*Holotype, male*: Yim Na San, Eastern Kwantung, Southern China, June 13, 1936 (L. Gressitt). In the collection of the Museum of Comparative Zoology.

The curious hooks at the apex of the tenth tergite lobes will differentiate this species from all others described in the genus. In addition, the ventral aspect of the clasper is very unusual. It is closely related to *mitis*.

### Oblongatus Group

**oblongatus** Martynov (1913a:18). Caucasus. Fig. 355.
**truncatus** Martynov (1913a:14). Caucasus.

### Monticolus Group

I have been fortunate in being able to study not only the New Guinea collections of Mr. Hoogstraal, but also the Australian material assembled at the British Museum by the late Martin E. Mosely. In tabulating characters to assist in deducing phylogenetic relationships, a survey was possible for all the known species in the group. These make it feasible to present a key for the identification of species.

#### KEY TO SPECIES

1.  Anterior projection or angulation of the ninth segment well below the midlateral line. From New Guinea . . . . . . . . . . . . . . . . 2
    Anterior projection or angulation of ninth segment near or above midlateral line. From Australia . . . . . . . . . . . . . . . . . . . . . . 4
2(1).  Cerci slender, elongate, and slightly clavate (Fig. 348) . . . . . . . . . . . . . . . . . . **latosus**
    Cerci not more than twice as long as deep, stout and short . . . . . . . . . . . . . . . . . . . . . . 3
3(2).  Lobe of tenth tergite nearly quadrate, clasper without apical tooth (Fig. 346) . . . . **ulmeri**

Lobe of tenth tergite irregular, with 2 small dorsal teeth at and near apex; clasper with apical tooth (Fig. 347) . . . . . . . . . . **jafiwi**
4(1).  Anterior projection or angulation of ninth segment well above midlateral line (Figs. 351, 352) . . . . . . . . . . . . . . . . . . . . . . . . . 5
    Anterior projection or angulation of ninth segment near midlateral line (Figs. 349, 350) . . . . . . . . . . . . . . . . . . . . . . . . . . . 7
5(4).  Tenth tergite elongate, its tip with a dorsal point (Fig. 352) . . . . . . . . . . **monticolus**
    Tenth tergite shorter, its tip depressed and without a dorsal point (Fig. 351) . . . . . . . . 6
6(5).  Clasper with apical tooth reflexed upward and slightly anteriad (Mosely & Kimmins 1953, Fig. 337) . . . . . . . . . . . . . . . . **tasmanicus**
    Clasper with apical tooth pointing directly mesad (Fig. 351) . . . . . . . . . . . . **kimminsi**
7(4).  Clasper with apicomesal tooth at extreme tip and with a small setose process at extreme base (Fig. 349) . . . . . . . . . . . . . . . **evansi**
    Clasper with apicomesal tooth situated definitely below the apex (Fig. 350); no basal process present . . . . . . . . . . . . . . . . . . . . . . 8
8(7).  Tenth tergite with dorsal profile enlarged and arcuate, projecting above level of ninth (Mosely & Kimmins 1953, Fig. 338) . . **crala**
    Tenth tergite with dorsal profile straight (Fig. 350) or slightly depressed, not higher than ninth . . . . . . . . . . . . . . . . . . . . . . 9

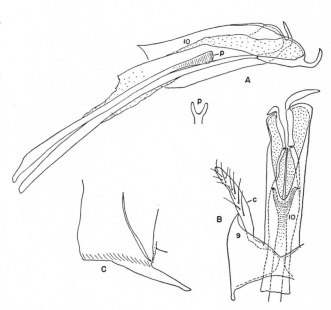

FIG. 370. Parts of male *Agapetus hamatus*. A, aedeagus and lobes of tenth tergite, lateral aspect; B, same, dorsal aspect; C, sixth sternite. c, cercus; p, phalicata (dorsal view of tip shown in detail below A).

9(8).  Apex of aedeagus simple (Mosely & Kimmins
1953, Fig. 339)..............pontona
Apex of aedeagus profile with a sharp ventral
point (Fig. 369C, D)..............dayi

LIST OF SPECIES

**crala** (Mosely), *Synagapetus* (*in* Mosely & Kimmins
1953:500). Tasmania. Fig. 353.
**jafiwi** Ross (1951c:354). New Guinea. Fig. 347.
**latosus** Ross (1951c:354). New Guinea. Fig. 348.
**monticolus** Banks (1939b:503). Australia (New South
Wales). Fig. 352.
**pontona** (Mosely), *Synagapetus* (*in* Mosely & Kimmins
1953:500). Australia (New South Wales).
The original series of this species contained a number of paratypes mounted dry on points. When Mrs.
Ross cleared these for examination it was found that
they actually represented three additional species.
These are described below. In view of these findings,
the species *pontona* is now known from a single locality, Hampton, New South Wales.
**tasmanicus** (Mosely), *Synagapetus* (*in* Mosely & Kimmins 1953:498). Tasmania.
**ulmeri** Ross (1951c:353). New Guinea. Fig. 346.

### Agapetus dayi new species

*Male*: Length 5.5 mm. Color dark brown, almost
black, and general structure typical for *monticolus*
group. Genitalia as in Fig. 350. Ninth segment with
a long anterior process, narrow and finger-like at
apex, the posterior margin arcuate and the dorsal
portion very narrow. Cercus moderately long and
bean-shaped, with a cluster of long setae. Tenth
tergite lobes nearly regularly rhomboidal, the dorsal margin nearly straight, the ventral margin moderately evenly sclerotized and with a clear space
in the lobe immediately above it. Clasper short,
tapering to a rounded apex, the mesal margin with
a moderately small spine at apex and a large triangular spine a short distance below the apex.
Aedeagus elongate, its apex with a pair of slender
rods, a pair of membranous lobes which are moderately spinate, and a sclerotized ventral portion
whose apex is cleft in ventral view and hooked in
lateral view (Fig. 369C, D).

*Holotype, male*: Bathurst, New South Wales,
2,300 ft. elevation, February 8, 1884. Known only
from the single type deposited in the British Museum. This specimen was formerly a paratype of
*Synagapetus pontona*.

This species is a close relative of *pontona*, differing in the slightly longer cercus, the almost straight
dorsal margin of the tenth tergite, and especially
in the profile of the aedeagus (Fig. 369C).

It is with pleasure that I name this species after
Dr. Max Day who has always been ready to further
cooperation between entomologists of Australia and
other parts of the world.

### Agapetus evansi new species

*Male*: Length, color and general structure as for
the preceding. Genitalia as in Fig. 349. Ninth segment with anterior margin forming almost a right
angle near midlateral line, posterior margin sinuate.
Cercus elongate and pointing considerably ventrad,
clothed with a brush of long hair. Lobes of tenth
tergite large and irregular, the dorsal portion forming a large membranous lobe angled dorsad, the
ventral portion forming a slightly downcurved and
tapering part; just below the middle of each lobe
there extends a broad sclerotized point. Clasper
with lateral aspect tapering evenly from base, the
ventral margin concave, and the mesal margin giving rise to a finger-like lobe bearing a brush of
short hair at its apex; ventral aspect simple with a
single mesal point at apex. Aedeagus simple.

*Holotype, male*: Ebor, New South Wales, Jan-
uary 1916. *Paratypes*: same data as for holotype, 5
males. The holotype is in the British Museum, the
paratypes in the British Museum and in the collection of the Illinois Natural History Survey. These
were formerly paratypes of *Synagapetus pontona*.

Several characters indicate that this species is in
a complex of its own, in particular the setose processes at the base of the clasper, and the unusual
shape of the tenth tergite (Fig. 349). It is probably
more closely related to the *tasmanicus* complex than
to the *pontona* complex.

Named in honor of Dr. J. W. Evans, whose collections from Tasmania have been of such great
aid in obtaining an understanding of the caddisfly
fauna of that interesting region.

### Agapetus kimminsi new species

*Male*: Length, color and general structure similar to *dayi*. Genitalia as in Fig. 351. Ninth segment
with anterior margin acutely rounded and widened
close to the dorsal margin; this causing the posterior and anterior margins of the ninth segment
to be somewhat parallel. Cercus pointed, the base
broad and extending along the edge of the ninth
segment so that the cercus points considerably forward; cercus clothed with an angular single row
of long setae. Tenth tergite almost uniform in struc-

ture, the apex of each lobe narrowed fairly evenly into a rounded apical process. Clasper generally tapered, the lateral aspect having the apical one-third entirely triangular, the ventral aspect being fairly narrow and bringing to view the apical mesal process which is small, spinelike, and projects mesally.

*Holotype, male*: Fernshaw, Victoria, Dec. 21, 1884. In the British Museum, formerly considered a female paratype of *Synagapetus pontona*.

This species is a close relative of *tasmanicus*, differing in the more pointed profile of the clasper, more sharply constricted tenth tergite, and the more primitive brush of apical spines on the clasper, which point mesad.

It is with a deep sense of gratitude that I name this species for Mr. D. E. Kimmins, who was of such great assistance to Mrs. Ross and me when we were studying caddisfly types at the British Museum.

## Subgenus **Tagapetus** Ross

*Agapetus* subgenus *Tagapetus* Ross (1951c:354). Type species: *Agapetus curvidens* Ulmer (original designation).

The two known species in this subgenus are the smallest members of the genus. In external appearance they bear a close resemblance to members of the Protoptilinae.

### KEY TO SPECIES

Clasper with base little wider than apical portion, the whole sinuate and extending considerably beyond tenth tergite (Fig. 354) . . . . . . . . . . . . . .**curvidens**
Clasper with base much thicker than apex, which is fairly short (Ulmer 1951, Pl. 1, Figs. 14-20) . . . . . . . . . . . . . . . . . . . . . . . . . . . . . . . . . . . . **abbreviatus**

### LIST OF SPECIES

**abbreviatus** Ulmer (1913:79; 1951:52). Java and Sumatra.
**curvidens** Ulmer (1930:374); Ross (1951c:354). Philippine Islands. Figs. 295E, 296I, 354.

## Subgenus **Agapetus** Curtis

*Agapetus* Curtis (1834:217). Type species: *Agapetus fuscipes* Curtis (subsequent designation of Westwood).
*Allagapetus* Martynov (1936:304). Type species: *Allagapetus punjabicus* Martynov. Present designation.

### LIST OF SPECIES
### Bidens Group

*Kirgisorum Subgroup.* Judging from Martynov's descriptions, the two species *triangularis* and *jakutorum* appear to be close relatives of *kirgisorum* and are so considered in this section.
**jakutorum** Martynov (1934:104). Siberia (Yakutsk).
**kirgisorum** Martynov (1927b:169). Turkestan. Fig. 359.
**triangularis** Martynov (1935:108). India (United Provinces).

*Bidens Subgroup.*
**bidens** McLachlan (1875:43; 1879:482), Martynov (1934:104). Turkestan.
**bidens** forma **brevidens** Martynov (1927b:172; 1934:107). Turkestan.
**kashmirensis** Kimmins (1953d:176). Kashmir.
**membrosus** Ross (1951c:355). China (Szechuan). Figs. 295D, 296G, 360.
**tridens** McLachlan (1875:44; 1879:482), Martynov (1934:108). Turkestan.

*Cocandicus Subgroup.* The two species, *cocandicus* and *punjabicus*, in this subgroup were considered to be a distinct genus, *Allagapetus*, by Martynov.
**cocandicus** McLachlan (1875:44; 1879:483), Martynov (1934:108). Kirghiz (Kokand). Fig. 362.
**punjabicus** (Martynov), *Allagapetus* (1936:305). India (Punjab).
**sindis** Kimmins (1953d:175). Kashmir.

### Comatus Group

**comatus** Pictet (1834:194); McLachlan (1879:479). Europe, widespread.
**delicatulus** McLachlan (1884:67) (also misidentified as *laniger*, McLachlan 1879:480). Pyrenees, Scotland.
**laniger** Pictet (1834:195), McLachlan (1884:67). Europe, widespread.
*Agapetus pactus* McLachlan (1879:481).

### Fuscipes Group

**caucasicus** Martynov (1913a:20). Caucasus, Mesopotamia. Fig. 361.
**cyrnensis** Mosely (1930a:173). Corsica.
**fuscipes** Curtis (1834:217), McLachlan (1879:477). Europe, widespread. Fig. 296H.
*?Agapetus ochripes* Curtis (1834:217).
*Rhyacophila tomentosa* Pictet (1834:189).
*?Rhyacophila incolor* Pictet (1834:192).
*Rhyacophila lanata* Pictet (1834:194).
*Potamaria Pictetii* Kolenati (1848:100).
*Agapetus odonturus* Navas (1916c:750).
**incertulus** McLachlan (1884:66). Portugal.
**nimbulus** McLachlan (1879:479). Central Europe.
**quadratus** Mosely (1930a:174). Corsica.

### Celatus Group

The species of this group occur in North America.
**arcita** Denning (1951:157). California.
**artesus** Ross (1938a:106). Missouri.

**bifidus** Denning (1949a:112). Oregon.
**boulderensis** Milne (1936:108). Colorado.
**celatus** McLachlan (1871:139); Kimmins & Denning (1951:111). California.
   *ophionis* Ross (1947:133).
**crasmus** Ross (1939a:66). Tennessee.
**denningi** Ross (1951c:356). Oregon.
**gelbae** Ross (1947:132). Indiana.
**hessi** Leonard & Leonard (1949:1). Michigan.
**illini** Ross (1938a:106; 1944:40). Ozarks. Figs. 295C, 296E.
**iridis** Ross (1944:269). New York.
**malleatus** Banks (1914:202); Ross (1938c:3). California.
**marlo** Milne (1936:108). California.
**medicus** Ross (1938a:107). Arkansas.
**minutus** Sibley (1926:79); Betten (1934:141). New York.
**montanus** Denning (1949b:38). Montana.
**occidentis** Denning (1949a:112). Oregon.
**orosus** Denning (1950b:116). California.
**pinatus** Ross (1938a:107). Tennessee. Fig. 296F.
**rossi** Denning (1941:200); Leonard & Leonard (1949: Pl. 1). Northeastern states.
**taho** Ross (1947:133). California.
**tomus** Ross (1941:44). Georgia.
**vireo** Ross (1941:43). Georgia, Tennessee.
**walkeri** (Betten and Mosely). *Synagapetus* (1940:8). Ontario.
   The female type of this species has, in the front wing, the tip of R₁ only faintly indicated. This condition is typical of the great bulk of the Nearctic species, hence it seems certain that *walkeri* belongs to this *celatus* group rather than a more primitive one.

### SPECIES NOT PLACED AS TO GROUP

**adejensis** Enderlein (1929:230). Canary Islands.
**aj-petriensis** Martynov (1916:166; 1934:98). Russia (Crimea).
**armatus** (McLachlan), *Pseudagapetus* (1879:486). Austria.
**hieianus** (Tsuda), *Synagapetus* (1942:250). Japan (Honshu).
**himalayanus** (Martynov), *Synagapetus* (1935:107). Northern India.
**yasensis** (Tsuda), *Synagapetus* (1942:251). Japan (Honshu).

## Misplaced Species in the Agapetini

**Agapetus niger** Navas (1932a:932) should be transferred to the genus *Apsilochorema* on the basis of the female type in the Paris Museum. The species is described from Tonkin.

**Catagapetus niger** Navas (1916d:82), described from Spain, has been shown by Schmid (1949: 314) to belong to *Hydropsyche*.

## Subfamily Protoptilinae

This report does not cover this subfamily, except to orient it in relation to other members of the family. In so doing, particular attention centers on the archaic species heretofore referred to as *Protoptila jeanae*, for which a new genus must be erected.

## Matrioptila new genus

Type species: *Protoptila jeanae* Ross (1938a: 112).

*Diagnosis*: In general typical for the subfamily Protoptilinae. Diagnostic features are in wings and genitalia. Front wing (Fig. 365) with R 5-branched, M 2-branched and weak, and Cu₁ simple and strong; Cu₂ extends free to the wing margin. Hind wing with R₁ joining Sc, Rs 3-branched, M 2-branched as in the front wing, and Cu₁ 2-branched. Male genitalia (Fig. 364) with tenth tergite divided into a pair of lateral lobes, cerci lacking, and claspers long and simple, situated close together.

This genus differs from related genera in which Cu₁ is branched in the hind wing by (1) the separate course of Cu₂ in the front wing, (2) the strong, convex Cu₁ in the front wing, (3) the similar branching of M in both wings, and (4) the distinct claspers in the male genitalia.

The genus contains only the type species, known from clear, rapid streams around the base of the Great Smoky and Cumberland Mountains in southeastern North America.

## Other Families

### Genus Electracanthinus Ulmer

Among the Baltic amber material was a curious form which Ulmer (1912:54) described as *Electracanthinus klebsi* Ulmer new genus and species. Ulmer placed this in the family Philopotamidae, but remarked that the ocelli were difficult to identify with certainty. The male genitalia and wing venation are suggestive of the family Psychomiidae, particularly some genera of the *Psychomyiinae*. If the species really lacks ocelli, *Electracanthinus* would be placed in this latter family without a reservation.

Considering these possibilities, it seems more prudent at this time to attempt no definite phylogenetic placement of *Electracanthinus*; rather, to invite further thought on its placement.

chapter six COMMON DISPERSAL
CHARACTERISTICS

In each of the three families, Philopotamidae, Rhyacophilidae, and Glossosomatidae, there are many individualistic details of phylogeny and dispersal. Underlying these, however, are phenomena which are remarkably similar in all three families: this is illustrated in the following listing of traits in common.

1. There is a sufficient survival of various morphological steps to permit the tracing of the evolution of many characters in minute detail. This development of individual characters actually shows the evolutionary path followed by the species; hence it has been possible to utilize this information to reconstruct family trees in considerable detail. Cases in which many characters are integrated must be remarkably close to the actual or true family tree. Others based on less evidence need more testing by future findings, as indicated at pertinent points in the text.

2. The great bulk of existing species can be segregated into many compact, monophyletic species groups, each group containing a few to a few dozen species. The geographic distribution patterns of these species groups have been of the utmost aid in deducing the dispersal trends for larger taxonomic categories.

3. Within each family there has evolved one (and only one) large, warm-adapted branch which has a different dispersal pattern from its cool-adapted, more primitive relatives. These warm-adapted branches are: in the Philopotamidae, the genus *Chimarra;* in the Rhyacophilidae, the subfamily Hydrobiosinae; in the Glossosomatidae, the subfamily Protoptilinae. Available evidence indicates that there was no community of development

of these branches. Probably each arose at a different time or place. No attempt is made here to explore the possible explanations for this similar but independent development of warm-adapted lines. Not only is it a problem extraneous to our study of the cool-adapted biota, but it is one which is so poorly understood that examples from many other groups would need to be studied in detail in order to extract comparative data and to establish possible bases for a theoretical analysis.

4. The great majority of the species groups comprising the cool-adapted forms are restricted in distribution. In most cases each group is confined to a single, relatively small area. In the Northern Hemisphere these areas are chiefly mountainous. A few exceptions occur, such as the *Wormaldia moesta* group, the *Wormaldia anilla* group, and the *Glossosoma intermedium* group, each of which contains one or two species which are widespread through hilly country, in addition to other members of the group which are restricted to more mountainous terrain.

5. Some groups from each family indicate that certain mountain areas have been separated from each other by arid or warm lowland areas for considerable periods of time. The intervals of isolation have been sufficient to allow extensive evolutionary development of the caddisflies within each area. The mountain areas of South America, Africa, and Australasia each support certain of these distinct phylogenetic groups. The great number of such groups occurring in the Northern Hemisphere in each family studied indicate that in this hemisphere there have been four primary areas of mountain isolation:

*a.* The European mountains, including the Caucasus and the mountains of the western portion of Asia Minor

*b.* The Asiatic mountains, including the Himalayas

*c.* The western montane region of North America

*d.* The eastern montane region of North America

Of these four, the last has the smallest number of endemic groups, and on this basis would seem to have been the most remote.

6. There has been a dispersal of ancestral forms between these Northern Hemisphere montane areas, and at different times. Each dispersal has not always encompassed all four areas. The greatest interchange seems to have occurred between the Asiatic area and the western montane region of North America. Next in frequency are indicated interchanges between Asia and Europe, then those between the two North American mountain areas. The net result, in all families, has been a moderately frequent dispersal from Europe through Asia to western North America and subsequently to eastern North America.

7. The foregoing implies that there was no transAtlantic montane connection linking western Europe with eastern North America during the development of the modern caddisfly fauna. The extremely few cases which might be interpreted as indicating the occurrence of such a bridge are those in which two closely related groups occur, one in Europe and the other in eastern North America, with no annectent forms known from Asia or western North America. Two groups in *Rhyacophila* are good illustrations. The European *stigmatica* group is closely related to the *glaberrima* group, known only from eastern North America. This might indicate that the ancestral form of both groups spread directly across an Atlantic land bridge. The weight of evidence shown by many other groups necessitates seeking an alternate explanation for the distribution pattern of these two groups of *Rhyacophila*. One possible alternative is that since both groups appear to have an extremely low rate of speciation, no annectent forms evolved or if they did evolve, the survival of species has been poor in relation to other caddisflies in the same areas. The *glaberrima* group is represented by only a single rare species, the *stigmatica* group

by 6 species. It is possible, therefore, that related species in Asia or western North America became extinct or have not yet been collected.

8. Species in groups which are represented in both eastern Asia and western North America show an interesting characteristic. In almost all such groups the western North American species are most closely related to species occurring in the northern portion of eastern Asia. In *Wormaldia* subgenus *Doloclanes* and in *Himalopsyche*, it is evident that the primitive stock developed in southeastern Asia, gave rise to a more northern phyletic line, and only this northern line eventually spread to North America.

9. Dispersals into South America, Australasia and Africa have been much less frequent than the intermontane dispersals in the Northern Hemisphere. Available data suggest that the avenues of dispersal to these southern areas were of infrequent occurrence. In every case studied, the evidence indicates that each dispersal had its origin in the Northern Hemisphere. There is no indication that these southern areas formed a cohesive biotic unit separate from the Northern Hemisphere. If such a condition ever did exist, either it occurred before the dispersal events studied here, or it was the result of a lack of avenues suitable for the spread of caddisflies.

This is the only one of the ten traits discussed in this chapter which is not exemplified by all three families studied. African dispersals include the Philopotamidae and Glossosomatidae, but not the Rhyacophilidae. South American and Australasian dispersals include members of all three families. This, together with data mentioned in other chapters, indicates that Africa has been connected with other land masses by corridors possessing a cool climate at unusually infrequent intervals.

10. There is no strong evidence in any of these three families for a dispersal route directly between Australasia and South America. A satisfactory explanation for existing data can be made, based on the assumption that all dispersals of these families between these areas occurred via the Northern Hemisphere. On the other hand, the distribution patterns of *Sortosa* and the Hydrobiosinae could be explained equally well on the basis of some direct connection between South America and Australia.

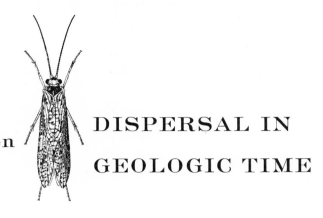

## chapter seven

# DISPERSAL IN GEOLOGIC TIME

We have assembled data on the evolution and dispersal patterns for the greater portion of three caddisfly families. Now we shall attempt to correlate these data with the geologic time scale. Many difficulties are inherent, for there is no empirical method by which phylogeny and dispersal can be integrated directly with geological time. It is necessary to use various bits of evidence as they occur, in the hope that we can finally deduce an explanation which is in harmony with all the known facts of the case.

*Evidence from Fossils.* In some groups such as the termites (Emerson 1933) there are many fossil species available to assist in dating various parts of the family tree. In the three caddisfly families under consideration such is not the case. Only a few fossils are known in each family, and all of these are from the same time and place (the Baltic amber of Germany). They provide us with some extremely valuable reference points, but time estimates for all other parts of the various family trees must be deduced from other evidence.

*Rate of Evolution.* Certain species living today appear to have been changeless for a long period. The species *Sortosa sisko*, for example, exhibits almost all the charcteristics which we deduce for the ancestor of the entire subfamily Philopotaminae. Along other lines, this ancestor has given rise to such highly specialized and much-changed species as *Gunungiella reducta* and *Chimarra aterrima* (see Charts 4 and 15). The phyletic lines leading to all three species have been evolving for very nearly the same length of time since they had a common ancestor, yet the amount of change which has occurred in each line is different. Logically, then, the

*amount of evolutionary change cannot be used as a measure of geologic time.*

*Survival of Phyletic Lines.* In many of the groups studied on the preceding pages (*Chimarra*, Chart 15, again is a good example) living forms show the step-by-step progress in evolutionary change from one form to a quite different one. This means that species representing these steps have survived to the present, because all these phyletic reconstructions are made on the basis of living forms. It seems evident, therefore, that in many groups there has been a remarkable survival of insect species, at least since the origin of the ancestral forms of present-day subfamilies and genera.

To students familiar with other invertebrate groups this situation should be no surprise. In the Mollusca, Crustacea, and Oligochaeta there are many examples of Mesozoic and Paleozoic fossils which are not only congeneric with living forms, but in addition show striking affinities to living species (Schrock & Twenhoffel, 1953).

*Differential Dispersal of Ancestral Types.* In the past there has been a widespread dispersal of many ancestral types. This has occurred even in the most restricted family studied, the Rhyacophilidae. There are cases, however, which indicate that some groups dispersed when others did not. Compare for instance, genera such as *Wormaldia* and *Chimarra*, which have spread and respread between many parts of the world, with the New Zealand genera of the subfamily Hydrobiosinae which has been restricted to New Zealand since the early formation of the subfamily. It is clear, therefore, that dispersal pattern, like rate of evolution, varies with each group.

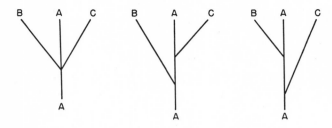

CHART 34. Hypothetical time relationships of lines arising from a common ancestor.

## THEORETICAL PROBLEMS

With the preceding points in mind, certain questions must be approached with a wider latitude of thinking than may at first be suggested by the data.

### Interpretation of Fossils

When a fossil form is identified, one may perhaps be prone to think that it marks both the time of origin and the main range of the species. This is certainly possible, but not necessarily so.

The fossil proves that the species was in existence at that time; that it did not arise later. If it represented a line evolving rapidly, the fossil would also give a close approximation of the earliest and latest dates of occurrence of that species or stage. If, however, it represented a line evolving very slowly, or the line of a living fossil, it would provide little data regarding either the earliest possible, or latest possible, dates of occurrence. It could be anywhere within a rather long expanse of existence of that particular type. For a good illustration, see the account of the Agapetini on p. 142.

The situation is further complicated by our inability to know which circumstance of evolutionary rate prevailed with regard to an isolated fossil form. Hence, in insect studies in which only isolated fossils are encountered (and this applies to most groups) this factor of the indeterminate time element of fossils is of considerable importance.

A locality record based on a fossil may be at any point in the species range. With insects this introduces a great deal of latitude. Known insect ranges vary greatly in extent. Examples of extremes are *Rhyacophila teddyi,* known only from a single small ~~of~~ mountains, and *Glossosoma intermedium,* points across Eurasia and North Amer- reason to believe that similar revailed in past times, and

that fossils represent species having variable ranges.

A fossil record, then, tells us (1) that a species occurred at a particular time, but not how long before or after; and (2) that it occurred at a particular spot, but not where else it might have occurred at that time.

### Relation of Phyletic Branches

It frequently happens that two or more groups of related forms are found to have essentially the same deduced ancestor. On a strictly morphological basis, these groups appear to have arisen from the same ancestor and at the same point on the family tree (Chart 34, *A*). When we consider the possibility that the ancestral form *A* might have been evolving at an extremely slow rate it becomes evident that we cannot be sure of the time relations of these branches at all. Let us postulate in Chart 34, *B* and *C*, that Ancestor A existed with little change through a considerable period of the time scale. Our morphological data can tell us that branches B and C each arose at some point on this line, but they cannot tell us whether B arose first, C second, or whether the two arose simultaneously.

The first impulse is to try to apply a measure of the amount of morphological difference between the various ends of the branches, and to consider that the branch differing the most from the common ancestor arose first. We have already shown, however, that evolutionary rates differ, and are individual with each group. Hence we cannot logically make this transfer of morphological difference into time difference. It seems that to obtain conclusions regarding time, we must have data which are basically concerned or associated with time.

If abundant and pertinent fossil material is available, there is a possibility of obtaining evidence which will solve this problem, because each fossil is chronologically identifiable and associated with a time scale. Even a few fossils may give clues of the utmost importance in deciding which of several alternative explanations to consider.

The second source of time data comes from the analysis of geological possibilities of dispersal and isolation. These possibilities can be compared with the phylogeny, dispersal indications, and geographic range of components of a group. Correlations between these sets of data give clues as to when certain dispersals may have occurred, or when certain groups may have been isolated. In this fashion inferences as to time may be introduced into the phylogenetic chart. An example of this type of evidence is presented in explaining the Australasian dispersal of *Sortosa* and *Chimarra*.

It must be realized that these last conclusions are only inferences, and that not until a large number of cases uphold an explanation, or a large number of points check with fidelity, will the conclusions approach reliability. It must be realized equally, however, that such conclusions may give us our only working hypotheses against which to compare other results or with which to explain facts in hand.

### Dispersals in Time

There are instances in which we believe that a certain ancestral form became widespread, extending perhaps from Europe to Australia or the Americas, or other combinations of geographic units. We frequently have little evidence to ascertain whether the entire dispersal was made in a relatively short time, or in a series of smaller dispersals, each some time apart. If the dispersal involves a group for which we have living fossils the problem is troublesome, because in such forms not enough change occurs to give us morphological stepping stones to correlate with geographic stepping stones. Frequently we must make a tentative decision based on inference from some other group, corroborating this decision as best we can from other evidence.

. . . . .

The above explanations are given to acquaint the reader with some of the problems which cause difficulty in the attempt to apply a time scale to the preceding phylogenetic studies. In spite of these difficulties there is sufficient evidence from geologic data and dispersal data of other organisms to give much aid in dating movements of the montane caddisflies.

## THE BIOGEOGRAPHIC TIME SCALE

Correlating the preceding dispersal patterns with each other and with geologic time is like putting together a jigsaw puzzle. Even though certain branches of different large groups may show a correspondence, it is evident that there is no over-all dispersal pattern which fits all groups. Each one has followed a separate course, conditioned by ecological opportunity. Nor is there an obvious, sustained correlation of any of these dispersal chains with geologic time.

As a result, it is necessary to seek pieces of evidence that seem to offer some opportunity for solving a bit of the puzzle here and a bit there. After certain landmarks are thus established in time, it is easier to attempt a reconstruction of events in entire groups.

### Narrowing the Problem

In Chart 3, we gave a brief summary of the fossil record, indicating that the order was well established in the Jurassic. Judging from wing evidence (all that is available), the Jurassic caddisfly fauna had not evolved into a complex fauna and may have represented at most the early beginnings of the Trichoptera line. It is certain, however, that the great bulk of modern genera had evolved by the time of the Baltic amber deposits. These are early Oligocene in age, but were redeposited in the Baltic Sea beds, so that their actual time of imprisonment in the amber may have been somewhat earlier. Emerson has expressed the view that the Baltic amber fossils are probably of Eocene age, which seems reasonable on the basis of many considerations, and I am adopting this view here.

Since the genera *Rhyacophila*, *Electragapetus*, and *Wormaldia* are represented in the Baltic amber it is certain that they were Eocene or pre-Eocene in origin. This gives us one landmark in each family. It seems highly likely that *Chimarra* is of at least a similar age, judging by its varied and long history. This would mean that *Sortosa* (parent of *Wormaldia*) and *Anagapetus* (grandparent of *Electragapetus*) are even older.

From this it is clear that we must look to correlations with geologic events after Jurassic and before Oligocene for aid in dating the origin of the genera, pre-Eocene for older genera and probably in or near Eocene for the more recent genera.

### Australasian Dispersals

It is a curious fact that certain old genera, such as *Sortosa* and a primitive member of the Hydrobiosinae, reached Australia and New Zealand and appear to have been isolated on New Zealand ever since; whereas more recent genera, such as *Chimarra* and *Apsilochorema*, reached Australia and Fiji but did not reach New Zealand. It is further true of these caddisflies that the New Zealand groups are also found on New Caledonia (*Sortosa* and *Xanthochorema*), but not so the Fiji groups. An additional example is an undescribed species of *Hydropsyche* found on New Caledonia which is intimately related to the peculiar primitive group of the genus found elsewhere only in New Zealand.

All of these groups seem to have spread into Australasia from southeastern Asia, and appear to represent two dispersals, an earlier one of a group of primitive forms and a later one of more specialized forms.

The distribution pattern of these dispersals can be fitted with striking agreement into present concepts of the origin of the inner and outer Melanesian arcs. There is much difference of opinion (Bryan 1944, Glaessner 1950) regarding the geologic history of the large Australian land mass, which stretches eastward to near Samoa. There is, however, essential agreement on these points (Chart 35):

1. The Malay Archipelago was probably an extensive land area at the end of Mesozoic and the beginning of Eocene and was connected intermittently with the New Guinea area by the alternate rising and falling of the Banda Basin (Umbgrove 1947, 1949).

2. At this time the southern part of New Guinea was connected to Australia across what is now the Coral Sea.

3. The inner Melanesian arc connected New Zealand to the New Guinea corner of the land mass. The arc, pictured as a series of islands or a mountainous ridge, included New Caledonia. The time

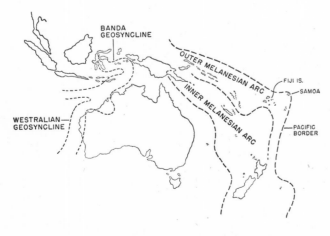

CHART 35. Geomorphic features of Australasia and adjoining areas (compiled from various sources).

of the arc is variously estimated as Cretaceous or early Cenozoic. The arc was apparently of short duration.

4. The outer Melanesian arc came into being at a later period. It extended from the northeastern part of New Guinea, through the Solomon Islands and the New Hebrides, to Fiji. This arc was probably of Miocene age. Certainly it would seem that no Trichoptera could traverse it before that time because much of it was below the sea from Jurassic to Oligocene. The arc probably was elevated at the same time as the northern highlands of New Guinea, many of which are the result of Miocene folding. The outer Melanesian arc has had a shorter but more violent geologic history than the inner arc, so that its parts also were undoubtedly connected for only brief periods.

5. It is likely that the Miocene folding producing the outer Melanesian arc brought about land connections between northern Australia and New Guinea, and between islands of the area between New Guinea and the Malay Archipelago.

This set of circumstances would have permitted this sequence:

1. In Cretaceous, a spread of ancestral forms such as *Sortosa* from southeastern Asia, across the Malay Archipelago, to New Guinea, Australia, New Caledonia, and New Zealand. The subsequent break in the inner Melanesian arc would have isolated the New Caledonia–New Zealand populations in the lower part of the arc. Parts of the Malay Archipelago also broke after this period, shutting off possibilities of continued faunal interchange with Asia.

2. In Miocene, a spread of *Chimarra*, *Agapetus* and other genera, again from southeastern Asia, through island chains to New Guinea, Australia, and the outer Melanesian arc. Some genera ultimately reached the Fiji Islands. Breaks in the chain resulted in the isolated faunas known today.

The monophyletic nature of the known *Agapetus* fauna of New Guinea and Australia suggests that either the connection between New Guinea and the Asiatic area broke first, resulting in an ancestral species common to both New Guinea and Australia; or that New Guinea was first connected, then disconnected, with a mainland dispersal route, and only later became connected with Australia. This latter seems to be a more likely method by which the stepping-stone nature of the fauna evolved.

It is significant that the older faunal units in Australia (*Sortosa* and the Hydrobiosinae *Taschorema* and allies) did not spread into New Guinea when *Chimarra* and its neighbors spread into Australia. Apparently the connection was of such an ecological nature that the older Australian fauna was restricted to the higher mountain levels at the time when the newer genera (*Chimarra* and *Agapetus*) were spreading at lower levels.

We have a further correlation to substantiate this time-dating. According to the above scheme, *Agapetus* would be pre-Miocene in origin, because the New Guinea–Australian species are moderately specialized members of the genus. *Agapetus* is an offshoot of an ancestral form preceding *Electragapetus* (Chart 42), which itself is pre-Oligocene. This certainly justifies the consideration of *Agapetus* itself as possibly pre-Oligocene, with branches spreading into eastern Asia in Oligocene and into Australasia in Miocene.

The virtual establishment of Miocene as the dispersal time of *Agapetus, Apsilochorema,* and *Chimarra* indicates strongly that the earlier spread of genera which reached New Zealand (*Sortosa* and the New Zealand Hydrobiosinae) occurred in the Cretaceous. The best corroborative evidence we have is the sequence of events leading from ancestral *Sortosa* to and through the development of *Chimarra* (see Chart 37).

*Chimarra* evidently developed as a subtropical genus in South America from an ancestral *Sortosa,* and evolved into several distinct groups. One of these spread to Asia, passed through several evolutionary stages, then spread presumably in Oligocene to New Guinea and, in Miocene, to Fiji and Australia. It seems likely (as explained in the next subsection), that, at the very latest, *Chimarra* spread from America to Asia during Eocene. The genus in its primitive form was therefore pre-Eocene, probably late Cretaceous, in actual time of origin. It is removed by several evolutionary steps from *Sortosa,* so that the time of arrival of *Sortosa* in South America may be inferred reasonably to have been about Middle Cretaceous. Certainly this supports the idea that *Sortosa* was in existence and widespread during Middle Cretaceous.

This rather devious path of reasoning corroborates well the original point in this discussion, that *Sortosa* spread from New Guinea into Australia and over the inner Melanesian arc to New Zealand during late Cretaceous.

*New Caledonia.* While we are at this point of the discussion let us examine the data for New Caledonia. We have three bits of evidence showing the montane fauna of this island to be monophyletic with that of New Zealand and with no other area. It is evident from this that the montane fauna of the inner Melanesian arc was cut off first from New Guinea, and developed distinctive features in the areas of the arc. While geologic evidence indicates that New Caledonia was probably part of the original Cretaceous pathway from New Guinea to New Zealand, there is some doubt as to whether or not it was resubmerged and later re-elevated in lower Tertiary. This gives us these two alternatives to explain the Trichoptera fauna:

1. If New Caledonia has remained above water since Cretaceous, then it has retained representatives of the primitive stocks of the montane lines on the arcs, with more specialized members developing on New Zealand.

2. If it was submerged and re-elevated, then it also was reconnected to New Zealand by montane terrain. In this case the New Caledonia species would represent the evolutionary stage of the various lines as they existed on New Zealand at that time.

*Other Australasian Connections.* De Beaufort (1951) records data from other groups, especially the Reptilia, which indicate that other connections possibly occurred between New Caledonia, New Zealand, and various islands of the outer Melanesian arc. Negative evidence from the montane caddisflies could be due to a lack of collecting and records. If not, it would not necessarily contradict De Beaufort's suggestion, but would simply indicate that these connections were not of a mountainous nature.

This point is well illustrated by the dispersal of the monotremes during the known Pleistocene connection between Australia and New Guinea. Concerning the monotremes De Beaufort writes "In early Tertiary times they spread over New Guinea and Australia; during the Tertiary isolation *Echidna* developed in Australia and *Zaglossus* in New Guinea. During the Pleistocene connection *Echidna* reached southern New Guinea and Tasmania, but *Zaglossus,* which lives in the mountains, could not reach Australia, as the connection was one of lowland only." Apparently no montane caddisflies spread between these areas at this time.

## The Bering Bridge

In the preceding section we mentioned the probable Eocene spread of subtropical *Chimarra* from North America to Asia. Emerson (1952) believes that plant evidence indicates late Cretaceous as the latest time when subtropical forms could move through the northern Bering Bridge area. There is, however, some evidence that such a crossing could have been made in early Cenozoic.

Using marine organisms as indices to minimum temperature conditions, Durham (1950) has calculated the past Cenozoic ocean temperatures of the North American region of the Pacific Coast. He shows that in early Eocene the 25° temperature line was situated at about 48° Lat. N (about Vancouver, B.C.), whereas at present it is situated at about 18° Lat. N (just above Acapulco, Mex.). Since the isotherms curve strongly north between 50° and 60° Lat. N, then we would expect that any subtropical species which can exist now as far north as southern Lower California, could have crossed the Bering Bridge in earliest Eocene. Many of the subtropical caddisfly groups which I believe may have done this (*Chimarra* subg. *Curgia, Marilia, Smicridea*) have the bulk of their range in Central and South America, but have one or two species occurring north to 20° or 30° Lat. N. All three of these groups eventually reached Australia, but it is not yet known from what area *Marilia* started. It seems reasonable to suppose that these groups dispersed in early Eocene. If the dispersal had occurred earlier we would expect to find greater evidence of redispersal.

Another pertinent point in Durham's data is that the early Eocene climate was fully as warm northward as the late Cretaceous climate.

Durham found little evidence relating to the Paleocene, but strong evidence that northern water temperatures have been declining steadily since early Eocene. There is no evidence from this source that interglacial periods were much warmer than average Pliocene climates. This situation seems to rule out rather definitely any northern intercontinental spread of warm-adapted organisms after early or middle Eocene.

These general conclusions corroborate very closely those of Chaney (1940) based on an analysis of Tertiary forest data. Plant fossils show that in Eocene, northern Alaska enjoyed temperate floras, that southern Alberta had a subtropical climate, and that intermediate types occurred around the southern fringe of Alaska and along the Aleutian chain. Chaney also considers that the climate has averaged cooler since that time.

The analysis of dispersal periods by Simpson (1947) gives definite clues as to actual times when land connections existed between Eurasia and North America. Certain evidence indicates that these connections were chiefly across the Bering Bridge. As Simpson points out, certain times of dispersal are inconclusively documented and doubtful, but strong evidence is present for the existence of at least the following connections:

1. Paleocene
2. Early Eocene (extensive interchange)
3. Late Eocene–early Oligocene (perhaps two separate dispersals)
4. Early to middle Miocene (a highly selective route)
5. Late Miocene–early Pliocene (faunal interchange not extensive, but more so than during the two preceding and the following)
6. Late Pliocene
7. Pleistocene (extensive interchange)

Different types of mammals involved in these dispersals indicate that each of the above seven bridges was of a different ecological type, as would be expected from the opinions of Chaney and Durham. This also explains why the caddisfly data follow dispersal patterns individual for each group.

## Inter-American Land Bridges

The situation with regard to land connections between North and South America has some puzzling aspects. There is evidence that certain animal groups dispersed between these two continents many times, but we have a satisfactory explanation for only a few cases.

The Cenozoic dispersal patterns for mammals (Simpson 1950) indicate several such crossings between the Americas, and the dispersal patterns for *Atopsyche* follow very well a proposed scheme based on Simpson's data (Ross & King 1952, Ross 1953a & b). The geologic maps of Weeks (1948) corroborate this situation in the Cenozoic, and suggest that the alternating land and sea conditions in Central America and Colombia acted as a sort of gate, sometimes open and sometimes shut, and involving various combinations of land areas in the vicinity. In this phenomenon it is similar to conditions in the islands of the south Pacific. There is, then, ample geologic evidence to support the sort of Cenozoic bridging suggested by distributional data of animals.

A problem arises in deducing the movement of such ancient forms as *Sortosa*, also ancient termites (Emerson 1952), saturniid moths, and undoubtedly many other insects (Ross 1953*a*). These forms were certainly in South America in pre-Paleocene times, perhaps early in Cretaceous, less likely as early as Jurassic; they were also in Asia in Cretaceous and probably also in North America. The data indicate an almost world-wide distribution of many early genera. The question is, what routes were followed, and when.

There is a possibility that the dispersal route of these ancient forms was from South America over an isthmus to Africa (Umbgrove 1947) or from South America via Antarctica to Australia or New Zealand. The evidence for the occurrence of such bridges in Cretaceous is poor, although it does not exclude them from consideration. It does, however, make it probable that a dispersal route existed between the Americas, and necessitates an examination of such possibilities.

According to Weeks (1948) northwestern Colombia was inundated by the sea from late Jurassic to early Paleocene except for a period in Middle Cretaceous when the Colombia–Venezuelan seaway was emergent (not shown in his maps). This piece of information provides a clue to a possible inter-American bridge via the Panamanian isthmus. Umbgrove (1947) suggests that at some time in Upper Cretaceous there was an orogenic movement of some of the West Indies. This and the peculiar mixture of Cretaceous deposits for some of the West Indies reported by Imlay (1944) introduces the possibility that the West Indies could have been a dispersal route between the two American continents.

With these two possibilities documented, there seems no real objection to considering that *Sortosa* and other primitive genera spread into South America from North America, or vice versa, in mid-Cretaceous.

## Mountains

The intercontinental connections we have discussed would be of little significance in relation to montane caddisflies if the connections were either not ecologically suited to such organisms, or if they connected areas not ecologically suited to them. To check on this point let us examine the record of the mountains.

The best summary of world-wide mountain conditions that I have found is given by Umbgrove (1947). From his accounts and maps it is clear that mountains have existed since early in the Cambrian, and that there have been numerous orogenic periods from the Silurian to the present. Certain areas, such as central Europe, have had a continuous montane topography since this early period; and in North America the Appalachian region, the Ouachita and Wichita region, and the frontal ranges of the Rockies have been mountainous to some degree since late Carboniferous or early Permian.

The caddisfly history presumably opened in early Mesozoic, on the heels of the Appalachian revolution which undoubtedly provided montane pathways across many parts of the world. Toward the end of the Mesozoic began the extensive Laramide revolution, reaching a crescendo in the Paleocene and continuing locally until at least Oligocene (Love, 1939). The Appalachian and Laramide systems together linked the great bulk of the world (except Africa) with a network of closely approximated mountain areas. Not only would this situation provide many avenues of dispersal for montane species, but it would also provide suitable ecological islands for cool-adapted organisms when the surrounding area was too warm for their existence.

This situation would apply especially to such an area as the southern two-thirds of North America, where during Cretaceous and Eocene subtropical conditions reached Lat. 51° N. Mountains in the south provided many areas in which cool-adapted forms could survive.

Mountain-making continued in Miocene, Pliocene, and Pleistocene and undoubtedly contributed some new avenues for dispersal. Possibly the present islands faunas of Asia and Melanesia are the result of dispersals over a large number of shifting and, in some places, very temporary land connections.

*Southeast Asia.* Of significance in almost every group is the old, stable land mass in southeastern Asia. This area was connected with the mountains north of the Gobi Desert area from Paleozoic to

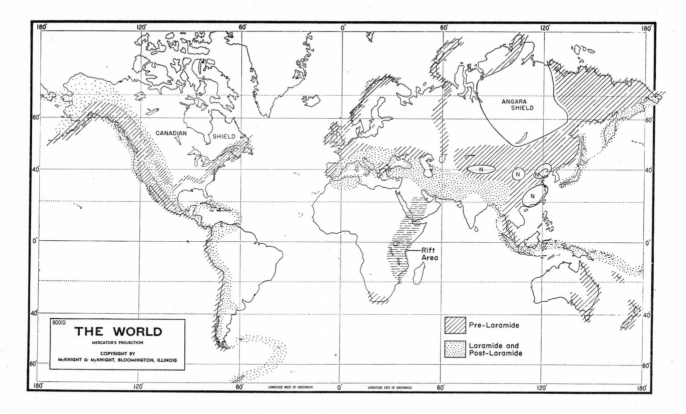

CHART 36. Principal orogenic areas of the world and associated features. N, stable nuclei of southern Asia.

mid-Mesozoic, when it became surrounded by Mesozoic mountains of an orogenetic movement including much of the territory (now islands) to the southeast. There is every likelihood that this movement set the stage for the spread to Australia of primitive Cretaceous phyletic lines. In Cenozoic the rise of the Himalayas and other ranges provided rejuvenated montane dispersal routes from the southeast Asian stable land mass to the west and with peninsular India.

One of the greatest aggregations of endemic groups is found centered around this area. At the present time it appears to form a single topographic and ecological unit with the Himalayan region, but its basic elements are far older than the Himalayas and could have constituted the more restricted range of ancestral forms dating back to earliest Mesozoic.

*Africa.* Although few of the cool-adapted montane caddisflies are found in Africa, it is highly desirable to know when mountainous routes to the

north were available for dispersal. The present mountains of eastern Africa are considered to be of Miocene age, and probably account for movements of young groups such as *Agapetus* and possibly *Chimarra* into that continent. Older semimontane conditions must have existed from Africa, possibly north into India, during late Cretaceous, if Umbgrove is correct in believing that domelike elevations preceded the volcanism and rifting in Africa and Arabia. It is entirely possible, therefore, that a montane dispersal route of sufficient elevation for cool-adapted organisms was present in this area fairly continuously from late Cretaceous to mid-Cenozoic, broken by the down-faulting of the Pliocene (Schuchert 1924, Umbgrove 1947).

To summarize the entire mountain situation, it appears that there have been mountains for a long time in many parts of the world, sufficient for the correlations proposed in this paper. Detailed points will be treated in reference to problems concerning individual groups.

## The Appalachian Area

A puzzling aggregation of montane caddisflies occurs in the Appalachian Mountain region of eastern North America. Archaic forms such as *Sortosa major* and *Rhyacophila montana* suggest that montane ancestral forms reached this area as early as Cretaceous and have been isolated in it ever since. Other groups, such as the *Rhyacophila carolina* group, appear to have reached the Appalachian region in mid-Cenozoic, and also to have remained isolated in that general area. Still a third group, exemplified by *Rhyacophila acropedes* and *angelita*, contain predominantly western forms which appear to have reached the Appalachian region in almost Recent time.

There is no evidence that the Appalachian system has been connected directly by mountain chains with the western North American systems except during late Carboniferous and Permian, which is too long ago for application to the cases in hand. There are still in existence remnants of some of the intervening mountains (the Wichita, Ouachita, and Arbuckle Mountains) which could have been of sufficient height in Cretaceous for some montane dispersal, but it is doubtful if such West to East crossings could have taken place then because of the great embayments extending northward from the Gulf of Mexico. Later it is still more doutbful if this route would have proved useful because of its areas of low elevation in regions of warm climate. Such information as we have points to a more northern route, presumably through hilly country well supplied with cold streams.

Regarding the supposed Cretaceous dispersal, we have one small bit of tangible evidence in addition to deduced dispersal hypotheses. A fossil caddisfly (?*Dolophilus praemissus* Cockerell) is known from the Coffee Creek (Eutah, Upper Cretaceous) formation of western Tennessee. Only the front wing of the specimen is well preserved. This wing could be either *Sortosa* or *Wormaldia*, or more likely a form very near the primitive psychomyiid genus *Phylocentropus*. To be certain of the family placement would require knowledge of head and body characters, but without these it is possible to narrow the identification down to these three. It is not likely (but still possible) that *Wormaldia* had evolved at this early date, so that the choice seems to narrow down to *Sortosa* or an ancestral *Phylo-centropus*, with the weight of evidence favoring the latter. The interesting point here is that *Sortosa* and *Phylocentropus* both occur as living fossils at the present time in the Great Smoky Mountains of eastern Tennessee, and it is highly likely that the two forms have been associated both ecologically and geographically throughout their history. Even if the fossil is a primitive *Phylocentropus* and not a *Sortosa*, the presence of this Cretaceous fossil in eastern North America is a good indication that *Sortosa* was there at that time also.

The postulated mid-Cenozoic dispersal involving the *Rhyacophila carolina* group and others is probably associated with the trans-Holarctic dispersal of the temperate forests. When arid conditions in central North America caused a division of these temperate forests into eastern and western elements, the range of the previously widespread ancestors of these caddisfly groups also were divided into the same geographic units. During this period, however, there were apparently no transverse mountain chains across North America. We are left with no alternative but to postulate that hilly country and a cool climate extended across the northern part of the continent, thus providing rapid streams with cool summer temperatures in which these caddisflies could live. Support for the dating of this Appalachian isolation as mid-Cenozoic is found in other insects, such as the leafhopper genus *Erythroneura*, which are associated with trees and which evidently had a dispersal pattern comparable to that of their hosts (Ross 1953a).

## Method of Range Extension

The extension of the ranges of *Rhyacophila acropedes* and *angelita* from the western montane region to the Appalachian area is one of the most intriguing phenomena we have encountered and brings us to a topic of general application. Both species are recently differentiated forms belonging to western species groups. The almost exact morphological identity of eastern and western specimens of these two species would indicate that their west to east dispersal is extremely recent; the location of all the eastern records in the northwestern or northern portion of the Appalachian system would further suggest that the dispersal occurred on the fringes of the last glacier as it retreated northward. Although western populations are found in mountain cascades, the eastern populations of these two species live in cold, rapid trout streams in hill country. These streams appear to represent the lower edge of temperature and velocity tolerances for the species. We know little of the caddisfly fauna in the intervening area between the known eastern and western records, but it seems certain that there is or was in the immediate past a pathway of such streams extending across the continent.

Why did only these two of the more than 50 western species of *Rhyacophila* extend their ranges eastward? Some of the western species are restricted to the western and southern ranges of the western mountains, and may not have had access to the dispersal opportunity. The others apparently do not have as wide a range of ecological tolerance as *acropedes* and *angelita*, and hence are unable to spread through an area without actual montane conditions. In other words, of the 50 species of pre-Wisconsin *Rhyacophila* which inhabited the western montane region of North America, the greater proportion had already evolved ecological tolerances which tied them effectively to montane conditions. It is possible that their tolerances include much colder conditions than those in which they occur, but limiting cold conditions would not normally occur in combination with good caddisfly streams close to the glacial front in the flat country of central North America. Only two of the western montane species had an ecological tolerance which permitted them to spread beyond the mountains and traverse the wooded hills eastward.

Let us examine another aspect of this situation. The 50 western species of *Rhyacophila* represent all nine major branches of the genus and 19 species groups. This Late Wisconsin crossing has set the stage for two, but only two, of these branches and species groups to colonize another montane area. If these colonizations are successful, the Appalachian fauna will become more complex to this extent.

Two types of *Rhyacophila* do not seem to have crossed between these two montane areas:

(1) No old eastern species crossed to the western montane areas. One possible reason for this could be that none of the eastern species were sufficiently cold-adapted to use the same path as *acropedes* and *angelita*, but this is undoubtedly not true. We have collected larvae of the widespread eastern species *fuscula* in Michigan streams having a maximum temperature of 45° F., which is 10 degrees colder than the average western Cascade stream. The most plausible explanation is that the ice fields retreated from west to east (Flint 1947), and that when the eastern end of the *Rhyacophila* ecological bridge joined the Appalachian region, the western end had already broken its connection with the western montane region, or the central portion of the bridge was ecologically untenable.

(2) There is excellent evidence that at some earlier period a branch of the *sibirica* group spread from the western montane region to the Appalachian, and produced the two species *manistee* and *minora*. Both species occur in the northern portion of the Appalachian region in the same general areas as do the eastern populations of *acropedes* and *angelita*. It scarcely seems reasonable that *manistee* and *minora* would not be able to spread through the same territory as did *acropedes* and *angelita*, which adds additional evidence to the one-way nature of the trans-American *Rhyacophila* bridge as explained above.

We can divide the American *Rhyacophila* fauna into three categories on this dispersal basis:

1. Many western species that had access to the bridge but could not cross it because of their limited ecological tolerance.

2. Perhaps many eastern species that could have crossed it, except that the western connection of the bridge was broken too early.

3. The very few western species which had access to the bridge, had the necessary wider ecological tolerance, and did cross it.

One more point may be drawn regarding these west to east crossings in North America. From Charts 16 and 21 it will be seen that there is good evidence for believing that one species from each of at least seven western phyletic lines spread into and colonized the Appalachian region. It is probable that three or possibly more times of dispersal were involved. It is noteworthy that each line dispersed only once. The *invaria* and *carolina* lines, for instance, apparently spread eastward in mid-Cenozoic but not again in Pleistocene with the *acropedes* and *angelita* lines. From this it can be inferred that either (1) the various connecting areas were of a different ecological type, (2) the various lines were not advantageously situated geographically at each possible opportunity, or (3) the breadth of tolerance (but not necessarily its mean) may change in time within each phyletic line.

The dispersal of groups across a dispersal route is thus seen to be a highly random phenomenon. In the case of these montane insects seldom (if ever) is there a wholesale interchange of faunas across such a connection, but rather the spread of that unpredictable number of species whose ecological tolerance fits the conditions of the connecting area.

Actually the significant point is that the ecological mean of a bridge may not coincide at all with the ecological means of the areas connected. Hence on the part of the species the premium quality for dispersal is likely to be breadth of ecological tolerance, a characteristic distinct from its adjustment to its parental environmental mean.

## PROBABLE CHRONOLOGY OF DISPERSAL PATTERNS

### The Philopotamidae

The phylogeny and general distribution of this family are summarized in Charts 4 to 15, Chapter 3. The main outlines of its chronology have been discussed in earlier parts of this chapter dealing with Australasia and South America. Based on these discussions, the proposed dispersal pattern has been plotted against geologic time in Charts 37 and 38.

In Chart 37 data are presented for the genera *Paulianodes, Sortosa* and its subgenera, the small branch *Philopotamus,* and the main features of the *Protarra-Chimarra* line.

The origin of the subfamily Paulianodinae is obscure. As suggested for the *Apsilochorema* line (Ross 1951e), this group also could have been isolated in early Cretaceous in Peninsular India, eventually reaching Africa and Madagascar. At present it is known only from the latter area. If these surmises are correct, this would also indicate that the ancestor for the entire family was in Asia, and that Asia was also the original range of the *Sortosa* Ancestor.

The *Sortosa* Ancestor became widespread, according to our previous reasoning, during middle to late Cretaceous. There seems little doubt from the montane habitat occupied by primitive living forms that the *Sortosa* Ancestor was at least a cool-adapted form requiring clear, rapid streams. The

series of compression movements occurring throughout the Mesozoic seem to have formed a complete band of mountains around the north Pacific, from the Chinese nuclei in southeast Asia, north and across to Alaska, and down the west coast of North America. According to Umbgrove (1947) the later orogenic movements continued around the Antilles, then across South America and down its west coast. Umbgrove refers this latter extension (the Subhercynian compression) to late Cretaceous; the period of elevation of parts of northern South America is given as mid-Cretaceous by Weeks (1948). It is probable that either the two movements were actually contemporaneous or that the two events overlapped in time, to some extent. Whichever is true, the general picture for the mountains of the Northern Hemisphere and South America corresponds to a remarkable degree with both the dispersal pattern of the caddisflies and other data offering clues as to their actual time of spread.

After this initial wide range extension, various populations of *Sortosa* became isolated in different areas. The South American segregate apparently gave rise to the subgenus *Sortosa* and the *Protarra-Chimarra* line. It is probable that there were actually two original *Sortosa* populations segregated in South America, and that the more northern one gave rise to the *Protarra-Chimarra* line, the one in extreme southern South America to the subgenus *Sortosa.*

It is difficult to speculate far on the chronology of the subgenera and small branches of the *Sortosa* Ancestor, as indicated by the following efforts:

*Subgenus Sortosa.* The three known species represent two dichotomies, but it is impossible to say when they occurred.

*Subgenus Fumonta.* Only one species is known, restricted in present-day range to the Great Smoky Mountains of eastern North America. No dating evidence.

*Subgenus Sisko.* The single known species of this North American group occurs in two restricted and widely separated areas, the Coast Range of Oregon and northern California, and the Georgia foothills of the eastern Great Smoky Mountains. Although only few specimens are available, it can be seen that the eastern and western populations differ only minutely in proportions of parts. The habitat, however, is peculiar, being cold streams in warm temperate areas. Judging again from the correspondence between this and the data from decidu-ous forests and leafhoppers, these two populations have in all likelihood been separated since the Miocene. This is the last time when a transconti-nental corridor of suitable conditions appears to have been in existence. This case points to the possibility of separated species populations persist-ing for millions of years with little or no change.

*Subgenus Dolophilodes.* Although there are a number of branches in the subgenus (Chart 8), there is some doubt both as to the phylogenetic placement of these branches and their dates of origin. Judging partly by the nebulous criterion of distinctive structure, and partly by its heterozygous condition for primitive wing characters (fork $R_{2+3}$ near *s*), *dorca* was the earliest branch of the group, and may indicate an origin in North America, with perhaps a spread of the group to Asia in Paleocene. From this point on, the home of ancestral forms is purely guesswork, with the bulk of evidence favor-ing an Asiatic site for the main lines of develop-ment with occasional species spreading to North America. If so, three distinct lines dispersed in this fashion, represented in North America by the west-ern *novusamericana,* the eastern *distincta,* and the western pair *aequalis* and *pallidipes* representing the *aequalis-ornata* complex. It is impossible to date these dispersals. The amount of species multiplica-tion is too small to afford many clues. Because of its eastern distribution, it may be surmised that *distincta* was a Miocene dispersal; the extreme sim-ilarity within the *aequalis-ornata* complex suggests a more recent date, possibly late Pliocene. This would indicate that the *novusamericana* dispersal occurred later than the *dorca* dispersal, but before the *aequalis-ornata* dispersal.

The uncertainties encountered in tracing the paths of this subgenus draw our attention to the lack of information regarding the present and past fauna of the stable Angara Shield of central Si-beria.

*Subgenus Kisaura.* There seems little doubt that this subgenus arose in southeastern Asia, develop-ing during Cretaceous in the mountains surround-ing the nuclei of southeastern Asia, and spreading into the Himalayan area in Cenozoic. The more recently evolved forms (Chart 6) have developed from parental populations moving toward the north. The species numbered 2 to 5 on Chart 6 make a re-markably clear chain of morphological events, sug-gesting the solid line dispersal. It is more likely that the line of parental populations actually moved along the mainland, the island species having spread to their present location as indicated by the dotted-line route in Chart 6. When this hap-pened is uncertain. A better understanding of the mainland fauna of this area would help to clarify the picture.

The restriction of this subgenus to the south-eastern Asiatic nuclei is in sharp contrast to the previous subgenus *Dolophilodes,* but it is in agree-ment with information concerning the primitive Asiatic lines of *Glossosoma* and many species groups of *Rhyacophila.* Many of these latter are evidently of great antiquity phylogenetically, and several of these forms may have formed a closely knit ecological complex in this area from early Cretaceous to the present.

*Genus Philopotamus.* The Baltic amber species *siculus* indicates that the genus has probably been in Europe continuously since early Cenozoic. It could well have originated from a Cretaceous dis-persal through the Ural Mountains into the older mountains of central Europe. The isolated position of some species in Portugal, Corsica, and Caucasia (Chart 7) will ultimately give some valuable clues as to the time that some of the dichotomies of the genus occurred.

*Philopotamus* forms another circumscribed Euro-pean species flock comparable to the *Rhyacophila vulgaris* group. In the case of *Philopotamus* the amount of species multiplication has been much smaller. Undoubtedly a detailed study of the two groups would do much to clarify the history of montane life in these areas. Unquestionably glacial advances have distorted the past ranges of many European species; hence, the most significant data will come from peripheral, restricted species which may have been little affected by these movements.

*Subgenus Thylakion.* The two South African spe-cies of this subgenus present a perplexing combi-nation of circumstances. The structure of their male genitalia indicates a common lineage with *Philopo-tamus.* This would suggest that sometime before *Philopotamus* became morphologically differenti-ated, considerably before late Eocene, an ancestral form from west Asia or Europe spread into Africa. The path by which this form crossed the Tethys geosyncline or sea is not known. If the genitalic similarities between *Thylakion* and *Philopotamus* are the result of parallel evolution, then ancestral *Sortosa* may be postulated to have crossed the Assam Bridge in the Cretaceous, eventually spreading to Africa, and forming the ancestor of *Thylakion*.

The time of actual entry into and dispersal through Africa is problematic. Data on siluroid fishes given by De Beaufort (1951) suggests either an early Cenozoic or late Cretaceous dispersal.

Depending on the ecological tolerances of the *Sortosa* caddisflies and these early siluroid fishes, they may or may not have spread into Africa at the same time. It is pertinent to note, however, that De Beaufort postulates two major phases of fish dispersal into Africa, an early one including the siluroids, and a later one including chiefly cyprinoids. Might not this pattern account also for the two evident montane caddisfly dispersals into the continent, the earlier including the progenitors of *Thylakion* and *Paulianodes*, the second including *Wormaldia* and *Chimarra?*

The extremely restricted nature of these early philopotamid forms in Africa (*Paulianodes* in Madagascar and *Thylakion* in the mountains of South Africa) is reminiscent of the situation in the freshwater crayfishes of the family Parastacidae. Of this ancient family, the only African member is *Astacoides* found only in Madagascar. Petit (1927) reports that it occurs only in brooks in forests and that it disappears from the streams when shade is removed by clearing. He believes that, after the crayfish reached Madagascar, the mainland of Africa underwent periods of more xeric conditions, reducing and thinning the forests, and exterminating the mainland populations. This idea will have an interesting application later when we consider *Wormaldia* and *Chimarra*.

*Subgenus Hydrobiosella.* The probable dispersal pattern for this genus has been given in detail in the preceding part of this chapter dealing with Australia and New Zealand. In brief, the original *Sortosa* Ancestor spread in Cretaceous to the East Indies, then into New Guinea, and from there to Australia and New Zealand. Representatives of these primitive faunal elements have become restricted to mountain streams of Australia, New Zealand, and New Caledonia. There is doubt as to whether the New Caledonia fauna is a primitive element of an Inner Melanesian arc fauna, or whether it represents a more recent mid-Cenozoic dispersal of the fauna which evolved in New Zealand.

When Chart 5 was prepared, I was hopeful that the dispersal pattern of the Australian and Tasmanian fauna, together with the well-marked phylogenetic relationships, could be interpreted in the light of the geologic history of the continent. When, however, the material for *Agapetus* was summarized (Chart 33), it was difficult to integrate information from the two groups because of uncertainties regarding the ecological tolerances of the animals, the location of corresponding areas in Australia, and the complete distribution pattern of the caddisflies. However, there are clues in these data to the ecological cycles that have occurred on the continent.

### The Chimarra Line

The peregrinations of the *Chimarra* line are treated chiefly to assist in dating the activities of the *Sortosa* Ancestor, and the two are plotted together in Chart 37 for a visually better comparison. The primitive character of much of the Neotropical *Chimarra* fauna demonstrates beyond a doubt that the line began there. First evolved a genus somewhat like *Protarra*, then true *Chimarra*, and so on (see Chart 15). If the *Sortosa* Ancestor reached South America in mid-Cretaceous, then (based on Week's account) it seems unlikely that *Chimarra* could have spread out of South America until early Eocene. Many lines reached Africa, probably simultaneously, and probably along with the cyprinoids as reported by De Beaufort, for the *Chimarra* line at this stage of its evolution was relatively warm-adapted although preferring cool, swift streams. Very likely this dispersal was during the Miocene, which De Beaufort believes was a period of wet climate in Africa. Such a date fits well into our postulates regarding other dispersal dates of the *Chimarra* line. Nonetheless, one problem remains unsolved: Not only did many lines of *Chimarra* reach Africa proper, but many species are known also from Madagascar. When they reached this latter area I do not know. Madagascar was supposedly severed from the mainland in Eocene. Perhaps studies in progress on the phylogeny of the Madagascar forms will throw some light on this subject.

The respread of advanced forms of *Chimarra* to North America probably occurred in early Oligocene or early Miocene, since these presumably provided warmer connecting areas than did later connections across the Bering Bridge. This dispersal

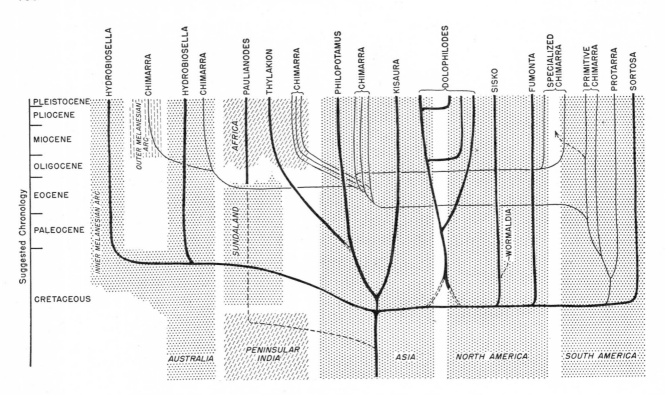

CHART 37. Phylogenetic dispersal chart of *Sortosa* (heavy lines) and *Chimarra* (thin lines).

(whichever time was involved) may have been contemporaneous with the dispersal of both the temperate deciduous forest and other insects such as certain leafhoppers and mosquitoes (Ross 1953*a*). Once in the Americas, the specialized forms of *Chimarra* increased greatly in number of species, and these in turn became adapted to different habitats. Those species which evolved in eastern North America became relatively cold-adapted, and are sometimes found in the same streams with *Sortosa distincta*. Other closely related species of *Chimarra* in the Neotropical region are still warm-adapted and do not extend north of the frost line.

The genus *Chimarra* is abundant and widespread in all the tropical and subtropical parts of the world. I feel sure that it will eventually assist in deducing faunal dispersals in many areas, but at present this study is only well started.

### The Wormaldia Line

We meet here the combination of circumstances that make the dating of northern cool-adapted forms such a difficult problem. There are no branches into Australasia or out of South America to aid in dating population movements; there are several phyletic lines, all of which arose from essentially the same morphological type and consequently show little indication of the chronological relationship of the various branches (see Chart 13); and the original ancestor spread over several continents, with little indication of the chronology of the actual dispersals.

Some evidence of time relations can be obtained from a few Baltic amber fossils and from a few points of distribution pattern. These are indicated in Chart 38, which represents the dispersal pattern of *Wormaldia*.

In the Baltic amber collections (Ulmer 1912) there are at least three species which are all closely related and have a mesal flap on the seventh sternite. The best diagnostic character by which to identify the genus *Wormaldia* is the loss of 2A in the hind wing, but this character is hidden in the two Baltic amber specimens I have examined, and the area is incompletely or doubtfully illustrated in the species treated by Ulmer. There is another diagnostic character, however, that is helpful. In *Sortosa, Philopotamus* and a few primitive species of *Wormaldia* such as *anilla,* the intercostal vein is nearly midway between the base of the stigmal area and the base of the wing. In most species of *Wormaldia,* especially the European groups *pulla* and *occipitalis,* the intercostal vein is much nearer the base of the wing. This same condition holds in the Baltic amber fossils, so that there is no doubt that they belong to *Wormaldia.*

We have definite proof, then, that *Wormaldia* was not only in existence by at least late Eocene, but had undergone some evolution of its own. Since with few exceptions the species groups are confined to mountain areas, and each group stems from a primitive form, it seems reasonable to suppose that the genus became widespread soon after its formation. On circumstantial evidence (see Chart 38), it also seems certain that the genus arose sometime in late Cretaceous. The original widespread dispersal of the group would therefore be between late Cretaceous and late Eocene.

To restrict the period further, the group is cool-adapted, and would probably require a montane route. It seems to me that such a period could best

have been that of the Laramide Revolution. This orogenic movement was at its peak in very early Cenozoic, or Paleocene, and could well have provided the cool avenues of dispersal for these caddisflies.

Returning our attention to Chart 38, there are a few more points that offer dating help. In the *kyana* group, one of the two species is known from Africa and the other from Madagascar. Assuming that these two areas were separated in late Eocene, this would indicate that the *kyana* group reached Africa in very early Cenozoic.

In the *anilla* group there exists the same situation in regard to western and eastern montane groups in North America that was discussed earlier in this chapter. The *thyria-hamata* complex comprises only two species, *thyria* in California, and *hamata* in North Carolina. It seems clear that the ancestral form was western, and that it spread at one time into the eastern mountains. Since the two species are known from the ends of their respective mountain chains, it seems likely that their ancestral form spread east at the time of the transcontinental temperate deciduous forest in mid-Cenozoic. The *strota-shawnee* complex is entirely

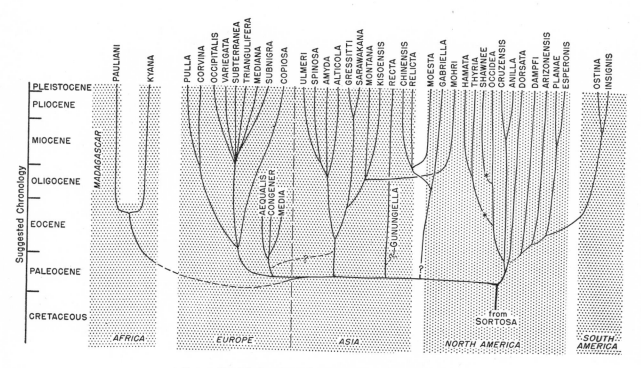

CHART 38. Phylogenetic dispersal chart of *Wormaldia.*

eastern, but is undoubtedly a relative of some species such as *occidea* which spread to the east. The scattered nature of the known collections of these species throughout the eastern deciduous forest, plus the considerable morphological difference that has developed between them, supports the idea that this complex also resulted from a dispersal at the same time as the *thyria-hamata* ancestor. Apparently neither group spread back to the western part of the continent.

Two other dispersals are to be accounted for. The subgenus *Doloclanes* is entirely Asiatic except for the species *mohri* from the southern Appalachian region in eastern North America. The entire subgenus occurs along the southern edge of the range of the genus as a whole and this suggests that *mohri* represents a mid-Cenozoic dispersal with the temperate deciduous forest. The other dispersal concerns the *moesta* group. If the phylogeny and dispersal possibilities suggested in Chapter 3 are valid, then we could conclude that *gabriella* was a strictly montane species, whereas the "widespread Holarctic ancestor" of Chart 11 had become a more temperate animal. Thus a temperate dispersal route in mid-Cenozoic would allow the *moesta* complex to become virtually world-wide, while restricting *gabriella* to the mountains of western North America. It must be realized that in this case the phylogeny is based on few characters and therefore these remarks are somewhat a challenge for further investigation.

Leaving the *moesta* group out of consideration for the moment, all the other data are in agreement in suggesting that the ancestral form of *Wormaldia* became world-wide before the Oligocene and possibly as early as late Paleocene or early Eocene.

There is no definite information on several points. One point concerns the time that the *pulla*, *copiosa*, and *occipitalis* groups arrived in Europe. It is entirely possible that the common ancestor of these three groups was also the ancestor of the *aequalis* Baltic amber group, in which case there must have been a differential survival of the four groups in Europe. Also there was either a differential fossilization in the amber, or the first three groups occurred in a different part of Europe in Eocene than did the *aequalis* group.

Information is also lacking for the ancestry of *Doloclanes* and *recta*. Both could be direct descendents of Paleocene segregates of the widespread ancestral *Wormaldia*. *Doloclanes* and the *aequalis* group may have had a common ancestor, but if so it probably antedated the amber fossils and could have originated in Asia. Certainly *Doloclanes* evolved in the area of the southeast Asian nuclei. A third point about which we have no clue is the chronology of the *arizonensis* group revolving around Central America. There are insufficient known dispersals and too little known of past climates in this area to furnish a basis for analyzing our present meager data. At some period or periods in its pre-Pleistocene history this area must have had cooler and more mesic conditions to allow the redistribution and species multiplication of which we have record.

*Gunungiella* is one of the rarest of caddisfly genera, with only about half a dozen specimens known, comprising four species. Their distribution, however, tallies in general with that of several other insect groups such as the *Rhyacophila castanea* group. These are suggestive of a Miocene distribution in the Oriental region. This pattern is discussed more fully in the account of the *Rhyacophila castanea* group on p. 91.

### Summary of the Philopotamidae

Reviewing and comparing Charts 37 and 38, we see that there have been two major dispersals of cool-adapted groups—*Sortosa* in middle or late Cretaceous, and *Wormaldia* in Paleocene or possibly early Eocene. Subsequent redispersal of these forms has been limited. The warm-adapted *Chimarra* line provides another widespread dispersal, probably in early Eocene, but this line has become redistributed to a greater extent than the first two.

The more restricted cool-adapted groups have formed closely knit species flocks centered around mountain areas and they illustrate the dependence on the persistence of montane ecological areas for continued existence of these caddisflies.

The two dispersals of these groups indicate that at least twice since early Mesozoic such ecological areas were more widespread and continuous than at present. The dispersals into Africa and Australia indicate also that conditions across the equator were unusually cool and/or mountainous at least during the times of the *Sortosa* and *Wormaldia* movements, and that they have not been so since. Otherwise we would expect evidence of a redispersal of cool-adapted forms stemming from Africa or Australia.

The dispersal patterns indicate even more clearly that at least for the greater portion of late Mesozoic and all Cenozoic, the areas and climates between these mountain areas have been inimical for the survival of the cool-adapted montane forms. Otherwise, the result would be many more intergrading lines relating the faunae of distant montane regions.

### The Rhyacophilidae

The two subfamilies of the Rhyacophilidae have had an entirely different history from the standpoint of dispersal. This difference makes it easy to correlate the Hydrobiosinae with events just discussed, but difficult to do so for the Rhyacophilinae.

### The Hydrobiosinae

In most respects this is the specialized member of the family (Chart 26), but it is discussed first because of its aid in establishing a possible time for the origin of the Rhyacophilinae.

One branch of the Hydrobiosinae has a range embracing South America, Australia, and the inner Melanesian arc (Chart 39). This branch fits the points discussed for a mid-Cretaceous dispersal. As with *Sortosa*, each geographic segregate has developed within its own area with little redispersal. No counterpart of *Chimarra* has arisen in South America. The closest approach is *Atopsyche*, which may have developed from a Central American isolate of the widespread ancestral form (Ancestor 4 in Chart 26). *Atopsyche* has spread back and forth between the Americas several times (Ross & King 1952, Ross 1953a and b), but apparently was too restricted by either stream temperatures or velocities to be able to spread across the Bering Bridge to Asia as did *Chimarra*.

Establishing the dispersal of Ancestor 4 as probably mid-Cretaceous reaffirms the reasoning previously used (Ross 1951) in considering that Ancestor 3 existed at least as early as Lower Cretaceous. In the earlier study I suggested that the form ancestral to *Apsilochorema* evolved from a

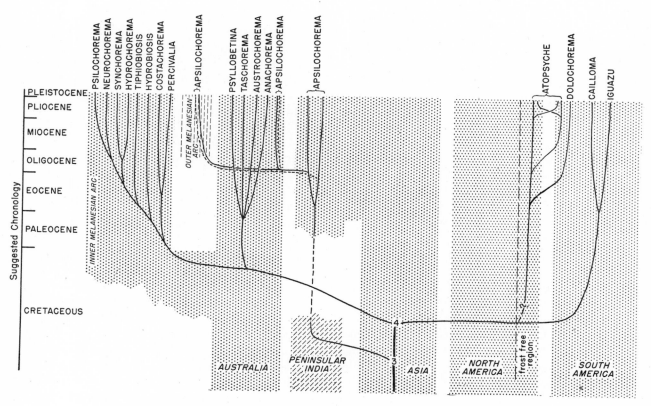

CHART 39. Phylogenetic dispersal chart of the *Hydrobiosinae*.

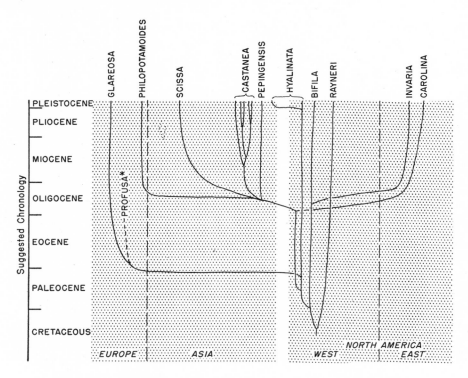

CHART 40. Phylogenetic dispersal chart of Branch 6 of *Rhyacophila*.

population of Ancestor 3 which crossed the Assam Bridge and became isolated in Peninsular India. This seemed a logical surmise if Ancestor 4 did not cross from Australia to South America by way of Antarctica. The dispersal pattern of *Sortosa* supports the Bering Bridge route. While this indicates that there was a Cretaceous dispersal from Australia to Asia and North America, it does not *ipso facto* prove that another population did not cross Antarctica directly to South America. Cretaceous dispersals, however must remain an open question.

### The Rhyacophilinae

The ancestral form of the Hydrobiosinae (Ancestor 3 of Chart 26) must definitely have existed before mid-Cretaceous Ancestor 4, and Ancestor 1 of Chart 26 antedated Ancestor 3. Thus it seems reasonable to suppose that the Rhyacophilinae branch started out at least as early as the end of Jurassic or the beginning of Cretaceous, and that Ancestor 2 may have been early Cretaceous in age. In point of definition Ancestor 2 is practically the genus *Rhyacophila*, since in most respects the genus *Himalopsyche* is simply a specialized offshoot of a primitive *Rhyacophila*.

The problem of ascertaining time of development in *Rhyacophila* is the most perplexing I have encountered. It is rendered difficult first because the exact phylogenetic sequence at the base of the *Rhyacophila* tree is not clear (see Chart 16), and secondly because no line of the genus seems to have crossed a land bridge with restrictive dating. There are a few points, however, that can be approached with admittedly devious reasoning to produce what I believe are fairly sound conclusions, at least the best that can be obtained with the data at hand.

*Branch 6.* The only branch having a fairly well identified fossil is Branch 6. The Baltic amber fossil *profusa* cannot be identified exactly but seems beyond much doubt to be an offshoot of the *hyalinata-glareosa* stem, as shown in Charts 19 and 40. There is a lesser possibility that it belongs in the *castanea-philopotamoides* group. In relation to our time scale, this latter alternative would add some age to the suggested chronology for this *castanea* complex. In this account I am going on the assumption that *profusa* is an offshoot of ancestral *glareosa*. Since there is evidence of only a single crossing of the *glareosa-hyalinata* complex from America to

Europe, the first available pre-Oligocene opportunity is the reasonable one to have occasioned this dispersal. Europe was separated from Asia during Eocene by a northern arm of the Tethys Sea, hence a connection in Paleocene is indicated. This coincides nicely with the postulates deduced for *Wormaldia*, also a cool-adapted group, and it is highly likely that the ancestral *Wormaldia* and the *Rhyacophila* both spread at the peak of the Laramide Revolution.

Turning to the *philopotamoides-castanea-carolina* groups, all the evidence points to a mid-Cenozoic dispersal associated with the temperate deciduous forest. The *carolina* group in eastern North America occurs through the hill country of the deciduous forest area, ranging into the reduced Ouachita Mountains in southeastern Oklahoma, but centering around the Appalachian Mountains area. The Asiatic *castanea* group has spread further into warmer areas than any other complex in southeastern Asia and would therefore appear to be more of a deciduous forest type than a restricted montane type. The European *philopotamoides* occurs in temperate deciduous areas. This suggests that all three groups arose from an ancestral form which spread with the temperate deciduous forest

in mid-Cenozoic, became trans-Holarctic, and later broke up into isolates in several parts of the previously larger range. None of the resulting groups has since spread out of these restricted general areas. Each has developed into a small, compact species group.

The most interesting of these is the *castanea* group (Chart 19). Its most primitive species is in Ceylon; others occur in southern China, Sarawak, and the Philippines. This distribution pattern fits very well the postulates presented by Hora (1938) for similar cases in the fishes. Hora believed that this pattern, characterized by existing records in southern India and others in southeast Asia, with a wide gap between the two areas, is the result of a Miocene dispersal pattern. He suggests that during this period hill-country forms spread from the Himalayan region, diagonally across central India through the elevated Satpura country into the Western Ghats and the hills of southern India. Presumably more arid conditions prevailed soon afterward, making the dispersal route (the Satpura country) untenable for cool-adapted forms. According to the phylogenetic data available for the *castanea* group, in its case the Satpura dispersal route was available when the earliest definitive member

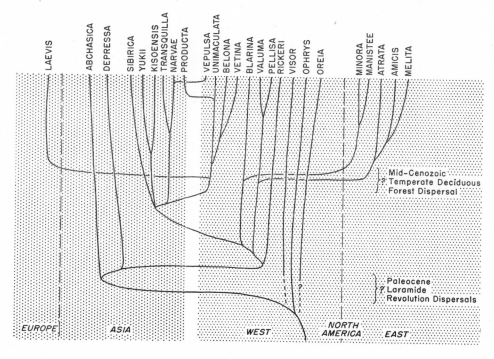

CHART 41. Phylogenetic dispersal chart of the *Rhyacophila sibirica* group.

of the group had evolved. The ecological changes in central India apparently foreshadowed restrictive climatic changes in other parts of the group's range, because after the isolation of the Ceylon segregate, the southeast Asiatic form also went through a stage of species multiplication to form a number of species now known from that region.

In the opinion of De Beaufort, this distribution pattern was brought about by the extensive and intensive vulcanism which produced the Deccan Traps, as suggested by Sarasin (1910). The Deccan Traps, however, were formed in Cretaceous, and there is certainly no evidence in the *Rhyacophila* data that even hints at such an early date for initiating the dispersal pattern found in the *castanea* group. I therefore agree with Pradhan (1952) that Hora's explanation fits the known facts of the situation admirably. Pradhan studied aquatic Hemiptera of the family Gerridae, and his distribution pattern fits well into this scheme. Many other cases are known of a similar sort, and it is obvious that, whatever was its exact date, the biologic unit influenced by the Satpura dispersal route was a flourishing community of aquatic organisms.

*The Sibirica Group of Branch 7.* The result of plotting the phylogenetic arrangement shown in Chart 21 on a dispersal chart is illustrated by Chart 41. Its rather bizarre appearance is due in part to the troubles associated with drawing it so that the least number of lines cross, hence the lower rungs of the ladder appear unduly long. But it is unusual in the number of intercontinental connections indicated between western North America and Asia. There are seven in all, and by a coincidence this is the number of Simpson's better-documented dispersal periods (see p. 172). It is doubtful, however, if the two sets coincide, because the ecological requirements of the *Rhyacophila* species are all within nearly the same limits, whereas the Mammalia include aggregations of many ecological types.

In attempting to correlate the dispersal pattern with time, the central lines which spread to Europe and to eastern North America seem to offer the best basis for surmise. It is entirely possible that all three of these lines (the horizontal offshoots near the middle of Chart 41) were contemporaneous, and were associated with the mid-Cenozoic dispersal of the temperate deciduous forest. If this is the case, the earlier dispersal lines would probably

represent periods dating back to Paleocene. The most recent dispersal, the *narvae-vepulsa* spread, is sufficiently recent that the two species are extremely closely related, if indeed they are distinct.

*Other Intercontinental Dispersals.* There is evidence of only a few additional intragroup dispersals. In the *naviculata* group (Chart 23) a single primitive species, *arnaudi*, indicates a spread of an Asiatic population to western North America. The *acropedes* group (Chart 18) shows evidence of the spread of the original group ancestor to North America from Asia, and the respread of one group back. Further back on the generic tree (Chart 16) it is evident that the ancestral forms of Branches 5 and 8 were widespread, as were also the ancestors of the *stigmatica-glaberrima* groups, the *rotunda-vulgaris* groups, and the *viquaea-clemens* groups. There is no evidence as to when these dispersals may have occurred, but judging from the amount of species multiplication which has taken place in some and the large amount of morphological difference which has developed between units within related pairs of lines, most or all of them must have taken place at least as early as Paleocene. There is, in essence, no reason to believe that these dispersals are any younger than the deduced Paleocene spread of the ancestor of the *glareosa-hyalinata* groups.

A second set of truly remarkable phenomena are shown by the diverse lines arising from Branches 1 and 9 (Chart 16). Each branch has seven main lines. Eleven of these fourteen are each known from a single montane area, and many of the lines are represented by bizarre morphological developments, as in *verrula* (Fig. 272) and *vagrita* (Fig. 273). The complete and uniform loss of annectent forms throughout both branches, the almost uniform restriction of each group to a single montane area, and the great diversity of structure which has evolved, together suggest that the ancestral forms of these branches were of greater age than those of other branches in the genus, perhaps early Cretaceous, and that the products of these ancestors have become thoroughly dependent on ecological conditions associated only with mountains.

The situation in these two branches emphasizes the thought expressed earlier in this chapter (concerning the Appalachian fauna) that the major montane areas may seldom if ever have been united by areas of continuous high mountains, but rather by foothills or semimountainous country. Those montane caddisflies having a moderately wide ecological tolerance could disperse through areas of this type.

The genus *Himalopsyche* adds little to the conclusions based on *Rhyacophila*. Although *Himalopsyche* may stem from a very early line, there is no information telling us when the genus as we know it evolved. The dispersal pattern (Chart 25) is similar to that found in the *naviculata* group. There is a good possibility, however, that *Himalopsyche* will ultimately divulge valuable information concerning the history of the montane fauna in the Asiatic mountains.

### The Glossosomatidae

The Baltic amber fossil *Electragapetus* gives the best clue for attempting to correlate the dispersal of this family with geologic time, hence the tribe Agapetini is taken up first in our discussion.

### The Tribe Agapetini

The phylogenetic arrangement shown in Chart 33 is transferred into a proposed time-dispersal system in Chart 42. The position of the fossil *Electragapetus* proves that the Agapetini ancestor reached Europe well before Oligocene. The small number

of crossings between continents (only one to Australia and one to North America) indicates that evolution within the tribe beyond the genus *Agapetus* took place in the Cenozoic. It seems probable, therefore, that populations of Ancestor 2 (see Chart 27) spread from North America during the Paleocene, through avenues provided by the Laramide orogenic movements. It is probable that the spread of the genus to New Guinea and Australia was in Miocene, in company with *Chimarra* and *Apsilochorema*. To date no species of *Agapetus* are known from either New Zealand or Fiji, so that no direct correlation can be made with the Melanesian arcs.

The members of the typical subgenus *Agapetus* are primarily brook species rather than montane cascade species. From that it seems probable that the population of this subgenus which spread into North America did so in the mid-Cenozoic dispersal of the temperate deciduous forest. The North American line has developed in both eastern and western North America, but little has yet been learned from the American forms which would aid in dating their movements more accurately.

Around this scant framework it is possible to obtain a reasonable idea of the evolution of the

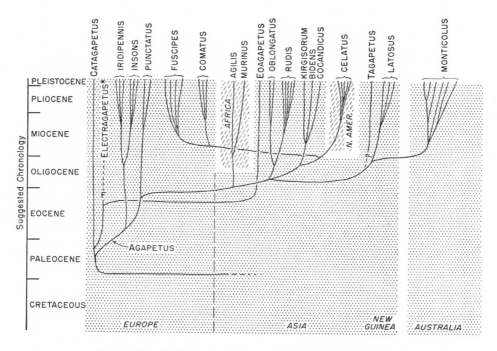

CHART 42. Phylogenetic dispersal chart of the *Agapetini.*

tribe. The original ancestral stock presumably became isolated in Europe in Paleocene and evolved into a *Catagapetus-Electragapetus*-like form, from which soon arose a line continuing the reduction of wing venation, and becoming the ancestral form of *Agapetus*. From this line in turn developed a more warm-adapted brook form (Ancestor 3 of Chart 33) which at the end of Eocene spread to Asia and presumably radiated from there into Africa and into the area of Malay and the East Indies.

The species now known from south and central Africa and from Ceylon belong to this early primitive group, the subgenus *Synagapetus*. According to De Beaufort, Africa and India were connected by a mesophytic land area from at least early Miocene, to a considerable time later. It would have been possible, therefore, for these southern Asiatic ancestral forms to spread into Africa at almost any period after they moved out of Europe. There is even greater apparent latitude regarding the time that they might have reached Ceylon, which is said by Sarasin to have been joined to India until Pleistocene. So little is known regarding the details of the Trichoptera fauna of this area that no further elucidation can be given.

The subgenus *Agapetus,* in which the male developed the pouches on the fifth abdominal segment, must have arisen as a northern Asiatic segregate of this widespread form, probably also in Eocene. The reason for thinking this lies in the fact that, presumably about mid-Cenozoic, the subgenus *Agapetus* spread back into Europe and also into North America at the same time that the simpler forms of the more primitive subgenus *Synagapetus* were spreading into Africa and into the southeastern and east-central areas of Asia. One has the impression that these developments took place one on each side of the rising Himalayan area, and that these mountains formed an effective barrier for the prevention of further intermingling between members of the two groups.

The restriction of the *iridipennis-insons* line and the *fuscipes* and *comatus* groups to Europe is good testimony that the area connecting the mountains of western Asia with the mountains of eastern Europe has been poorly suited for the dispersal of cool-adapted stream species for most of Cenozoic. The dispersals of cool-adapted caddisflies which have occurred between these two areas are reminiscent of those between eastern and western North America. In both the Eurasian and American cases, the entire dispersal pattern can be explained by assuming that a few short periods occurred which allowed the spread of an occasional species having a wider ecological tolerance than its neighboring relatives.

### The Tribe Glossosomatini

There is little to aid in deducing the time relations of this tribe. The only certain fact is that the Glossosomatini did not arise later than the Agapetini, because the two came from essentially the same primitive ancestor. If we follow the logical assumption that both groups arose from the same widespread dispersal of Ancestor 2, then we can also assume that *Glossosoma* arose from an Asiatic Paleocene segregate of that line. It is also probable that the *Anseriglossa* line and the *nigrior* branch of *Eomystra* both spread to North America in mid-Cenozoic (Chart 43).

The subgenus *Glossosoma* spread to Europe after this time. Between this dispersal and that of *Anseriglossa* to North America enough time had to elapse to permit the evolution of certain distinctive features of the subgenus *Glossosoma* and also considerable evolution within the subgenus, for only a specialized branch spread to Europe. That the dispersal route was of short duration is amply attested by, first, the monophyletic nature of the European fauna, indicating that only a single species made a successful colonization, and, secondly, the lack of evidence of a redispersal from Europe into Asia.

The subgenus *Eomystra*, unlike the others, shows definite evidence of several faunal interchanges between Asia and North America. Several species in the group occur in cold streams in hill country, independent of mountain conditions, and are common in some of the low mountain areas in the north, such as the Altai Mountains in Asia and the rolling areas of the Rocky Mountains in the Yukon. This is the only subgenus of *Glossosoma* to reach the Appalachian Mountains of eastern North America, and is the only one containing a widespread Holarctic species (*intermedium*). In spite of these evidences of ease of dispersal and its Miocene age, *Eomystra* is greatly limited in its southern distribution in Eurasia, and moderately so in the western montane region in North America. The ecological factors which cause this restriction are not known.

They might be climatic, topographic, or the results of competition.

The interesting item, however, is that the subgenus differs from the others in the genus ecologically, and also in dispersal pattern. It is the equivalent in this respect to the *sibirica* group in *Rhyacophila* (see Chart 41). By their contrast with other members of their own genera, these two groups give a striking demonstration of the differential dispersal pattern one can expect to find in a single taxonomic unit.

I have no doubt that many of the intercontinental dispersals of *Eomystra* occurred at the same time as later ones of the *Rhyacophila sibirica* group, but it is impossible with present information to attempt a step-by-step correlation between the two.

### Evolution in the Rocky Mountains

One of the most intriguing problems of the family concerns the subgenus *Ripaeglossa*, restricted to the western montane region of North America. This subgenus very likely arose from a population of a primitive *Protoglossa*-like ancestor which spread to North America in late Paleocene. It is also possible that the ancestral form of the entire tribe developed around the Angara Shield in central Siberia at a time when this area and North

America were connected, so that *Ripaeglossa* might have resulted from the isolation of part of this ancestor through a break in the Bering Bridge. Just when the subgenus as we know it today developed, with its peculiar hooded genitalia, is difficult to say, because no intermediate forms have yet been found. After this structure had evolved, the *Ripaeglossa* line divided into three phyletic lines as shown in Chart 30. The problem of explaining and dating these events is an excursion into the orogenic history of western North America.

It has been shown by Love (1939) and Spieker (1946) that the chains of western mountains did not arise more or less simultaneously, but arose unevenly, some of the links at one time, some at another. In particular, Spieker's work indicates that at least in some areas the mountains have been elevated, then worn down, then their sediments re-elevated, as many as three times. He further stresses the fact that many orogenic movements were very local in nature. When the progenitor of *Ripaeglossa* first spread through the western mountains, these were probably areas of fairly stable ranges, with random bridging ranges joining them into an irregular mountainous network. Many of the bridges eroded to the status of low hills probably unsuited for montane species, resulting in the

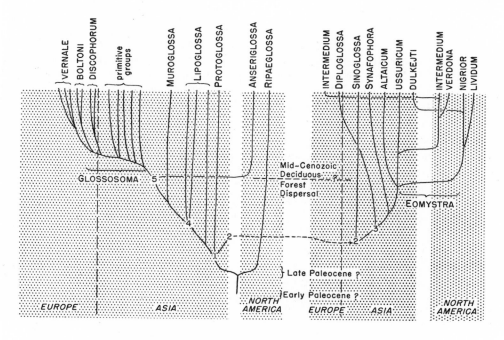

CHART 43. Phylogenetic dispersal chart of *Glossosoma*.

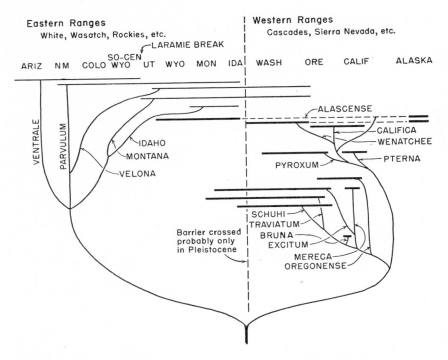

CHART 44. Phylogenetic dispersal chart of *Glossosoma* subgenus *Ripaeglossa*.

complete isolation of any group that had spread across the bridge. Later orogenic movements might restore parallel or neighboring bridges, allowing dispersal away from the restricted range of new species which perhaps resulted from the preceding isolation.

If the *Ripaeglossa* ancestor did colonize western North America in the Paleocene, it undoubtedly had an opportunity to spread to several ranges, because during that period the mountains of Laramide time were supposedly newly elevated and extensive. According to Schuchert, however, two events characterized the next period, the Eocene. In the first place it was a long period of accelerated and sustained erosion, and in the second place the climate was uniformly warm. If the range of the ancestral *Ripaeglossa* population had become extensive, these two conditions would have combined to break it up into isolated units on different mountain areas, and each unit would evolve on an individual path. Did this combination of eroding mountains and warm climate proceed so far in reducing caddisfly habitats that finally it wiped out all the *Ripaeglossa* populations but one? Or was the original *Ripaeglossa* unable to spread southward, so

that it changed into its present form before it broke up into a number of species?

Whatever the answers to these questions concerning its early history, the fact is that a typical *Ripaeglossa* species did ultimately reach the southern end of both the eastern Rocky Mountains and the western Coastal or Sierra Nevada ranges. I believe it is certain that only one species was involved because the existing eastern and western groups are each monophyletic and closely related to each other.

If we consider that the orogenic movements described by Spieker are also typical of many of the middle and late Cenozoic compression periods, then it is a simple matter to apply this concept to a widespread ancestral form of *Ripaeglossa* and arrive at the fauna and distribution pattern known today (Chart 44). Such an explanation demands the following conditions *with relation to the ecological tolerances of Ripaeglossa*:

1. The dispersal pathways that permitted the first spread into the eastern and western ranges became untenable, so that faunal interchange between the eastern and western ranges ceased. This divided the group into an eastern and a western species.

2. Dispersal routes permitted the spread of the eastern form, the *parvulum* group, into the central and southern parts of the Rocky Mountain system.

3. Some of the dispersal units within this system became untenable for *Ripaeglossa*, resulting in the isolation of at least three segregates.

4. Presumably a repetition of these conditions affected the northern of these three segregates to produce ultimately three more species.

5. In the western ranges a parallel series of events occurred, to produce two groups of five or six species each.

6. Presumably in Pleistocene there occurred the *first opportunity* for a remingling of the eastern and western faunal units. This would entail either (1) a change in climate permitting streams to maintain montane conditions for a greater distance away from the mountains on which they originated, or (2) the elevation in the Pleistocene of additional mountains connecting the two areas. Possibly both factors occurred simultaneously.

The evidence for this contention regarding the recent nature of faunal intermingling is summarized on Charts 30 and 44. Six of the 16 known species in the subgenus have a range crossing the east-west dividing line, as follows: in the eastern *parvulum* branch, only *velona*; in the western *alascense* branch, *alascense* and *wenatchee*; and in the western *traviatum* branch, *schuhi*, *traviatum* and *excita*. There is no evidence that a species population of one group has spread to and become isolated in the opposite area long enough ago to evolve into a distinctive species. The only case that might be an exception is *alascense*, but it is even more plausible to consider that *alascense* represents a northern spread, possibly in late Pliocene, to Alaska, rather than a direct west-east dispersal.

On the basis of the *Ripaeglossa* data, it seems to me that the Pleistocene (possibly also late Pliocene) has not yet brought about a multiplication of the species in this group, but has instead effected a most significant dispersal of species previously isolated rigidly within separate montane systems.

If one might project some thought into the future, it is possible that there might be a return of the previous isolating factors, restricting or prohibiting faunal interchange between the eastern

and western ranges. Such an isolation, superimposed on the situation we see now, would sever the populations of the six species now possessing an intersystem range. This subsequent isolation would then complete a process of species multiplication, the possibility for which was brought about by the dispersal opportunities of the Pleistocene.

### Summary of the Glossosomatidae

The dispersal patterns of both the Agapetini and Glossosomatini fit well with the concept of a Laramide distribution of their ancestral forms. Since

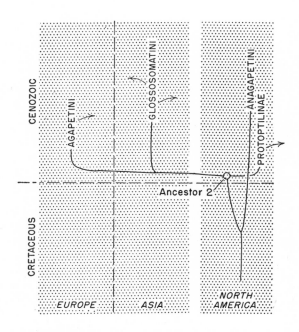

CHART 45. Summary of dispersal suggestions for the *Glossosomatidae*.

*Anagapetus* is not their direct ancestor but the "father" of their ancestor, it seems probable that *Anagapetus* is of at least middle Cretaceous age. It could be older. Perhaps some information on this question will come from an analysis of the Protoptilinae, although the time for such an attempted project seems some distance in the future. Without this, however, the time relations in Chart 45 seem to be certainly on the conservative side of the time ledger.

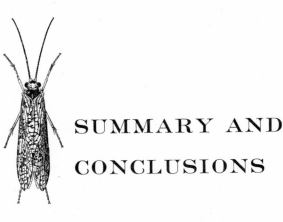

chapter eight

# SUMMARY AND
# CONCLUSIONS

The dispersal data outlined in the preceding chapters and tabulated in Charts 37 to 45 are condensed in the following summary. This is correlated with the geologic time table.

*Triassic-Jurassic.* The dawn of modern caddisflies is shown primarily by fossils from Australia and Europe, the European fossils giving indications that by middle Jurassic some of the primary divisions of the order had already occurred. Evidence from living forms appears insufficient to deduce biogeographic events this far into the past.

*Cretaceous.* By this time at least the primitive existing families and perhaps subfamilies had come into being, and it seems certain that by mid-Cretaceous many living genera had evolved. We have evidence that in middle or upper Cretaceous there occurred ecological and topographic conditions permitting certain genera such as *Sortosa* and a primitive Hydrobiosinae to disperse throughout Eurasia, Australia, and the Americas, possibly also into Africa. These were apparently on the warm-tolerant side of cool-adapted, but not so warm-adapted as some of their progeny. At the same time that this dispersal occurred, there was undoubtedly some spreading of truly cool-adapted genera such as *Rhyacophila* in the Holarctic region, but the extent of this is conjectural.

Conditions allowing intercontinental dispersal apparently lasted for only a brief period, after which the ranges of the dispersed forms became separated into isolated segments. Many of these continued with little change, others evolved into new genera such as *Wormaldia, Protarra,* and *Chimarra.*

*Paleocene.* The Laramide orogeny seems to have set the stage in this period for the most extensive, deducible faunal interchange of cool-adapted forms. This faunal interchange effected chiefly an intermingling of the Eurasian and North American faunae, in particular *Wormaldia,* various branches of *Rhyacophila,* and possibly the glossosomatine form giving rise to the Agapetini and Glossosomatini. For most of this fauna the dispersal period would again seem to have been short, followed by a long period of isolation for the resulting geographic isolates. Following this dispersal period additional genera, such as *Catagapetus, Agapetus,* and *Glossosoma,* appear to have evolved.

An exception to this seems to be the cool-adapted faunal elements existing in the neighborhood of the Angara Shield. There is some evidence suggesting that this fauna crossed the Bering Bridge between Asia and North America several times.

*Eocene.* This period was marked by the development in isolated areas of the cool-adapted fauna, and by a remarkable world-wide dispersal of some of the warm-adapted subtropical genera such as *Chimarra.* Studies in progress suggest that many other warm-adapted Trichoptera genera spread in the same movement. There is a good possibility that certain other warm-adapted insect genera such as *Erythroneura, Culex,* some Saturniidae, and perhaps some of the termites, treated by Ross (1953*a*) as dispersing in late Cretaceous or early Cenozoic, were involved in this dispersal. If true, this would be one of the most important points in the evolution of the modern warm-adapted forms.

*Oligocene—Early Miocene.* At some point during the latter part of this period there seems to have been another extensive interchange of forms between Asia and North America, this time associated chiefly with the spread of the temperate deciduous forest. It is difficult to assign these dispersals within close time limits, but the facts are that (1) there is no evidence of such an interchange of subtropical groups, (2) there is no evidence of an interchange of the extremely cold-adapted groups, but (3) the distribution of many temperate groups, such as certain branches of *Chimarra* and the more temperate lines of *Rhyacophila, Wormaldia,* and the Glossosomatinae, can be readily explained only on the basis of an Asian–North American dispersal at about this time. This I have simply referred to as mid-Cenozoic. It is probable that its termination was at the time of the early Miocene re-elevation of the Rocky Mountains in North America.

*Miocene.* In this period there was considerable movement of faunas in the Old World. Subtropical genera such as *Chimarra* and *Apsilochorema* spread into Australia and the outer Melanesian arc. There is a good possibility that genera such as *Agapetus* reached Africa, and that other forms, such as the *Rhyacophila castanea* group, became widespread through the Oriental region. Also at this time or later in the Miocene some cool-adapted lines of *Wormaldia, Glossosoma,* and *Agapetus* spread from Asia to Europe.

*Pliocene.* There is little evidence of intercontinental dispersal of the montane fauna during this period, except again for the groups centering around northeastern Asia and northwestern North America. Otherwise the mountainous areas seem to have been separated by intervening areas of flat or arid country.

*Pleistocene.* The glacial periods probably provided ecological conditions which permitted a small amount of dispersal of montane species from one major area to another, as for instance the spread of two species of *Rhyacophila* from the western montane region to the Appalachian system in North America. In the montane fauna there is no evidence of a widespread dispersal, with the single exception of the Holarctic species *Glossosoma intermedium,* which does appear to have become widespread in this period. This species, however, exists sucessfully in cold springs in flat country and is not truly montane.

Probably the greatest effect of glaciation on these montane caddisflies has been the redistribution *within* mountain systems of species previously isolated in component parts of the system. The subgenus *Ripaeglossa* of *Glossosoma* is a good example of this type of dispersal.

The major features of dispersal for the montane caddisflies may be stated briefly as follows:

Cretaceous: widespread dispersal of primitive forms.

Paleocene: greatest dispersal of cold-adapted forms.

Eocene: greatest dispersal of subtropical forms.

Mid-Cenozoic: greatest dispersal of temperate forms.

Pliocene, Pleistocene: chiefly intrasystem dispersal of montane elements.

### The Cool-Adapted Biota

Referring again to Charts 2 and 3, it is evident that the cool-adapted elements of the montane caddisflies have continued in an unbroken line of cool-adapted forms since the time of their inception in the Traissic or Jurassic to the present time. Warm-adapted forms have developed from offshoot lines, but the primitive parental lines have continued in virtually the same habitat as their progenitors.

The evidence is unassailable that these cool-adapted lines have been associated with mountain regions for their entire history, and actually confined rigidly to them for long periods in Mesozoic and Cenozoic when the surrounding country was too hot or dry to provide the kind of ecological conditions they required. It is especially significant that biogeographic analysis shows this to have been the case not only with forms requiring high stream velocities and therefore restricted to mountains at any time, but also with species that inhabit brooks and streams of hilly country, and therefore not dependent on mountains as a topographic necessity for their survival.

The biogeographic record thus points to the fact that at least during the warm periods of Cretaceous and early Cenozoic, the mountains provided continuous ecological conditions suited for survival of cool-adapted caddisflies and very likely for the entire cool-adapted biota.

Viewed in this perspective, data from other groups, hitherto puzzling, fall into an orderly sequence. In earlier studies of the Holarctic sawfly genus *Dolerus* (Ross 1929), there was noted the existence of well-marked morphological groups showing evidence of both steplike advances in morphological evolution and the need for past periods of isolation during which these groups could develop. The great majority of these groups in *Dolerus,* however, are now widespread and abundant across the entire Holarctic region. *Dolerus* is primarily a cool to cold-adapted genus, with most of the species occurring in cool temperate to subarctic or arctic areas. The early cool-adapted *Dolerus* species were undoubtedly restricted to mountainous areas for long periods, with occasional dispersals comparable to those of the montane caddisflies. Then in late Pliocene and Pleistocene, during periods of widespread cool or cold climate, a great many species of *Dolerus* each became widespread throughout the Holarctic region. Possibly this pattern repeated itself more than once during the period.

The fact that the Asiatic–American Pliocene–Pleistocene dispersal routes were freely used by *Dolerus,* many other cool-adapted sawflies, and a considerable number of mammals (Simpson 1947), yet were crossed by only a few species of montane caddisflies, signifies that these dispersal routes were nonmountainous in character. This is further emphasized by the pond and lake caddisflies of the genus *Limnephilus,* which have spread readily from North America to Asia and/or vice versa. Some of these same *Limnephilus* species are today equally numerous in the tundra pools of the flat terrain in northern Saskatchewan and in the high altitude montane ponds of the Colorado Rockies.

This ecological restriction of the montane caddisflies is one of those happy chance occurrences which has allowed us to look with more surety into the past history of an interesting biota.

The record of the mountains themselves stretches far back of our possible period of interpretation with biogeographic means. Mountains have been present and have provided suitable conditions whereby the cool-adapted biotas of the Carboniferous or Permian could have existed continuously from then to now. Every intervening period of widespread warm climates has had many mountain areas of considerable extent. Here we see the explanation of Tillyard's most illuminating statement quoted on p. 20. Obviously the details of the alternating periods of restriction to mountains

and periodic widespread dispersal at times of cool climates, are different with each cool-adapted group, but this rhythmic oscillation is the general pattern for them all.

## The Warm-Adapted Biota

The warm-adapted nature of some elements of the terrestrial biota seems to be of long standing. Among the insects, cockroaches are a good example. Fossil roaches from the Carboniferous are much like their living relatives, and from their ecological associates in the Carboniferous fossil beds, it would appear that the cockroaches were then primarily a tropical and subtropical group as they are now. Available evidence indicates that the earliest termites also were warm-adapted, the group originating in early Mesozoic if not earlier. In both the cockroaches and the termites, a few phyletic lines have become adapted to warm temperate conditions, but these lines have never developed into large groups. Possibly the Orthoptera and many groups of Hemiptera have followed the same general pattern.

A sharp contrast to these groups is found in the warm-adapted caddisflies, which became warm-adapted relatively recently, *Chimarra* possibly in the Upper Cretaceous, and *Gunungiella* probably not until early Cenozoic. Both arose from older, cool-adapted groups.

It is therefore evident that warm-adapted lines are of various ages. It follows that each line will have its own peculiar evolutionary history, which will reflect the age of the group and the possibilities it has had for dispersal and development.

## The Cretaceous-Cenozoic Biotic Boundary

Much has been written regarding the division between the Cretaceous and the Cenozoic (Spieker 1946). The boundary now in common use is based on fossil evidence showing the last appearance of dinosaurs (the end of Cretaceous) and the first appearance of placental mammals (the beginning of the Cenozoic). This is primarily a biotic boundary, and it is therefore pertinent to include here some remarks on the montane caddisfly situation at this time.

The end of the Cretaceous was apparently a period of generally warm climates. Immediately preceding this the montane caddisflies had spread to many parts of the world, and during this warm climate had evolved in the mountains of many scattered localities.

The unusual dispersal of the cool-adapted Trichoptera which we have attributed to the Paleocene orogenies would certainly indicate that at this period or near it there occurred an equally unusual combination of mountainous areas in close proximity, and cool climates in the intervening areas. It seems logical that a period apparently ideal for the spread of cool-adapted forms would have been equally inimical for warm-adapted ones, and may help to explain the reduction and disappearance of the dinosaurian reptiles.

The unusual dispersal of cool-adapted forms during the Paleocene was followed by an even more widespread dispersal of warm-adapted forms apparently in early Eocene.

Thus in the montane caddisflies many forms which evolved in late Cretaceous suddenly became widespread in the early part of the Cenozoic, ultimately leading to a tremendous increase of the caddisfly fauna. The fossil record is so poor for this order in the Cretaceous that we have no knowledge of that part of the fauna which may have become extinct.

### Age of the Insect Fauna

In his extensive correlation of the Coleoptera fauna of North America, Van Dyke (1939) visualized the dispersal pattern as having occurred moderately recently, that is, from the Miocene to the present. The data from the caddisflies indicate an older time of origin for most groups, in some cases as long ago as Paleocene and Cretaceous. This antiquity of dispersal pattern fits also with data presented by Emerson (1952) for the termites, with data for a few other groups presented by Ross (1953a), and probably fits also the relationships pointed out by Mills (1939) between north and south occurrence and primitiveness in the Collembola.

### Problems

This study has proved to be an over-all survey of the primitive montane caddisfly fauna rather than an exhaustive and detailed analysis of every small group. It is my hope that this survey will stimulate much more interest in the problem, including the accumulation of needed new material from all parts of the world.

Many problems have been encountered and mentioned in the preceding pages, but certain ones merit more discussion or emphasis, and are again outlined briefly here.

*Species Flocks.* Certain large monophyletic aggregates of species which have evolved within circumscribed areas can be classified as true species flocks. The finest example is the *Rhyacophila vulgaris* group, but others include the subgenus *Hydrobiosella* of *Sortosa*, the genus *Philopotamus*, and the *occipitalis* group of *Wormaldia*. Detailed study and phylogenetic analysis of each of these species flocks, coupled with detailed information on the range of each species, will undoubtedly throw much light on biogeographic problems of the region.

*The Siberian Route.* There are quite a number of instances treated in this report in which groups spreading between Europe, Asia, and North America appear to have by-passed completely the Oriental Region proper. This includes the following: in *Agapetus* the subgenus *Agapetus*; in *Rhyacophila* the *stigmatica-glaberrima* groups, the *vulgaris-rotunda-fuscula* groups; in *Glossosoma* the subgenus *Eomystra*; and others. Certain species contained in these groups, such as *Glossosoma altai*, are known only from southern Siberia and Japan; others have close relatives in Siberia and Japan, or in Siberia and northwestern North America. There is here a suggestion that the mountains north of the Gobi Desert and the mountain chains of southern Siberia (Mirov 1951) have served as the northern dispersal route for this group of caddisflies. Too little is yet known of the inland caddisfly fauna of Asia to present this idea as more than a suggestion.

The distribution of certain species of ants (Formicidae) is further suggestive of the existence of such a route. Kuznetzov-Ugamskij (1929, Figs. 2 and 4) has illustrated the range of two species, *Formica uralensis* and *Lasius carniolicus,* which follow this supposed dispersal path almost perfectly, and illustrate the continuity of ecological conditions along it.

*Effects of Glaciation.* In addition to effects mentioned previously, there is a possibility that the glacial advances may have caused other unknown changes in the montane caddisfly fauna. Some answers to this question will undoubtedly come from future collecting in glaciated areas or neighboring areas in northern Asia and northwestern North America.

# BIBLIOGRAPHY

ADAMS, C. C. 1902. Southeastern United States as a center of geographical distribution of flora and fauna. Biol. Bull., 3:115-29.

ALLAN, ROBIN S. 1948. Geological correlation and paleoecology. Bull. Geol. Soc. Amer., 59:1-10.

BANKS, NATHAN. 1895. New neuropteroid insects. Trans. Amer. Ent. Soc. 22:313-16.

———. 1897. New North American neuropteroid insects. Trans. Amer. Ent. Soc., 24:21-31.

———. 1900. Papers from the Harriman Alaska expedition. Entomological results (4). Neuropteroid insects. Proc. Washington Acad. Sci., 2:465-73.

———. 1904. Neuropteroid insects from New Mexico. Trans. Amer. Ent. Soc., 30:97-110.

———. 1905. Descriptions of new Nearctic neuropteroid insects. Trans. Amer. Ent. Soc., 32:1-20.

———. 1906. New Trichoptera from Japan. Proc. Ent. Soc. Washington, 7:106-12.

———. 1907. Descriptions of new Trichoptera. Proc. Ent. Soc. Washington 8:117-33.

———. 1911. Descriptions of new species of North American neuropteroid insects. Trans. Amer. Ent. Soc., 37:335-60.

———. 1913. Synopses and descriptions of exotic Neuroptera. Trans. Amer. Ent. Soc., 39:201-42.

———. 1914. American Trichoptera—notes and descriptions. Can. Ent., 46:149-56, 201-5, 252-58, 261-68.

———. 1918. New neuropteroid insects. Bull. Mus. Comp. Zool. (Harvard Univ.), 62:3-22.

———. 1920. New neuropteroid insects. Bull. Mus. Comp. Zool. (Harvard Univ.), 64:299-362.

———. 1924. Descriptions of new neuropteroid insects. Bull. Mus. Comp. Zool. (Harvard Univ.), 65:421-55.

———. 1930a. Trichoptera from Cape Breton, Nova Scotia. Bull. Brooklyn Ent. Soc., 25:127-32.

———. 1930b. New neuropteroid insects from the United States. Psyche, 37:223-33.

———. 1931a. Neuropteroid insects from the Malay Peninsula. Jour. Fed. Malay Museums, 16:391-404.

———. 1931b. Some Oriental neuropteroid insects. Psyche, 38:56-70.

———. 1934. Supplementary neuropteroid insects from the Malay Peninsula and from Mt. Kinabalu, Borneo. Jour. Fed. Malay Museums, 17:567-78.

———. 1936. Four new Trichoptera from the United States. Arbeiten über morphologische und taxonomische Entomologie aus Berlin-Dahlem, 3:265-68.

———. 1937. Philippine neuropteroid insects. Philippine Jour. Sci., 63:125-74.

———. 1938. Further neuropteroid insects from Malaya. Jour. Fed. Malay Museums, 18:220-35.

———. 1939a. Neuropteroid insects from the Philippines. Philippine Jour. Sci., 69:133-45.

———. 1939b. New genera and species of neuropteroid insects. Bull. Mus. Comp. Zool. (Harvard Univ.), 85:439-504.

———. 1940. Report on certain groups of neuropteroid insects from Szechwan, China. Proc. U. S. Nat. Mus., 88:173-220.

———. 1947. Some neuropterous insects from Szechwan, China. Fieldiana-Zoology (Chicago Nat. Hist. Mus.), 31:97-107.

BARNARD, K. H. 1934. South African caddis-flies (Trichoptera). Trans. Roy. Soc. S. Africa, 21:291-394.

———. 1940. Additional records, and descriptions of new species, of South African alder-flies (Megaloptera), may-flies (Ephemeroptera), caddis-flies (Trichoptera), stone-flies (Perlaria) and dragon-flies (Odonata). Ann. S. African Mus., 32:609-61.

BENSON, ROBERT B. 1942. Blasticotomidae in the Miocene of Florissant, Colorado (Hymenoptera: Symphyta). Psyche, 48-49; 47-48.

BETTEN, CORNELIUS. 1934. The caddisflies or Trichoptera of New York State. Bull. N.Y. State Museum, 292:576.

———, and Martin E. Mosely. 1940. The Francis Walker types of Trichoptera in the British Museum. London. 248 pp.

BLANCHARD. 1851. In Gay, Historica fisica y politica de Chile, Zoologia, 6:135-42.

BOTOSANEANU, L. 1952a. Rhyacophila furcifera (Klap.) Bots. syn. Rh. meyeri var. furcifera Klap. 1904. Comunicarile Academiei Rep. Pop. Romane, 2: 547-50.

———. 1952b. *Rhyacophila orghidani* n. sp. (Trichoptera Rhyacophilinae) din muntii apuseni ai Republicii Populare Romane. Comunicarile Academiei Rep. Pop. Romane, 2:721-24.

BRAUER, FRIEDRICH. 1857. Neuroptera Austriaca. 23 + 80 pp. Wein.

BRYAN, W. H. 1944. The relationship of the Australian continent to the Pacific Ocean—now and in the past. Jour. & Proc. Royal Soc. N. S. Wales, 78:42-62.

CAIN, STANLEY A. 1944. Foundations of Plant Geography. New York. 556 pp.

CARPENTER, F. M. 1933. Trichoptera from the mountains of North Carolina and Tennessee. Psyche, 40:32-47.

CHANEY, R. W. 1940. Tertiary forests and continental history. Bull. Geol. Soc. Amer., 51:469-88.

———. 1947. Tertiary centers and migration routes. Ecol. Mono., 17:139-48.

CURTIS, JOHN. 1834. Descriptions of some hitherto nondescript British species of mayflies of anglers. London and Edinburgh Philosoph. Mag. and Jour. Sci., 4:120-25, 212-18.

DARLINGTON, P. J., JR. 1948. The geographical distribution of cold-blooded vertebrates. Quart. Rev. Biol., 23:1-26, 105-23.

DAVIS, H. S. 1953. Culture and Diseases of Game Fishes. Berkeley, Calif. 332 pp.

DAVIS, JARED J. 1950. Two new species of caddisflies (Trichoptera) from Washington state. Ann. Ent. Soc. Amer., 42:448-50.

DE BEAUFORT, F. L. 1951. Zoogeography of the Land and Inland Waters. London. 208 pp.

DENNING, D. G. 1941. Descriptions and notes of new and little known species of Trichoptera. Ann. Ent. Soc. Amer., 34:195-203.

———. 1942. Descriptions of new Trichoptera from the United States. Canadian Ent. 54:46-51.

———. 1947. New Trichoptera from Puerto Rico. Ann. Ent. Soc. Amer., 40:656-61.

———. 1948a. New and little known species of Nearctic Trichoptera. Psyche, 55:16-27.

———. 1948b. A review of the Rhyacophilidae (Trichoptera). Canadian Ent., 80:97-117.

———. 1949a. New and little known species of caddis flies. Amer. Mid. Nat., 42:112-22.

———. 1949b. New species of Nearctic caddis flies. Bull. Brooklyn Ent. Soc., 44:37-48.

———. 1950a. Records and descriptions of Nearctic caddis flies, Part I. Bull. Brooklyn Ent. Soc., 45:97-104.

———. 1950b. Records and descriptions of Nearctic caddis flies. Part II. Jour. Kansas Ent. Soc., 23:115-20.

———. 1951. Records and descriptions of Nearctic caddis flies. Jour. Kansas Ent. Soc., 24:157-62.

———. 1954. New species of western Trichoptera. Jour. Kansas Ent. Soc., 27:57-64.

DEORAS, P. J. 1944-45. On the comparative morphology and evolution of adult Trichoptera. Indian Jour. Ent., 5:177-88; 6:35-48.

DESPAX, R. 1933. Rhyacophila vandeli sp. nov. Trichoptere Nouveau des Pyrenees. Bull. Soc. Hist. Nat. Toulouse, 65:625-27.

———. 1944. Quelques Formes Critiques du Genre Rhyacophila Pict. Bull. Soc. Hist. Nat. Toulouse. 79:270-72.

DOHLER, WALTER VON. 1950. Zur Kenntnis der Gattung Rhyacophila in mitteleuropäischen Raum (Trichoptera). Archiv. für Hydrobiologie, 44:271-93.

DONOVAN, EDWARD. 1813. The Natural History of British Insects. Vol. 16. 91 + 10 pp., pls. 541-76. London.

DURHAM, J. W. 1950. Cenozoic marine climates of the Pacific Coast. Bull. Geol. Soc. Amer., 61:1243-64.

DZIEDZIELEWICZ, J. 1911. Noury gatunek z rzedu owadow chroscikowatych (Trichoptera): Rhyacophila furcata n. sp. z2 rycinami (une nouvelle espèce du genre Trichoptera). Krakow Spraw. Kom. Fizyogr. Cz. II, 44:107-109.

EMERSON, ALFRED E. 1933. A revision of the genera of fossil and recent Termopsinae. Univ. California Publ. Ent., 6:165-96.

———. 1952. The biogeography of termites. Bull. Amer. Mus. Nat. Hist., 99:217-25.

ENDERLEIN, GUNTHER. 1929. Entomologica Canaria II. Zool. Anz., 84:221-34.

FLINT, R. F. 1947. Glacial Geology and the Pleistocene Epoch. New York. 589 pp.

FORSSLUND, K. H. 1935. Schwedisch-chinesische wissenschaftliche éxpedition nach den nordwestlichen Provinzen Chinas. Trichoptera. Arkiv för Zoologi, 27(31):1-21.

GLAESSNER, M. F. 1950. Geotectonic position of New Guinea. Bull. Amer. Assoc. Pet. Geol., 34:856-81.

GILLULY, J. 1949. Distribution of mountain building in geologic time. Bull. Geol. Soc. Amer., 60:561-90.

GUERIN, F. E. 1837. Iconographie du regne Animal de G. Cuvier. Paris. 576 pp. (Pt. 7-Insects).

HAGEN, HERMAN A. and F. J. PICTET. 1856. Die in Bernstein befindlichen Neuropteren der Vorwelt. *In* Berendt's Organische Reste der Vorwelt, 2:41-126.

HAGEN, HERMAN A. 1858. Synopsis der Neuropteren Ceylons. Part 1. Verh. Zool. Bot. Gesell. Wien, 8:484-87.

———. 1859a. Die Phryganiden Pictet's nach Typen bearbeitet. Stett. Ent. Zeit., 20:131-70.

———. 1859b. Synopsis der Neuropteren Ceylons. Part 2. Verh. Zool. Bot. Gesell. Wien, 9:208-12.

———. 1860. Die Phryganiden Pictet's nach Typen bearbeitet. Stett. Ent. Zeit., 21:274-90.

———. 1861. Synopsis of the Neuroptera of North America, with a list of the South American species. Smithsonian Inst. Misc. Collect. 347 pp.

———. 1864. Phryganidarum synopsis synonymica. Kaiserlich-Köninglichen Zool. Bot. Gesell. Wien. Verhandlungen, 14:799-890.

HANDLIRSCH, ANTON VON. 1938. Neue Untersuchungen über die fossilen Insekten mit Ergänzungen und Nachträgen sowie Ausblicken auf phylogenetische, palaeogeographische und allgemein biologische Probleme. II. Teil. Annalen des naturhistorischen Museums in Wien, 49:1-240.

HORA, S. L. 1938. Changes in the drainage of India, as evidenced by the distribution of freshwater fishes. Proc. Nat. Inst. Sci. India, 4:395-409.

IMLAY, RALPH W. 1944. Correlation of Cretaceous formations of the Greater Antilles, Central America, and Mexico. Bull. Geol. Soc. Amer., 55:1005-46.

IWATA, MASATOSHI. 1927a. Trichopterous larvae from Japan. Annot. Zool. Japonenses, 11:203-33.

———. 1927b. Trichopterous larvae from Japan II. Dobuts. Zasshi, 39:389-94.

———. 1928. Five new species of Trichopterous larvae from Formosa. Annot. Zool. Japonenses, 11:341-51.

KIMMINS, D. E. 1952. Indian caddis flies.—VI. New species and a new genus of the subfamily Rhyacophilinae. Ann. & Mag. Nat. Hist. (12), 5:347-61.

———. 1953a. Miss L. E. Cheesman's expedition to New Caledonia, 1949—Orders Odonata, Ephemeroptera, Neuroptera and Trichoptera. Ann. & Mag. Nat. Hist. (12), 6:241-57.

———. 1953b. Entomological results from the Swedish expedition 1934 to Burma and British India. Trichoptera. The genus Rhyacophila Pictet (Fam. Rhyacophilidae). Arkiv för Zoologi (2), 4:505-55.

———. 1953c. A Key to the European species of *Wormaldia* (Trichoptera, Philopotamidae), with descriptions of two new subspecies. Ann. & Mag. Nat. Hist. (12), 6:801-808.

———. 1953d. Entomological results from the Swedish expedition 1934 to Burma and British India. Trichoptera: (Rhyacophilidae, subfamilies Hydrobiosinae, Glossosomatinae and Agapetinae). Arkiv för Zoologi (2), 6:167-83.

———. 1955. Results of the Oxford University expedition to Sarawak. 1932. Order Trichoptera. Sarawak Museum Jour., 6:374-442.

———, and D. G. DENNING. 1951. The McLachlan types of North American Trichoptera in the British Museum. Ann. Ent. Soc. Amer., 44:111-40.

KINSEY, ALFRED C. 1930. The gall wasp genus *Cynips*. A study in the origin of species. Indiana Univ. Studies 16 (Studies Nos. 84, 85, 86). 577 pp.

———. 1936. The origin of higher categories in *Cynips*. Indiana Univ. Publ., Science Ser., 4:1-334.

KLAPALEK, FRANZ. 1892. Trichopterologicky Vijzkum Cech. v.r. 1891. Ropz. Ceske Acad. Cis. Frant. Jos., Praze, 5:1-22.

———. 1894. Descriptions of new species of Raphidia L., and of three new species of Trichoptera from the Balkan Peninsula, with critical remarks on Panorpa gibberosa, McLachlan. Trans. Ent. Soc. London, 489-95.

———. 1898. Fünf neue Trichopteren-Arten aus Ungarn. Termes. Fuzetek, 21:488-90.

———. 1902. Zur Kenntnis der Neuropteroiden von Un-

garn, Bosnien, und Hercegovina. Termes. Fuzetek, 25:161-80.

———. 1904. Zprava o Vysledich Cesty do Transsylvanskych Alp a Vysokych Tater. Věst. České Akad., 13:719-30.

———. 1905. Zprava o Vysledich Cesty do Transsylvanskych Alp a Vysokych Tater. Věstn. České Akad. Cisare Frant. Jos. Rocnik, 13:1-12.

KLOET, G. S., and W. D. HINCKS. 1944. Nomenclatorial notes on two generic names in the Trichoptera. The Entomologist, 77:97.

KOLENATI, F. A. 1848. Genera et species Trichopterorum. Pars prior. Moscow. 108 pp.

———. 1859. Genera et species Trichopterorum. Pars altera. Moscow. 135 pp.

KUZNETZOV-UGAMSKIJ, N. N. 1929. Die Ameisen des Süd-Ussuri-Gebietes. Zool. Anz., 83:16-34.

LEACH, WILLIAM ELFORD. 1815. Entomology, *in* Brewster's Edinburgh Encyclopedia 9(1):52-172.

LEONARD, JUSTIN W., and FANNIE A. 1949. Noteworthy records of caddisflies from Michigan, with descriptions of new species. Occ. Papers Mus. Zool. Univ. Michigan, 250:1-8.

LESTAGE, J. A. 1925. Trichoptera collected in Algeria by M. H. Gauthier and list of known North African species. Bull. Soc. d'Hist. Nat. Afr. Nord, 16:13-118.

LING, SHAO-WIN. 1938. A few new caddisflies in the collection of the California Academy of Sciences. Pan-Pacific Ent., 14:59-69.

LOBECK, A. K. 1939. Geomorphology. New York. 731 pp.

LOVE, J. D. 1939. Geology along the south margin of the Absaroka Range. Geol. Soc. Amer., Special Paper No. 20:116-17.

MARTYNOV, A. B. 1909. Les Trichoptères du Tibet Oriental et du Tsaidam d'après les Matériaux Collectionnes par l'Expédition de la Société Imp. Georg. Russe sous la Direction de P. K. Kozlow en 1900-1901. Ann. Mus. Zool. Acad. Imp. Sci. St. Petersbourg, 14:256-309.

———. 1910. Les Trichoptères de la Sibérie et des Régions Adjacentes, II. Ann. Mus. Zool. Acad. Imp. Sci. St. Petersbourg, 15:351-429.

———. 1912. On two collections of Trichoptera from Peru. Ann. Mus. Zool. Acad. Imp. Sci. St. Petersbourg, 17:1-40.

———. 1913a. Contribution to the knowledge of the Trichopterous Fauna of the Caucasus. (In Russian.) Trav. Labr. Zool. Univ. Warsaw. 111 pp.

———. 1913b. Contributions à la faune des Trichoptères du Caucase. (In Russian.) Horae Soc. Ent. Ross. 40(7):1-30.

———. 1914a. Notes on the Trichoptera collected by Prof. P. Sushkin's expedition to the Altai during 1912. Rev. Russe d'Ent., 14:72-84.

———. 1914b. Contributions à la faune des Trichoptères de la Chine. Ann. Mus. Zool. Acad. Imp. Sci. Petrograd, 19:323-39.

————. 1915. Contributions à la faune des Trichoptères des possessions Russes dans l'Asie centrale. Petrograd. Ann. Mus. Zool. Acad. Sci., 19:402-37.

————. 1916. Notice sur la faune des Trichoptères de la Crimée. (Russian with English résumé.) Ann. Mus. Zool. Acad. Imp. Sci. Petrograd, 21:165-99.

————. 1922. Sur une nouvelle espèce de la tribu des Apataniini, et quelques autres formes provenant du pays de Minoussinsk. Ann. Mus. Zool. Acad. Sci. Russie, Petrograd, 22:45-63.

————. 1925. Contributions to the knowledge of the Trichopterous fauna of the Eastern Transcaucasia. (Russian with English résumé.) Rev. Russe d'Ent., 19:119-27.

————. 1926. To the knowledge of Trichoptera from Central Kaukasus and their metamorphoses. (Russian with English resumé). Trav. Station Biol. in Caucase du Nord, (I), 3:19-62.

————. 1927a. Supplementary notes on the trichopterous fauna of the Caucasus. (Russian with English resumé.) Rev. Russe d'Ent., 21:119-27.

————. 1927b. Contributions to the aquatic entomofauna of Turkestan. I. Trichoptera Annulipalpia. Ann. Mus. Zool. Acad. Sci. USSR, 28:162-93.

————. 1928. Contributions to the aquatic entomofauna of Turkestan. II. Trichoptera Integripalpia. Ann. Mus. Zool. Acad. Sci. USSR, 28:457-95.

————. 1930. On the Trichopterous fauna of China and Tibet. Proc. Zool. Soc. London, pp. 65-112.

————. 1931. Report on a collection of insects of the Order Trichoptera from Siam and China. Proc. U. S. Nat. Mus., 79:1-20.

————. 1933. On the interesting collection of Trichoptera from Japan. Annot. Zool. Japonenses. 14:139-56.

————. 1934. The Trichoptera Annulipalpia of the USSR. Leningrad. 343 pp.

————. 1935. On a collection of Trichoptera from the Indian Museum. Rec. Indian Mus., 37:93-209.

————. 1936. On a collection of Trichoptera from the Indian Museum. Part II. Integripalpia. Rec. Indian Mus., 38:239-306.

————. 1938. Note on the Trichoptera of Nachitschewan U.S.S.R. and neighboring districts. (In Russian, with English summary.) Trud. Zool. Inst. Baku, 8:65-73.

MATSUMURA, S. 1931. Six thousand illustrated insects of Japan-Empire. (In Japanese.) Tokyo. ii, iii, iii, 23, 1497 pp.

McFARLANE, A. G. 1939. Additions to New Zealand Rhyacophilidae. Part I. Trans. R. Soc. New Zealand, 69:330-40.

————. 1951. Additions to the N. Z. Rhyacophilidae. Part II. Records Canterbury Mus., 5:255-65.

McLACHLAN, ROBERT. 1862a. Notes on British Trichoptera. Ent. Annual: 21-37.

————. 1862b. Characters of new species of exotic Trichoptera; also of one new species inhabiting Britain. Trans. Ent. Soc. London (3),1:301-11.

————. 1863. Notes on British Trichoptera, with description of a new species of Rhyacophila. Ent. Annual, pp. 129-36.

————. 1865. Trichoptera Britannica. A monograph of British species of caddis flies. Trans. Ent. Soc. London (3), 5:1-184.

————. 1867. Bemerkungen über europäische Phryganiden, nebst Beschreibungen einiger neuer Genera und Species. Stett. Ent. Zeit., 28:50-63.

————. 1868. Contributions to a knowledge of European Trichoptera. Trans. Ent. Soc. London, pp. 289-308.

————. 1871. On new forms, etc., of extra-European Trichopterous insects. Jour. Linn. Soc. London, Zool., 11:98-141.

————. 1875. In Fedtschenko's Puteshestvie V Turkestan (Travels in Turkestan); Zoogeographichiskia Izsledovania Neuroptera. St. Petersburg and Moscow. pp. 1-60.

————. 1874-80. A monographic revision and synopsis of the Trichoptera of the European fauna. Pt. 1, 1874:1-46. Pt. 2, 1875:47-108. Pt. 3, 1875:109-44. Pt. 4, 1876:145-220. Pt. 5, 1876:221-80, w. supplement I-XII. Pt. 6, 1877:281-348. Pt. 7, 1878:349-428. Pt. 8, 1879:429-500. Pt. 9, 1880:501-23, w. supplement XIII-LXXXIV. London.

————. 1884. A monographic revision and synopsis of the Trichoptera of the European fauna. First additional supplement. London. 76 pp.

————. 1898. Some new species of Trichoptera belonging to the European fauna, with notes on others. Ent. Mon. Mag. (2), 9:46-52.

MILLS, HARLOW B. 1939. Remarks on the geographical distribution of North American Collembola. Bull. Brooklyn Ent. Soc., 34:158-61.

MILNE, LORUS J. 1936. Studies in North American Trichoptera, 3. Cambridge, Mass. 128 pp.

MILNE, MARGERY J. and LORUS J. 1940. A new species of Rhyacophila, described from metamorphotypes (Rhyacophilidae: Trichoptera). Bull. Brooklyn Ent. Soc., 35:153-56.

MIROV, N. T. 1951. Geography of Russia. New York. 362 pp.

MORTON, KENNETH J. 1884. Description of a variety of Philopotamus montanus, Donovan, from Scotland. Ent. Mon. Mag., 20:273.

————. 1900. Description of new species of Oriental Rhyacophilidae. Trans. Ent. Soc. London, pp. 1-7.

MOSELY, MARTIN E. 1930a. Corsican Trichoptera. Eos, Rev. Espanola Ent., 6:147-84.

————. 1930b. New European Trichoptera and Plecoptera. Trans. Ent. Soc. London, 78:237-53.

————. 1935a. New Trichoptera and Plecoptera in France: some Auvergne Plecoptera. Trans. Ent. Soc. London, 83:557-62.

————. 1935b. The genus Synagapetus McLachlan (Trichoptera). Ann. & Mag. Nat. Hist., (10), 16:304-13.

————. 1938a. A new Corsican Trichopteron. Ann. & Mag. Nat. Hist., (11), 2:204-205.

————. 1938b. Die Arthopodenfauna Madeira nach den Ergebnissen der Reise von Prof. Dr. O. Lundblad. VII. Trichoptera. Arkiv för Zoologi, 30(14): 1-8.

————. 1939. Ruwenzori Expedition 1934-5. Vol. III, No. 1. Trichoptera. British Museum (Natural History), London. 40 pp.

————. 1941. Fijian Trichoptera in the British Museum. Ann. & Mag. Nat. Hist. (11), 7:373.

————. 1942. Trichoptera from Foochow. Trans. R. Ent. Soc. London, 92:343-62.

MOSELY, M. E. and D. E. KIMMINS. 1953. The Trichoptera of Australia and New Zealand. British Museum (Natural History). London. 550 pp.

NAVAS, LONGINOS. 1907. Trichopteros nuevos. R. Sociedad Espanola de historia natural Boletin, 7:397-400.

————. 1916a. Neuropteros nuevos de Espana. Rev. Real Acad. Ci. Exactas, Fis. Nat. de Madrid. pp. 593-601.

————. 1916b. Tricopteros nuevos de Espana. Broteria, 14:5-11.

————. 1916c. Neuropteros nuevos de Espana (Tercera serie). Rev. Real Acad. Ci. Madrid, 15:739-51.

————. 1916d. Trichopteros de Aragon. Rev. Acad. Ci. Zaragoza, pp. 73-85.

————. 1917a. Neuropteros nuevos o poco conocidos (Octava serie). Mem. Acad. Ci. Barcelona, 13: 173-78.

————. 1917b. Tricopteros nuevos de Espana (Tercera serie). Broteria, 15:16-28.

————. 1918a. Neuropteros nuevos o poco conocidos (Decima serie). R. Academia de Ciencias y Artes de Barcelona Memorias, 14:339-66.

————. 1918b. Trichopteros nuevos de Espana (Quinta serie). Broteria, 16:7-20.

————. 1918c. Insectos Chilenos. Bol. Soc. Aragon. Zaragoza, 17:212-30.

————. 1918d. Excursiones entomologicas por el norte de la Provincia de Lerida. Bull. Inst. Catalana d'Hist. Nat., pp. 44-49.

————. 1919. Excursions entomologicas por Cataluna durante el verano de 1918. Mem. Real. Acad. Ci. Barcelona, 15:1-36.

————. 1920. Tricopteros nuevos de Espana (Sexta serie). Broteria, 18:23-27.

————. 1922. Mis excursiones entomologicas durante el verano de 1921. Bol. Soc. ent. Espana Zaragoza, 5:107-19.

————. 1923. Insecta nova. Mem. Pont. Accad. Nuovi Lincei, Rome, 6(2):1-27.

————. 1925a. Insectos exoticos nuevos o poco conocidos. Mem. Real Ac. Ci. Barcelona, 19(5):1-22.

————. 1925b. Mis excursiones del verano de 1925. Broteria, 22:137-39.

————. 1926. Veinticinco formos nuevos de insectos. Bol. Soc. iber. Cienc. Nat. Zaragossa, 26:48-75.

————. 1929. Insecta Orientalia. Mem. Pont. Accad. Nuovi Lincei, Rome, 12(2):33-56.

————. 1930a. Excursio entomologica a la vall de No-guera de Cardos (Lerida). Bull. Inst. Catal. Hist. Nat. Barcelona, 10:156-69.

————. 1930b. Excursion a Ribera de Cardos, Pallars (Lerida). Bull. Inst. Catal. Hist. Nat. Barcelona, 10:48-57.

————. 1932a. Insecta Orientalia. Mem. Pont. Accad. Nuovi Lincei, Rome, (2)16:913-56.

————. 1932b. Alcuni Insetti del Museo di Zoologia della R. Universita di Torino. Boll. Mus. Zool. Anat. Comp. Univ. Torino, 42(3):38.

————. 1932c. Bol. Soc. ent. Esp., 15:97.

————. 1933a. Neurotteri e Tricotteri del "Deutsches entomologisches Institut" di Berlin-Dahlem. Boll. Soc. Ent. Italiana, 65:105-13.

————. 1933b. Insecta Orientalia, 12 ser. Mem. Pont. Acc. Sci. Nuovi Lincei, Rome, 17:75-108.

————. 1933c. Nevroptères et insectes voisins. Chine et pays environnants. Notes ent. chinoise, Mus. Heude, Shanghai, 9:22.

————. 1934. Insetti neurotteri e affini del Piemonte. Mem. Soc. Ent. Italiana, Genoa, 12:150-62.

————. 1935. Insectos del Piamonte (Italia). Neuropteros y afines. Bol. Soc. iber. Cienc. nat. Zaragoza, 34:33-45.

————. 1936a. Nevroptères et insectes voisins. Chine et pays environnants. Notes ent. chinoise, Mus. Heude, Shanghai, 3:37-62, 117-32.

————. 1936b. Insectos de Berberia. Bol. Soc. Ent. Esp., Madrid, 18:45-52, 77-100.

NEEDHAM, PAUL R. 1938. Trout Streams. Ithaca, N. Y. 233 pp.

NIELSEN, ANKER. 1948. Postembryonic development and biology of the Hydroptilidae. Det Kgl. Danske Vidensk. Selskab, Biol. Skrifter, 5:1-200.

ORTMANN, A. E. 1902. The geographical distribution of freshwater decapods and its bearing upon ancient geography. Proc. Amer. Philos. Soc., 41:267-400.

PALMER, BOYD B. 1938. A contribution to the life history of Chimarrha albomaculata Kolbe from Puerto Rico. Ann. Ent. Soc. Amer., 31:69-73.

PETIT, G. 1927. Le genre Astacoides de Madagascar. C. R. Soc. Biogeogr., No. 33.

PICTET, Ed. 1865. Synopsis des Nevroptères d'Espagne. Geneva. 123 pp.

PICTET, FRANCOIS JULES. 1834. Recherches pour Servir à l'Histoire et à l'Anatomie des Phryganides. Geneva. 235 pp.

PRADHAN, K. S. 1952. On the distribution of the genus Amemboa Esaki (Hemiptera:Heteroptera), with the description of a new species. Rec. Indian Mus., 48:11-16.

PROVANCHER, M. ABBÉ. 1878. Additions et corrections aux Neuroptères de la Province de Quebec. Le Naturaliste Canadien, 10:124-47, 367-69.

PRYOR, M. G. M. 1951. On the abdominal appendages of larvae of Trichoptera, Neuroptera, and Lepidoptera, and the origins of jointed limbs. Quart. Jour. Micro. Sci., 92:351-76.

RADOVANOVIC, M. 1932a. Wormaldia subterrannea n. sp., ein neue, in den Höhlen Jugoslawiens aufgefundene Trichopteren. Art. Zool. Anz., 100:101-108.

———. 1932b. Results of the study of Balkan Trichoptera. (In Serbian.) Acta Soc. ent. jugosl., Belgrade, 5-6:159-92.

Ross, Herbert H. 1929. Sawflies of the subfamily Dolerinae of America north of Mexico. Ill. Biol. Monographs, 12:1-116.

———. 1938a. Descriptions of Nearctic caddisflies (Trichoptera) with special reference to the Illinois species. Bull. Ill. Nat. Hist. Surv., 21:101-83.

———. 1938b. Descriptions of new North American Trichoptera. Proc. Ent. Soc. Wash., 40:117-24.

———. 1938c. Lectotypes of North American caddisflies in the Museum of Comparative Zoology. Psyche, 45:1-61.

———. 1939a. New species of Trichoptera from the Appalachian Region. Proc. Ent. Soc. Washington, 41:65-70.

———. 1939b. Three new species of Nearctic Trichoptera. Ann. Ent. Soc. Amer., 32:628-31.

———. 1941. Descriptions and records of North American Trichoptera. Trans. Amer. Ent. Soc., 67:35-126.

———. 1944. The caddisflies or Trichoptera of Illinois. Bull. Ill. Nat. Hist. Surv., 23:1-326.

———. 1947. Descriptions and records of North American Trichoptera, with synoptic notes. Trans. Amer. Ent. Soc., 73:125-68.

———. 1948. New Nearctic Rhyacophilidae and Philopotamidae. Ann. Ent. Soc. Amer., 41:17-26.

———. 1949a. Xiphocentronidae, a new family of Trichoptera. Ent. News, 60:1-7.

———. 1949b. A classification for the Nearctic species of Wormaldia and Dolophilodes. Proc. Ent. Soc. Washington, 51:154-60.

———. 1950a. New species of Nearctic Rhyacophila (Trichoptera-Rhyacophilidae). Jour. Washington Acad. Sci., 40:260-65.

———. 1950b. A new Philippine Rhyacophila of unusual interest (Trichoptera, Rhyacophilidae). Ent. News, 61:131-34.

———. 1951a. The Trichoptera of Lower California. Proc. California Acad. Sci., 27:65-76.

———. 1951b. The caddisfly genus Anagapetus. Pan-Pacific Ent., 27:140-44.

———. 1951c. Phylogeny and biogeography of the caddisflies of the genera Agapetus and Electragapetus (Trichoptera: Rhyacophilidae). Jour. Washington Acad. Sci., 41:347-56.

———. 1951d. Relationships of the Fijian species of Apsilochorema (Trichoptera, Rhyacophilidae). Occasional Papers Bernice P. Bishop Mus., 20:175-82.

———. 1951e. The origin and dispersal of a group of primitive caddisflies. Evolution, 5:102-15.

———. 1953a. On the origin and composition of the Nearctic insect fauna. Evolution, 7:145-58.

———. 1953b. Additional material on the phylogeny and dispersal of Atopsyche (Trichoptera, Rhyacophilidae). Jour. Washington Acad. Sci., 43:287-93.

Ross, Herbert H., and Chi-Ling Hwang. 1953. Some interesting Chinese species of Glossosoma. Proc. Ent. Soc. Washington, 55:6-9.

Ross, Herbert H., and Edwin W. King. 1952. Biogeographic and taxonomic studies in Atopsyche (Trichoptera, Rhyacophilidae). Ann. Ent. Soc. Amer., 45:177-204.

Ross, Herbert H., and G. J. Spencer. 1952. A preliminary list of the Trichoptera of British Columbia. Proc. Ent. Soc. British Columbia. 48:43-51.

Sarasin, F. 1910. Über die Geschichte der Tierwelt von Ceylon. Zool. Jahrb., Leipzig, Suppl. 12.

Satori, J. 1938. Eine neue Trichopteren-Art aus dem Matra-Gebirge in Nordungarn. Konowia, 17: 42-4.

Schmid, F. 1947. Sur quelques Trichoptères suisses nouveaux ou peu connus. Mitt. Schweiz. Ent. Gesell., 20:519-35.

———. 1949. Les Trichoptères de la Collection Navas. Eos, Rev. Espanola Ent., 25:305-426.

Schrock, R. R. and W. H. Twenhoffel. 1953. Principles of Invertebrate Paleontology. 2nd ed. New York. 816 pp.

Schuchert, Charles. 1924. A Textbook of Geology. Part 2: Historical geology. 2nd ed. New York. 724 pp.

Scopoli, J. A. 1763. Entomologia Carniolica. Vindobon. 420 pp.

Sibley, Charles K. 1926. New species of New York caddis flies. Jour. N.Y. Ent. Soc., 34:79-81.

Simpson, G. G. 1944. Tempo and Mode in Evolution. New York. 237 pp.

———. 1947. Holarctic mammalian faunas and continental relationships during the Cenozoic. Bull. Geol. Soc. Amer., 58:613-88.

———. 1950. History of the fauna of Latin America. Amer. Scientist, 38:361-89.

Spieker, Edmund M. 1946. Late Mesozoic and Early Cenozoic History of Central Utah. U. S. Geological Survey, Professional Paper 205-D:117-61.

Stephens, James Francis. 1836. Illustrations of British Entomology. Vol. 6. London. 240 pp.

Thienemann, August. 1904. Ptilocolepus granulatus Pt., eine Übergangsform von den Rhyacophiliden zu den Hydroptiliden. Allgemeine Zeitschr. fur Ent., 9:418-24, 437-41.

Tillyard, R. J. 1917. Mesozoic insects of Queensland. No. 1, Planipennia, Trichoptera, and the new order Protomecoptera. Proc. Linn. Soc. N.S. Wales (Sydney), 42:175-200.

———. 1919. Mesozoic insects of Queensland. No. 5. Mecoptera, the new order Paratrichoptera, and additions to Planipennia. Proc. Linn. Soc. N.S. Wales (Sydney), 44:194-212.

———. 1924. Studies of New Zealand Trichoptera or Caddis-Flies. No. 2. Trans. N.Z. Inst. (Wellington), 55:285-314.

———. 1933. The Panorpoid complex in the British Rhaetic and Lias. Fossil Insects No. 3, London. British Museum (Natural History). 79 pp.

Tsuda, Matsunae. 1936. Untersuchungen über die japanischen Wasserinsekten I. Kitagamüdae, eine neue Familie der Trichopteren. Annot. Zool. Japonenses, 15:394-99.

————. 1939. Zur Kenntnis der japanischen Philopotamiden (Trichoptera). Annot. Zool. Japonenses, 18:295-97.

————. 1940a. Zur Kenntnis der japanischen Rhyacophilinen (Rhyacophilidae, Trichoptera). Annot. Zool. Japonenses, 19:119-35.

————. 1940b. Zur Kenntnis der japanischen Glossosomatinen (Rhyacophilidae, Trichoptera). Annot. Zool. Japonenses, 19:191-94.

————. 1941. Einige mandschurische Trichopteren. Annot. Zool. Japonenses, 20:159-61.

————. 1942. Japanische Trichopteren I. Systematik. Mem. Coll. Sci. Kyoto Imp. Univ. (B), 17:239-339.

ULMER, GEORG. 1905a. Zur Kenntnis aussereuropäischer Trichopteren. Stett. Ent. Zeit., pp. 1-119.

————. 1905b. Neue und wenig bekannte Trichopteren der Museen zu Brüssel und Paris. Ann. Soc. Ent. Belg., 49:17-41.

————. 1907a. Trichoptera. Catalogues de Collections zoologiques du Baron Edm. de Selys Longchamps, 6(1):1-102.

————. 1907b. Trichoptera. Genera Insectorum, 60:1-259.

————. 1908. Trichoptera und Ephemeridae. Die Fauna Südwestaustraliens, 2(3):25-46.

————. 1909. Einige neue exotische Trichopteren. Notes Leyden Mus., 31:125-42.

————. 1912. Die Trichopteren des baltischen Bernsteins. Beiträge zur Naturkunde Preussens, Königsberg 10. 380 pp.

————. 1913. Über einige von Edw. Jacobson auf Java gesammelte Trichopteren. Zweiter Beitrag. Notes Leyden Mus., 35:78-101.

————. 1926. Beiträge zur Fauna sinica. III. Trichopteren und Ephemeropteren. Arch. Natg., Berlin, 91(A5):19-110.

————. 1927. Einige neue Trichopteren aus Asien. Ent. Mitt., 16:172-82.

————. 1930. Trichopteren von den Philippinen und von den Sunda-Inseln. Treubia, 11:373-498.

————. 1932-33. Aquatic insects of China. Article III. Neue chinesische Trichopteren nebst Übersicht über die bisher aus China bekannten Arten. Peking Nat. Hist. Bull., 7:39-70.

————. 1938. Einige neue Trichopteren von Neu-Guinea aus dem Berliner Museum. S. B. Ges. Naturf. Fr. Berlin. f. 1937. pp. 398-403.

————. 1951. Kocherfliegen (Trichopteren) von den Sunda-Inseln. (Teil I). Archiv für Hydrobiologie, Suppl. Bd. 19: 528 pp.

ULMER, GEORG and HANS KRAWANY, 1938. Zwei neue Agapetinae (Trichoptera) aus Nieder-Österreich und ihre Metamorphose. Internationale Revue der gesamten Hydrobiologie und Hydrographie, 37:306-19.

UMBGROVE, J. H. F. 1947. The Pulse of the Earth. 2nd ed. The Hague, Martinus Nijhoff. 358 pp.

————. 1949. Structural history of the East Indies. Cambridge University Press. 63 pp.

VAN DYKE, EDWIN C. 1939. The origin and distribution of the coleopterous insect fauna of North America. Proc. Sixth Pac. Sci. Con., 4:255-68.

WALKER, FRANCIS. 1852. Catalogue of the specimens of neuropterous insects in the collection of the British Museum. Pt. 1. London. 192 pp.

WEEKS, L. G. 1948. Paleogeography of South America. Bull. Geol. Soc. Amer., 59:249-82.

ZETTERSTEDT, JOHANN WILHELM. 1840. Insecta Lapponica; sectio quinta. Leipzig. Neuroptera, 1025-74.

# INDEX

For entries of scientific names accompanied by a large number of page references, principal references have been indicated in boldface numbers. Author names have been given for the few cases involving homonyms, when this has been necessary for proper identification of the name.